THEORY OF
FUNCTIONS
OF A
COMPLEX VARIABLE

BY

C. CARATHEODORY
PROFESSOR, UNIVERSITY OF MUNICH

TRANSLATED BY

F. STEINHARDT
COLUMBIA UNIVERSITY

VOLUME ONE

Second English Edition

CHELSEA PUBLISHING COMPANY
NEW YORK

LIBRARY OF CONGRESS CATALOGUE CARD NUMBER 60-16838

PRINTED IN THE UNITED STATES OF AMERICA

TRANSLATOR'S PREFACE

THIS BOOK IS A translation of the last of Carathéodory's celebrated text books, *Funktionentheorie*, which he completed shortly before his recent death.

A number of misprints and minor errors have been corrected in this first American edition of the two-volume work.

It may be noted that in a first course in which considerations of time may necessitate the omission of some of the material, the chapter on Inversion Geometry (Part I, Chapter Three) may be bypassed without interruption of continuity, except for a short glance at § 86 where chordal (spherical) distance is defined. The spherical metric is used consistently, and to great advantage, throughout the rest of the book.

F. Steinhardt

EDITOR'S PREFACE

THE AUTHOR OF THIS book, shortly before he died, had the pleasure of being able to see it through the press. Like his *Vorlesungen über Reelle Funktionen* (Treatise on Real Functions), which was written during the First World War and which is today among the classics on the subject, the present work also was conceived and carried out in times of great external disorder and change. In spite of the extreme hardships imposed on him during these difficult years, Carathéodory lost none of his well-known creativity and endurance. Even the illness which after the end of the war confined him to bed again and again for weeks at a time scarcely slowed him down in the writing of this work. During this time, Carathéodory familiarized me with all the details of the book, and I undertook the task of going over the text from a critical point of view as well as from the student's point of view. With characteristic vitality, Carathéodory took great pleasure in acquainting friends and colleagues, who stayed for hours visiting, with the growing manuscript. Thus I always felt that he was especially devoted to the present work.

This book is primarily a textbook, even if its title does not make this explicit. However, the expert too will find in it much that is new and of interest as regards both subject matter and presentation. The division of the work into two volumes is not intended to imply a corresponding division of the material, but was done merely to make it easier for the student to purchase the book. For this reason, the usual practice of furnishing each of the two volumes with a subtitle has not been followed.

It is traditional for textbooks on the Theory of Functions written in German (and in English) to develop the theory of analytic functions as soon as possible after the introduction of complex numbers; at a later point there may be given, by way of application, a more or less brief account of the geometry of circles (theory of inversions and general Moebius transformations). The author of the present treatise has chosen the reverse order, placing the geometry of circles first. From it he evolves an effortless treatment of the Euclidean, Spherical, and Non-Euclidean Geometries and Trigonometries. When the student is then introduced to the Theory of Functions proper, he will have acquired a grasp of basic concepts and a certain familiarity with the way of thinking appropriate to the subject. Part Two of the book presents first some material from Point-Set Theory and from Topology that is needed for subsequent developments; this material is, in the main, compiled for purposes of reference rather than treated exhaustively. There follows an exposition of the basic concept of the complex contour integral and of the most important theorems attaching to this concept.

As is well known, there are various different ways of introducing the analytic functions. Carathéodory chose Riemann's definition, which is based on the property of differentiability of a complex function. This choice is significant for all of the further development of the theory of analytic functions, the main theorems of which are proved in Part Three. The fruitful concept of harmonic measure, which has assumed great importance in recent years, is introduced in its simplest form only, and its generalization is merely hinted at. A more detailed study would not lie within the scope of this work and will hardly be missed, especially since we have an unexcelled account of this subject in R. Nevanlinna's well-known book on single-valued analytic functions.

Part Four deals with the construction of analytic functions by means of various limiting processes. The approach followed here, offering great advantages and hardly explored in the textbook literature up to now, makes full use of the concept of normal families, due to P. Montel, and the concept of limiting oscillation, due to A. Ostrowski. This results in much greater elegance of proof and makes the theory very attractive.

The fifth and last part of the first volume consists of three chapters dealing with special functions. The author has taken particular care with the exposition of the trigonometric functions. In connection with the logarithm and the general power function, the student is introduced to the simplest types of Riemann surfaces. One of the points of interest in the study of these functions and of the gamma function, and not the least important one at that, is for the student to see that there is no fundamental difference between real and complex analytic functions and that the theorems of Function Theory can actually lead to numerical results.

It will be in keeping, I believe, with the wishes of my highly esteemed teacher if I express thanks in his name to all those who took an interest in this book and helped to further its progress. Particular thanks are due to Professor R. Fueter, who not only read all of the galley proofs but also conducted all of the negotiations with the publishers and was responsible for seeing it through the press. Professor E. Schmidt read large parts of the manuscript and deserves thanks for many a valuable suggestion and improvement. We also thank Professors R. Nevanlinna and A. Ostrowski for their active interest and help, the latter especially for his detailed critical appraisal. The publishers, Verlag Birkhäuser, are to be thanked for the excellence of workmanship of the book and for their untiring cooperation in carrying out our wishes.

May the spirit of this great teacher and master of the Theory of Functions continue through this work to inspire the hearts of students with love for this beautiful and important branch of our science.

Munich, May 1950   **L. Weigand**

AUTHOR'S PREFACE

THE THEORY OF Analytic Functions has its roots in eighteenth-century mathematics. It was L. Euler (1707-1783) who first compiled an enormous amount of material bearing on our subject, the elaboration of which kept the mathematicians of many generations fully occupied and which even today is not exhausted. The first mathematician who essayed to build a systematic theory of functions was J.-L. Lagrange (1736-1813), whose bold idea it was to develop the entire theory on the basis of power series. The state of the science at that time can best be gleaned from the comprehensive treatise by P. Lacroix (2nd ed., 1810-1819).

However, most of the results known at that time were not too well secured. For many individual facts, C. F. Gauss (1777-1855) supplied the first proofs that meet our present-day standards. But Gauss never published the most important of the ideas that he had conceived in this connection. Thus it remained for A.-L. Cauchy (1789-1857), who invented (in 1813) and systematically developed the concept of the complex contour integral, to create the first coherent structure for Function Theory. After the discovery of the elliptic functions in the years 1828-1830 by N. H. Abel (1802-1829) and C. G. J. Jacobi (1804-1851), Cauchy's theory was carried forward, especially by J. Liouville (1809-1882), and was set down in the treatise by Briot and Bouquet (1859) which even today is still worth reading. The genius of B. Riemann (1826-1865) intervened not only to bring the Cauchy theory to a certain completion, but also to create the foundations for the geometric theory of functions. At almost the same time, K. Weierstrass (1815-1897) took up again the above-mentioned idea of Lagrange's, on the basis of which he was able to arithmetize Function Theory and to develop a system that in point of rigor and beauty cannot be excelled. The Weierstrass tradition was carried on in an especially pure form by A. Pringsheim (1850-1941), whose book (1925-1932) is extremely instructive.

During the last third of the 19th Century the followers of Riemann and those of Weierstrass formed two sharply separated schools of thought. However, in the 1870's Georg Cantor (1845-1918) created the Theory of Sets. This discipline is one of the most original creations that mathematics has brought forth, comparable perhaps only to the achievements of the ancient mathematicians of the Fifth and Fourth Centuries B.C., who came up, so to speak, out of nowhere with strict geometric proofs. With the aid of Set Theory it was possible for the concepts and results of Cauchy's and Riemann's theories to be put on just as firm a basis as that on which Weierstrass' theory rests, and this led to the discovery of great new results in the Theory of Functions as well as of many simplifications in the exposition.

In yet another plane lie the developments that have in time led to the somewhat changed aspects of Function Theory today. For in the course of the present century, various processes were introduced that had a profound influence on the directions in which the theory grew. In the first place, we mention in this connection *Schwarz's Lemma*, which in combination with elementary mappings from the geometry of circles allows for new types of arguments such as were unknown prior to its discovery. The new methods thus created are equivalent to a general principle due to E. Lindelöf (1870-1946), discovered a little later than Schwarz's Lemma and used by some writers in place of this lemma. At almost the same time, the concept of *normal families* was introduced into Function Theory, and this concept has gradually taken over a central role in a large class of function-theoretic proofs. Although the beginnings of these developments can be traced back somewhat further, say to T. J. Stieltjes (1856-1894), it may be said that P. Montel first gave an exact definition of normal families and illustrated the usefulness of this concept by one new application after another. Likewise of great help is an idea of A. Ostrowski's, which is, to make use of the spherical distance on the Riemann sphere in order to avoid the exceptional role that is otherwise played by the number ∞ in various limiting processes. I have not hesitated to exploit systematically all of the advantages which these various methods have to offer.

The greatest difficulty in planning a textbook on Function Theory lies in the selection of material. Since a book that is too voluminous is impractical for various reasons, one must decide beforehand to omit all those problems the presentation of which requires very lengthy preparatory material. For this reason I have not even mentioned such things as the theory of algebraic functions, or the definition of the most general analytic function that can be obtained from one of its functional elements—things that have always been regarded as forming an indispensable part of a textbook of Function Theory. For the same reason, the general definition of a Riemann surface has not been given, nor is there an account of the theory of uniformization.

The book begins with a treatment of Inversion Geometry (geometry of circles). This subject, of such great importance for Function Theory, is taught in great detail in France in the "Classes de mathématiques spéciales," whereas in German-language (and English-language) universities, it is usually dealt with in much too cursory a fashion. It seems to me, however, that this branch of geometry forms the best avenue of approach to the Theory of Functions; it was, after all, his knowledge of Inversion Geometry that enabled H. A. Schwarz (1843-1921) to achieve all of his celebrated successes.

CONTENTS

Part One

COMPLEX NUMBERS

Part Two

SOME RESULTS FROM POINT SET THEORY AND FROM TOPOLOGY

Part Three

ANALYTIC FUNCTIONS

Part Four

Analytic Functions Defined by Limiting Processes

Part Five

Special Functions

THE COMPLEX NUMBERS FROM THE ALGEBRAIC POINT OF VIEW

which represents the *unit*, or *one*, of the complex number system, just as n was the complex number "zero."

We can summarize our results as follows: *The complex numbers are the elements of a commutative field in which all the ordinary laws of algebra are valid.*

6. Those complex numbers whose second component vanishes, and which are therefore of the form

$$a = (a_1, 0), \tag{6.1}$$

play a special role. They include $n = (0,0)$, as well as $e = (1,0)$. Such numbers will be called *real numbers in the complex domain*. This terminology is justified by the form taken on by the formulas for the elementary operations if

$$a = (\alpha_1, 0), \quad b = (\beta_1, 0) \tag{6.2}$$

is posited, viz.

$$a \pm b = (\alpha_1 \pm \beta_1, 0), \quad a\,b = (\alpha_1 \beta_1, 0), \quad \frac{b}{a} = \left(\frac{\beta_1}{\alpha_1}, 0\right). \tag{6.3}$$

As the above shows, when any of the elementary arithmetical operations are applied to real numbers in the complex domain, the results are always themselves real numbers in the complex domain; and what is more, those numbers constitute a field which is *isomorphic* to that of the ordinary real numbers $a, \beta, \cdots$.

The field of complex numbers may thus be considered as an extension of the field of real numbers, just as the fractions p/q appear as an extension of the domain of integers $p/1$. In the case of fractions, we leave out the fraction line and the denominator if the latter equals 1, writing p in place of $p/1$. Similarly, there will be no danger of confusion if the real number $(a, 0)$ in the complex domain is denoted simply by a, which will greatly simplify the appearance of many formulas. We shall do this consistently, and in particular we shall write 0 for $n = (0,0)$, and 1 for $e = (1,0)$.

7. It still remains to be shown that we have achieved the goal which we set ourselves in introducing the complex numbers in the first place, namely that to each complex number $a = (a_1, a_2)$ we can assign at least one complex number $x = (\xi_1, \xi_2)$ whose square x^2 equals a. Now by (3.4), we have

$$x^2 = (\xi_1^2 - \xi_2^2, 2\,\xi_1\,\xi_2); \tag{7.1}$$

and the equation

$$x^2 = a \tag{7.2}$$

is equivalent to the system of equations

$$\xi_1^2 - \xi_2^2 = \alpha_1, \quad 2\,\xi_1\,\xi_2 = \alpha_2. \tag{7.3}$$

From this it follows that

$$\alpha_1^2 + \alpha_2^2 = (\xi_1^2 - \xi_2^2)^2 + 4\,\xi_1^2\,\xi_2^2 = (\xi_1^2 + \xi_2^2)^2,$$

and we therefore have

$$\xi_1^2 + \xi_2^2 = \sqrt{\alpha_1^2 + \alpha_2^2}. \tag{7.4}$$

Comparing this last relation with (7.3), we find

$$\xi_1^2 = \frac{\sqrt{\alpha_1^2 + \alpha_2^2} + \alpha_1}{2}, \quad \xi_2^2 = \frac{\sqrt{\alpha_1^2 + \alpha_2^2} - \alpha_1}{2}.$$

Thus the only possible values for ξ_1 and ξ_2 are of the form

$$\xi_1 = \pm \sqrt{\frac{\sqrt{\alpha_1^2 + \alpha_2^2} + \alpha_1}{2}}, \quad \xi_2 = \pm \sqrt{\frac{\sqrt{\alpha_1^2 + \alpha_2^2} - \alpha_1}{2}} \tag{7.5}$$

This seems to furnish four solutions to our system of equations. However if $a_2 > 0$, then the second of equations (7.3) shows that ξ_1 and ξ_2 must have the same sign, so that in this case the only possible combinations of signs in (7.5) are $(+, +)$ and $(-, -)$; similarly, in the case $a_2 < 0$ the only possible combinations of signs in (7.5) are $(+, -)$ and $(-, +)$.

Finally, if $a_2 = 0$, i.e. if the given number a is real, then if $a > 0$ we obtain

$$\xi_1 = \pm \sqrt{a}, \quad \xi_2 = 0, \tag{7.6}$$

and if $a < 0$ we obtain

$$\xi_1 = 0, \quad \xi_2 = \pm \sqrt{-a}. \tag{7.7}$$

We can verify by substitution that the complex numbers found above do satisfy equation (7.2), and we may conclude that in all cases considered above, this equation has two opposite solutions, i.e. two solutions whose sum is zero. And finally, we see that in the case $a = 0$, the only case remaining, there is just the one solution $x = 0$.

8. As (7.7) shows, the complex number

$$i = (0, 1), \tag{8.1}$$

called the *imaginary unit*, is a solution of the equation

$$x^2 = -1. \tag{8.2}$$

Now since

$$i\,\alpha_2 = (0, 1)\,(\alpha_2, 0) = (0, \alpha_2),$$

it follows that every number

$$a = (\alpha_1, \alpha_2) = (\alpha_1, 0) + (0, \alpha_2)$$

may be writen in the form

$$a = \alpha_1 + i\,\alpha_2\,. \tag{8.3}$$

If we also take into account the equations

$$i^2 = -1, \qquad i^3 = -i, \qquad i^4 = +1, \ldots, \tag{8.4}$$

we see that all calculations with complex numbers can now be carried out very conveniently. Thus for example, we find, once more verifying equation (3.4), that

$$a\,b = (\alpha_1 + i\,\alpha_2)\,(\beta_1 + i\,\beta_2) \tag{8.5}$$

$$= \alpha_1\,\beta_1 + i\,\alpha_1\,\beta_2 + i\,\alpha_2\,\beta_1 - \alpha_2\,\beta_2$$

$$= (\alpha_1\,\beta_1 - \alpha_2\,\beta_2) + i\,(\alpha_1\,\beta_2 + \alpha_2\,\beta_1),$$

or, once more verifying (5.3), that

$$\frac{b}{a} = \frac{\beta_1 + i\,\beta_2}{\alpha_1 + i\,\alpha_2} = \frac{(\beta_1 + i\,\beta_2)\,(\alpha_1 - i\,\alpha_2)}{(\alpha_1 + i\,\alpha_2)\,(\alpha_1 - i\,\alpha_2)} = \frac{\alpha_1\,\beta_1 + \alpha_2\,\beta_2}{\alpha_1^2 + \alpha_2^2} + i\,\frac{\alpha_1\,\beta_2 - \alpha_2\,\beta_1}{\alpha_1^2 + \alpha_2^2}\,. \tag{8.6}$$

In equation (8.3), we call α_1 the *real part* and α_2 the *imaginary part* of a, and we write

$$\alpha_1 = \Re a, \qquad \alpha_2 = \Im a\,. \tag{8.7}$$

9. Now that we have defined the complex numbers, one and all, as the elements of a field that contains the real numbers in the complex domain and the number i as well, nothing remains of the difficulties which gave the mathematicians of the 18th century such headaches. These difficulties were all due to the fact that one wanted, at that time, to adjoin to the ordinary real numbers a number i which would not fit in anywhere.

In all that follows, we shall as a rule use only complex numbers in any of the formulas to be writen down, and when we speak of a real number we shall mean a real number in the complex domain. This will apply, for instance, to the 2 in $2a$, etc. The only exceptions to this will be letters that obviously stand for natural numbers, such as certain subscripts, or the exponents used in forming integral powers. (Cf., however, § 254,).

Thus, for example, to write

$$a_0\,x^n + a_1\,x^{n-1} + \cdots + a_{n-1}\,x + a_n = 0, \tag{9.1}$$

means to assign the following problem: With $a_0 \neq 0$, $a_1, \ldots, a_n$ standing for given complex numbers, we seek to determine a complex number x for which (9.1) holds. It will later turn out (cf. § 170) that for any given value of the natural number n, equation (9.1) always has solutions and that the process of extension of the domain of numbers, as described in § 1 for the first two cases $n = 1$ and $n = 2$, need not be carried any further. This important result, which is known as the *Fundamental Theorem of Algebra*, was first given expression by d'Alembert (1717-1783) in the 18th century; but it was first proved by Gauss in 1799.

Complex Conjugates (§ 10)

10. Along with a complex number

$$z = x + iy \tag{10.1}$$

having x as its real part and y as its imaginary part, consider the number

$$\bar{z} = x - iy, \tag{10.2}$$

called the *complex conjugate* of z.

The process of passing from z to $\bar{z}$ defines a mapping of the totality of complex numbers onto itself. This mapping is an *automorphism* of the field of complex numbers, which means the following: If

$$w = u + iv \qquad (u, v \text{ real}) \tag{10.3}$$

is any other complex number, then

$$\overline{(z + w)} = \bar{z} + \bar{w}, \qquad \overline{(zw)} = \bar{z}\bar{w}. \tag{10.4}$$

This automorphism is of the second order (or *involutory*), for we have

$$\bar{\bar{z}} = z. \tag{10.5}$$

Comparison of (10.1) and (10.2) shows that z is real if and only if

$$z = \bar{z}. \tag{10.6}$$

If $f(z, \bar{z})$ is any rational expression in z and $\bar{z}$ with real coefficients, then the complex conjugate of $f(z, \bar{z})$ is obtained by interchanging z and $\bar{z}$ in the given expression. Hence if $f(z, \bar{z})$ is symmetric in z and $\bar{z}$, then the function $f(z, \bar{z})$ is real-valued.

But if $f(z, \bar{z})$ also contains complex coefficients, then $\overline{f}(z, \bar{z})$ is obtained by the interchange of z and $\bar{z}$ and the replacement of the coefficients by their complex conjugates.

For example, the expressions

$$z + \bar{z} = 2\,x, \quad (z + \bar{z})^2 = 4\,x^2, \quad z\,\bar{z} = x^2 + y^2 \tag{10.7}$$

all are real-valued, while

$$(z - \bar{z}) = 2\,i\,y \tag{10.8}$$

is either a pure imaginary or zero. But

$$(z - \bar{z})^2 = -\,4\,y^2, \tag{10.9}$$

being a symmetric function, is always real-valued.

Note, incidentally, that the above equalities imply

$$(z + \bar{z})^2 \geqq 0, \quad (z - \bar{z})^2 \leqq 0. \tag{10.10}$$

Absolute Values (§§ 11-12)

11. By the *absolute value* or *modulus* of a complex number z, to be denoted by $|z|$, we shall mean the non-negative number whose square equals $z\bar{z}$; thus

$$|z|^2 = z\,\bar{z} = x^2 + y^2, \quad |z| = +\sqrt{x^2 + y^2}. \tag{11.1}$$

If $z = 0$ then $|z| = 0$; and *vice versa*, if $|z| = 0$ then $z\bar{z} = 0$, which in turn implies $z = 0$. If $z \neq 0$ and $z^2 = |z|^2$, then it follows that $z = \bar{z}$, and hence that z is real; and we then have $z = |z|$ or $z = -|z|$ according to whether z is positive or negative.

For any two complex numbers a and b, we find that

$$|a\,b|^2 = (a\,b)\,(\bar{a}\,\bar{b}) = (a\,\bar{a})\,(b\,\bar{b}) = |a|^2\,|b|^2.$$

From this we obtain

$$|a\,b| = |a|\,|b|. \tag{11.2}$$

Then if

$$a \neq 0, \quad a\,b = c, \quad b = \frac{c}{a},$$

we further obtain

$$\left|\frac{c}{a}\right| = \frac{|c|}{|a|} \qquad (a \neq 0, c \text{ arbitrary}). \tag{11.3}$$

12. Let us now compare the absolute values $|a + b|$, $|a|$, $|b|$, where a and b are any two complex numbers. To start with, we may write

$$\begin{aligned}
|a + b|^2 &= (a + b)\,(\bar{a} + \bar{b}) \\
&= a\,\bar{a} + b\,\bar{b} + (a\,\bar{b} + \bar{a}\,b) \\
&= |a|^2 + |b|^2 + (a\,\bar{b} + b\,\bar{a}).
\end{aligned} \tag{12.1}$$

Observing that the two numbers $a\bar{b}$ and $\bar{a}b$ are complex conjugates, we obtain from (10.10) that

$$(a\,\bar{b}+b\,\bar{a})^2 \geqq 0, \quad (a\,\bar{b}-b\,\bar{a})^2 \leqq 0. \tag{12.2}$$

On account of the identity

$$(a\,\bar{b}+b\,\bar{a})^2 = (a\,\bar{b}-b\,\bar{a})^2 + 4\,|a|^2\,|b|^2 \tag{12.3}$$

it therefore follows that, independently of the sign of the real number $a\bar{b}+b\bar{a}$,

$$a\bar{b}+b\bar{a} \leqq 2\,|a|\,|b| \tag{12.4}$$

always holds.

Comparison of (12.1) and (12.4) now yields the inequality

$$|a+b| \leqq |a| + |b|. \tag{12.5}$$

Using this last relation, we find further that

$$|a| = |(a+b)-b| \leqq |a+b| + |-b| = |a+b| + |b|, \tag{12.6}$$

and similarly that

$$|b| \leqq |a+b| + |a|,$$

so that we can finally write

$$\big||a|-|b|\big| \leqq |a+b| \leqq |a| + |b|. \tag{12.7}$$

To conclude, let us obtain the condition for the equality sign to hold in (12.5). It obviously holds if $a=0$; and if $a \neq 0$, then it is seen from the above calculation that the equality sign will hold in (12.5) if and only if both of the following two relations hold:

$$a\bar{b}-b\bar{a}=0, \quad a\bar{b}+b\bar{a} \geqq 0. \tag{12.8}$$

Setting $b=ac$, $\bar{b}=\bar{a}\bar{c}$ transforms (12.8) into the equivalent relations

$$c=\bar{c} \geqq 0, \tag{12.9}$$

which state that

$$c=b/a \tag{12.10}$$

is real and non-negative.

Unimodular Numbers (§§ 13-14)

13. If z is not real, then the *difference* $z-x$ of z and its real part x is a so-called *pure imaginary* number iy. Let us now turn to the consideration of the numbers u which are obtained, somewhat similarly, by forming the *quotient* of a number $a \neq 0$ and its absolute value $|a|$.

From the equation

$$a = |a| u \qquad\qquad (a \neq 0) \quad (13.1)$$

it follows that

$$u\bar{u} = 1, \qquad |u| = 1. \qquad\qquad (13.2)$$

Numbers u for which (13.2) holds are called *unimodular* (that is, of modulus one). If we set

$$u = x + iy, \qquad \bar{u} = x - iy, \qquad\qquad (13.3)$$

then we find

$$x^2 + y^2 = 1, \qquad\qquad (13.4)$$

so that the unimodular numbers may also be characterized by equation (13.4). The unimodular number -1 satisfies the equation

$$-1 = \frac{i}{-i} = \frac{i}{\bar{i}}. \qquad\qquad (13.5)$$

Furthermore, every unimodular number u satisfies

$$u(1 + \bar{u}) = u + u\bar{u} = 1 + u.$$

It follows that if u is any unimodular number other than -1, in other words if

$$a = 1 + u \neq 0, \qquad \bar{a} = 1 + \bar{u} \neq 0,$$

then the equality

$$u = \frac{1 + u}{1 + \bar{u}} = \frac{a}{\bar{a}} \qquad\qquad (1 + u \neq 0) \quad (13.6)$$

also holds.

Thus *every unimodular number can be represented as the quotient of two complex conjugates, and every such quotient represents a unimodular number.* Note that if u and v are unimodular, then so are the numbers

$$\bar{u}, \qquad 1/u, \qquad uv, \qquad u/v. \qquad\qquad (13.7)$$

14. If a and x are any two distinct complex numbers, then the number

$$\frac{x - a}{\bar{x} - \bar{a}} \qquad\qquad (14.1)$$

is unimodular. If, in addition, $|x| = 1$, then $-1/x$ is unimodular, and therefore so is

$$y = \frac{-1}{x} \cdot \frac{x - a}{\bar{x} - \bar{a}} = \frac{a - x}{1 - \bar{a}\, x}. \qquad\qquad (14.2)$$

In what follows, we shall assume throughout that

$$|a| \neq 1 . \tag{14.3}$$

Then if we compare the equation

$$y = \frac{a - x}{1 - \bar{a}\,x} \tag{14.4}$$

with its solution with respect to x,

$$x = \frac{a - y}{1 - \bar{a}\,y} , \tag{14.5}$$

and observe that each of the last two equations may be obtained from the other by interchanging x and y, we find that (14.4) and (14.5) give a one-to-one mapping of the totality of unimodular numbers onto itself.

From (14.4) we obtain further, for any complex number x different from $1/\bar{a}$:

$$|y|^2 = \frac{(a - x)\,(\bar{a} - \bar{x})}{(1 - \bar{a}\,x)\,(1 - a\,\bar{x})} \tag{14.6}$$

and

$$1 - |y|^2 = \frac{(1 - |a|^2)\,(1 - |x|^2)}{|1 - \bar{a}\,x|^2} . \tag{14.7}$$

Therefore if

$$|a| < 1 , \tag{14.8}$$

the two numbers $(1 - |x|^2)$ and $(1 - |y|^2)$ will have the same sign. Thus equations (14.4) and (14.5) map every number x whose modulus is ≤ 1 onto a number y having the same property; and we can obtain in this way every y for which $|y| \leq 1$.

We shall see later that the transformation or mapping (14.4) admits of a simple geometric interpretation. In this connection it will be important to have an estimate of $|y|$ in terms of $|a|$ and $|x|$. To obtain such an estimate, we replace the numbers a and x in (14.4) by $|a|$ and $\pm |x|$ respectively, introduce the notations

$$y_1 = \frac{|a| - |x|}{1 - |a|\,|x|} , \qquad y_2 = \frac{|a| + |x|}{1 + |a|\,|x|} \tag{14.9}$$

and find

$$1 - y_1^2 = \frac{(1 - |a|^2)\,(1 - |x|^2)}{(1 - |a|\,|x|)^2} , \quad 1 - y_2^2 = \frac{(1 - |a|^2)\,(1 - |x|^2)}{(1 + |a|\,|x|)^2} . \tag{14.10}$$

But by (12.7), we have

$$1 - |a|\,|x| \leq |1 - \bar{a}\,x| \leq 1 + |a|\,|x| ,$$

so that a comparison of (14.10) with (14.7) yields the relations

$$|y_1| \leq |y| \leq y_2 \leq 1 ,$$

which may also be written as follows:

$$\frac{||a| - |x||}{1 - |a||x|} \leqq \frac{|a - x|}{|1 - \bar{a}\,x|} \leqq \frac{|a| + |x|}{1 + |a||x|} \leqq 1, \quad (|a| < 1,\; 0 \leqq |x| \leqq 1). \quad (14.11)$$

The Amplitude of a Complex Number (§§ 15-17)

15. The unimodular numbers can be expressed in terms of a real parameter. For, in the representation

$$u = \frac{a + i\,b}{a - i\,b} \quad (a, b \text{ real},\; a^2 + b^2 > 0) \qquad (15.1)$$

of a unimodular number u, the number a is zero if and only if $u = -1$. Thus if we assume $u \neq -1$, we may introduce the notation

$$t = \frac{b}{a} \qquad (t \text{ real}) \quad (15.2)$$

and obtain

$$u = \frac{1 + i\,t}{1 - i\,t} = \frac{1 - t^2}{1 + t^2} + i\,\frac{2\,t}{1 + t^2}. \qquad (15.3)$$

If

$$u' = \frac{1 + i\,t'}{1 - i\,t'} \qquad (15.4)$$

represents a second such unimodular number, we find

$$u - u' = \frac{2\,i\,(t - t')}{(1 - i\,t)\,(1 - i\,t')}, \qquad (15.5)$$

which shows that $u' = u$ if and only if $t' = t$. Hence the unimodular numbers other than -1 can be mapped one-to-one onto the real t-axis.

16. If we presuppose the theory of the trigonometric functions in the real domain, we can obtain a more useful mapping of the unimodular numbers onto a real axis by assigning to every value of t a real number ϑ defined by the equation

$$\frac{\vartheta}{2} = \text{arc tg } t. \qquad (-\pi < \vartheta < \pi) \quad (16.1)$$

This yields

$$t = \text{tg}\,\frac{\vartheta}{2}, \qquad (16.2)$$

$$\frac{1 - t^2}{1 + t^2} = \frac{1 - \text{tg}^2\,\frac{\vartheta}{2}}{1 + \text{tg}^2\,\frac{\vartheta}{2}} = \cos\vartheta, \quad \frac{2\,t}{1 + t^2} = \frac{2\,\text{tg}\,\frac{\vartheta}{2}}{1 + \text{tg}^2\,\frac{\vartheta}{2}} = \sin\vartheta, \qquad (16.3)$$

and equation (15.3) assumes the form

$$u = \cos \vartheta + i \sin \vartheta. \tag{16.4}$$

We can verify conversely that the right-hand side of the last equation represents a unimodular number for every value of ϑ. The number ϑ is called an *amplitude*, or *argument*, of the unimodular number u.

If ϑ_0 is an amplitude of the unimodular number u, then because of the periodicity of the trigonometric functions, the number u has infinitely many further amplitudes, namely the numbers

$$\vartheta = \vartheta_0 + 2 k \pi, \quad (k = 0, \pm 1, \pm 2, \ldots). \tag{16.5}$$

Among these, there is exactly one *principal amplitude*, by which is meant the amplitude contained in the half-open interval

$$-\pi < \vartheta \leq \pi. \tag{16.6}$$

17. When multiplying unimodular numbers, one adds their amplitudes. For if

$$u_1 = \cos \vartheta_1 + i \sin \vartheta_1, \quad u_2 = \cos \vartheta_2 + i \sin \vartheta_2, \tag{17.1}$$

then

$$u_1 u_2 = (\cos \vartheta_1 \cos \vartheta_2 - \sin \vartheta_1 \sin \vartheta_2) + i (\sin \vartheta_1 \cos \vartheta_2 + \sin \vartheta_2 \cos \vartheta_1)$$
$$= \cos (\vartheta_1 + \vartheta_2) + i \sin (\vartheta_1 + \vartheta_2). \tag{17.2}$$

In a later chapter of this book (see § 234ff.) we shall define the functions e^z, $\cos z$, $\sin z$ for arbitrary complex values of z and we shall prove the identity

$$e^{iz} = \cos z + i \sin z. \tag{17.3}$$

There is nothing to prevent us at this point from introducing the symbol $e^{i\vartheta}$ as a *convenient abbreviation* for the unimodular number $\cos \vartheta + i \sin \vartheta$. In this notation, the functional relation expressed by (17.1) and (17.2) takes on the form

$$e^{i (\vartheta_1 + \vartheta_2)} = e^{i \vartheta_1} e^{i \vartheta_2}. \tag{17.4}$$

Roots (§§ 18-19)

18. Let a be an arbitrary complex number $\neq 0$, and let n be an arbitrary natural number. We propose to calculate all the roots of the equation

$$z^n = a . \tag{18.1}$$

If we set

$$a = |a| e^{i\vartheta} = |a| e^{i(\vartheta + 2k\pi)} \qquad (k = 0, 1, \ldots) \qquad (18.2)$$

and

$$z = |z| e^{i\varphi}, \qquad (18.3)$$

then

$$|z|^n = |a| \quad \text{and} \quad n\varphi = \vartheta + 2k\pi \qquad (18.4)$$

must hold. This determines

$$|z| = \sqrt[n]{|a|} \qquad (18.5)$$

uniquely. Among the numbers

$$\varphi_k = \frac{\vartheta}{n} + \frac{2k\pi}{n} \qquad (k = 0, 1, \ldots) \qquad (18.6)$$

there are, however, n distinct ones, namely

$$\varphi_0, \quad \varphi_1, \quad \varphi_2, \quad \ldots, \quad \varphi_{n-1}, \qquad (18.7)$$

which when substituted for φ in (18.3) yield n distinct solutions of (18.1). One verifies easily that (18.1) has no further solutions.

19. If we set $a = 1$ in (18.1), we obtain the equation

$$z^n = 1, \qquad (19.1)$$

every root of which, other than 1 itself, is called a *root of unity*. By (18.5) and (18.6) we have

$$|z| = 1, \qquad \varphi_k = \frac{2k\pi}{n}, \qquad (19.2)$$

so that

$$z = e^{\frac{2k\pi i}{n}}, \qquad (k = 1, 2, \ldots, n - 1). \qquad (19.3)$$

Thus for $n = 2, 4, 8$ and $k = 1$, we find

$$e^{i\pi} = -1, \quad e^{\frac{i\pi}{2}} = i, \quad e^{\frac{i\pi}{4}} = \frac{1+i}{\sqrt{2}}. \qquad (19.4)$$

For $n = 3$, we have

$$z^3 - 1 = (z - 1)(z^2 + z + 1). \qquad (19.5)$$

Thus the third roots of unity are simply the roots of the quadratic equation

$$z^2 + z + 1 = 0.$$

From this, and from the relations (19.4), we calculate successively

$$\left.\begin{aligned}
e^{\frac{2i\pi}{3}} &= \frac{-1+i\sqrt{3}}{2}, \\
e^{\frac{i\pi}{3}} &= e^{i\pi-\frac{2i\pi}{3}} =: \frac{1+i\sqrt{3}}{2}, \\
e^{\frac{i\pi}{12}} &= e^{\frac{i\pi}{3}-\frac{i\pi}{4}} = \frac{(\sqrt{3}+1)+i\,(\sqrt{3}-1)}{2\sqrt{2}}, \\
e^{\frac{i\pi}{6}} &=: \frac{\sqrt{3}+i}{2}.
\end{aligned}\right\} \qquad (19.6)$$

CHAPTER TWO

THE GEOMETRY OF THE COMPLEX NUMBERS

The Gaussian or Complex Plane (§§ 20-22)

20. A decisive step forward in the theory of complex numbers was taken early in the last century, when the idea of mapping the complex numbers on the points of a plane occurred almost simultaneously to a number of mathematicians. Gauss developed this idea systematically, and because of his great authority it was adopted universally.

Let us consider a plane, which we shall call the complex plane (or the Gaussian plane) and single out two points O and E in it. We shall introduce into this plane a Cartesian coordinate system whose origin is at O and whose x-axis has its unit point at E. We now map every complex number $z = x + iy$ on the point P of the plane whose coordinates are x and y. Conversely, with every point $P(x, y)$ of the plane we associate the number $z = x + iy$. In this manner we have, so to speak, identified the totality of complex numbers with the points of a plane.

The immediate advantage of this identification lies in the fact that most of the results of the preceding chapter now admit of simple geometric interpretations. Thus, for instance, our mapping makes the real numbers in the complex domain correspond to the points of the x-axis, which will therefore be called the *real axis* or the *axis of real numbers*. Also, two complex conjugates are represented by two points that are located symmetrically with respect to the real axis.

Furthermore, the absolute value

$$|a - b| = \sqrt{(a_1 - b_1)^2 + (a_2 - b_2)^2}$$

of the difference of two numbers

$$a = a_1 + i\,a_2, \quad b = b_1 + i\,b_2$$

measures the *distance* between their image points. The modulus $|a|$ of a complex number a therefore measures the distance from the origin O of the image point P of a. Finally, if $a \neq 0$ then the amplitude ϑ of a measures—in radians—the angle formed by the vectors OP and OE.

Now consider the triangle in the complex plane whose vertices coincide with

17

the (images of the) numbers a, b, and c. The lengths of the sides of this triangle are given by the quantities $|b-c|$, $|c-a|$, $|a-b|$. The relation

$$\left| |c-a| - |a-b| \right| \leqq |b-c| \leqq |c-a| + |a-b| , \qquad (20.1)$$

which follows from (12.7), is simply another way of expressing the theorem of elementary geometry to the effect that the length of any given side of a triangle is always between the sum and the difference of the lengths of the other two sides.

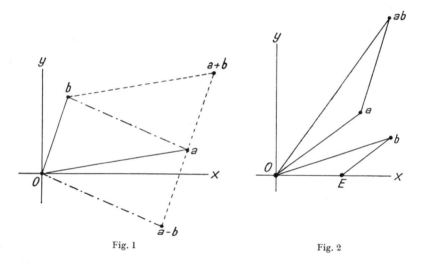

Fig. 1   Fig. 2

21. Even these very simple results would, because of their striking intuitiveness, justify the introduction of the geometric representation of the complex numbers. It is for deeper reasons, however, that a theory of functions in which complex numbers are not considered as geometric points, would nowadays be unthinkable. A ready appreciation of the connection between Function Theory and Topology—a connection discovered by A. L. Cauchy (1789-1857) and B. Riemann (1826-1865)—is possible only with the aid of our geometric interpretation. But even certain more elementary properties of the complex numbers that are of prime importance for Function Theory, would have been accessible only with great difficulty without the use of geometric ideas. These properties all stem from the fact that the straight line and the circle play a decisive role both in elementary geometry and in the complex plane. In this connection, we shall be concerned primarily with the circle-preserving transformations, which are represented by simple complex functions.

But before going into these matters, we shall first show how the arithmetical operations on complex numbers can be carried out by means of constructions in elementary geometry.

22. If a and b are two complex numbers whose ratio is not a real number, then the numbers $a + b$ and $a - b$ are obtained by drawing the parallelograms

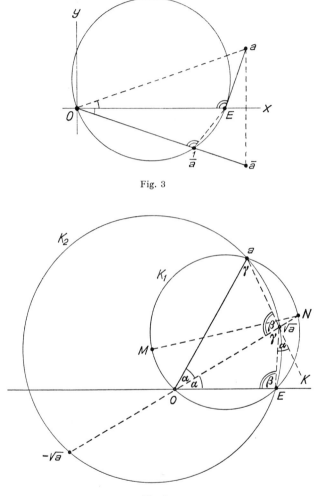

Fig. 3

Fig. 4

Applying to the circle K_1 the theorem on the equality of all angles subtended by the same chord, we find: $\alpha = \sphericalangle\, aON = \sphericalangle\, aEN$ and since $\overline{aN} = \overline{NE}$, we also have $\alpha = \sphericalangle\, NOE.$ The same theorem applied to the circle K_2—to which EN is tangent—yields $\sphericalangle\, E\,\sqrt{a}\,K = \sphericalangle\, a\,E\,N = \alpha.$ Hence the triangles $OE\,\sqrt{a}$ and $O\,\sqrt{a}\,a$ are similar.

shown in Fig. 1. Similarly, unless a and b are both real, the number ab is determined by means of a construction involving similar triangles, as shown in Fig. 2.

Furthermore, for any non-real $a \neq 0$, the point $1/a$ is obtained by intersecting the straight line that joins O to $\bar{a}$ with the circle that passes through the points O and E and is tangent to the line Ea; for, the two triangles $O(1/a)E$ and OEa are similar (see Fig. 3).

The construction which produces $\pm \sqrt{a}$ out of a is equally simple. We consider (cf. Fig. 4) the circle circumscribed about triangle OEa, and its diameter MN which intersects the chord Ea at a right angle, M being chosen such that $OM < EM$. Then the points $\pm \sqrt{a}$ are the intersections of the straight line ON with the circle that passes through E and a and has its center at M. To prove this, we need only verify that the three angles labeled with a in Fig. 4 are actually equal to each other; the validity of the construction then follows from the similarity of triangles $OE\sqrt{a}$ and $O\sqrt{a}\,a$.

Circles in the Complex Plane (§ 23)

23. According to § 20, the points z of the Gaussian plane that lie on a circle of radius R about a as the center satisfy the equation

$$|z - a| = R \tag{23.1}$$

But since

$$|z - a|^2 = (z - a)(\bar{z} - \bar{a}) = z\bar{z} - \bar{a}z - a\bar{z} + a\bar{a},$$

we may replace (23.1) by

$$z\bar{z} - \bar{a}z - a\bar{z} + a\bar{a} - R^2 = 0. \tag{23.2}$$

Now if A, B, C, and D are real numbers and if we set

$$A(z + \bar{z}) + iB(\bar{z} - z) + C(z\bar{z} - 1) + D(z\bar{z} + 1) = 0, \tag{23.3}$$

then equation (23.3) is equivalent with equation (23.2) provided that $A, B, C,$ and D are chosen in such a way that the equations

$$a = -\frac{A + iB}{C + D}, \qquad R^2 = \frac{A^2 + B^2 + C^2 - D^2}{(C + D)^2} \tag{23.4}$$

hold. Therefore (23.3) represents a circle of radius R about a as its center whenever the relations

$$C + D \neq 0, \qquad D^2 < A^2 + B^2 + C^2 \tag{23.5}$$

are satisfied. If

$$C + D = 0 \qquad (23.6)$$

then (23.3) represents the straight line

$$A(z + \bar{z}) + i B(\bar{z} - z) - 2C = 0,$$

that is,

$$A x + B y - C = 0 \qquad (z = x + i y) \qquad (23.7)$$

The Group of Moebius Transformations (§§ 24-25)

24. Let α, β, γ, and δ be four complex numbers satisfying the condition

$$\alpha \delta - \beta \gamma \neq 0. \qquad (24.1)$$

Let us study the equation

$$w = \frac{\alpha z + \beta}{\gamma z + \delta} \qquad (24.2)$$

First, if $\gamma = 0$ then both α and δ must be different from zero, because of condition (24.1), so that the two equivalent equations

$$w = \frac{\alpha}{\delta} z + \frac{\beta}{\delta}, \quad z = \frac{\delta}{\alpha} w - \frac{\beta}{\alpha} \qquad (24.3)$$

are meaningful. Relation (24.2) then represents a one-to-one mapping of the entire Gaussian z-plane onto the entire Gaussian w-plane.

Second, if $\gamma \neq 0$ then the right-hand side of (24.2) fails to represent a complex number in case $\gamma z + \delta = 0$, that is, in case $z = -\delta/\gamma$; but to every point of the z-plane other than $-\delta/\gamma$ there corresponds a value of w other than α/γ, since

$$w - \frac{\alpha}{\gamma} = \frac{-(\alpha \delta - \beta \gamma)}{\gamma (\gamma z + \delta)} \neq 0. \qquad (24.4)$$

We note furthermore that equation (24.2) is equivalent to

$$z = \frac{-\delta w + \beta}{\gamma w - \alpha}, \qquad (24.5)$$

and comparing this with the preceding set of relations, we see that (24.2) maps the z-plane "punctured" at $z_0 = -\delta/\gamma$ (i.e. the totality of all points z other than z_0) one-to-one onto the w-plane punctured at $w_0 = \alpha/\gamma$.

The mapping by means of (24.2)—subject to condition (24.1)—of the full (or punctured) z-plane onto the full (or punctured) w-plane is called a *Moebius transformation*,[1] since the first study of such mappings goes back to A. F. Moebius (1790-1868).

---

[1] Also called *fractional linear* or *linear* or *bilinear* transformation.

The above results do not hold true if condition (24.1) is dropped, that is if

$$\alpha\delta - \beta\gamma = 0. \qquad (24.6)$$

For in this case, we must have either $\gamma = 0$ and $\alpha\delta = 0$, which renders meaningless at least one of the two expressions on the right-hand sides of (24.2) and (24.5), or else $\gamma \neq 0$, which means, by (24.4), that all points of the z-plane except for $z_0 = -\delta/\gamma$ are mapped onto the single point $w_0 = \alpha/\gamma$ of the w-plane.

25. Let us now consider a second Moebius transformation,

$$W = \frac{\alpha_1 w + \beta_1}{\gamma_1 w + \delta_1} \qquad (\alpha_1 \delta_1 - \beta_1 \gamma_1 \neq 0), \qquad (25.1)$$

and let us here substitute for w the right-hand side of (24.2). We obtain

$$W = \frac{\alpha_1 (\alpha z + \beta) + \beta_1 (\gamma z + \delta)}{\gamma_1 (\alpha z + \beta) + \delta_1 (\gamma z + \delta)} = \frac{\alpha^* z + \beta^*}{\gamma^* z + \delta^*}, \qquad (25.2)$$

having set

$$\begin{aligned} \alpha^* &= \alpha_1 \alpha + \beta_1 \gamma, \quad \beta^* = \alpha_1 \beta + \beta_1 \delta, \\ \gamma^* &= \gamma_1 \alpha + \delta_1 \gamma, \quad \delta^* = \gamma_1 \beta + \delta_1 \delta. \end{aligned} \right\} \qquad (25.3)$$

We easily verify the identity

$$\alpha^* \delta^* - \beta^* \gamma^* = (\alpha\delta - \beta\gamma)(\alpha_1 \delta_1 - \beta_1 \gamma_1), \qquad (25.4)$$

which implies that

$$\alpha^* \delta^* - \beta^* \gamma^* \neq 0 \qquad (25.5)$$

From this it follows that the transformation (25.2), which is the product, or composite, of (24.2) and (25.1), is itself a Moebius transformation. This means that the Moebius transformations have the *group property* (more specifically, the *composition property* of a group). Furthermore, since the composite transformation (25.2) reduces to $W = z$ if we choose

$$\alpha_1 = -\delta, \quad \beta_1 = \beta, \quad \gamma_1 = \gamma, \quad \delta_1 = -\alpha,$$

it follows that every Moebius transformation has an *inverse*. Therefore the totality of Moebius transformations constitutes a *group*.

There is, to be sure, a complication involved in the fact that the Moebius transformation (24.2) is defined only in the z-plane punctured at the point $z_0 = -\delta/\gamma$ while (25.2) is defined in the z-plane punctured at $z_0^* = -\delta^*/\gamma^*$ But we shall resolve this difficulty later (§ 30) by means of a very simple device.

Circle-Preserving Mappings (§§ 26-28)

26. It is possible to obtain the most general Moebius transformations for which $\gamma = 0$, by composition of two more special types, namely

$$w = \alpha\, z, \quad w = z + \beta. \tag{26.1}$$

For if we write

$$w = \frac{\alpha}{\delta}\, w_1, \quad w_1 = z + \frac{\beta}{\alpha}, \tag{26.2}$$

we obtain

$$w = \frac{\alpha\, z + \beta}{\delta}. \tag{26.3}$$

The most general Moebius transformations can now be compounded of transformations (26.1) together with the transformation

$$w = 1/z, \tag{26.4}$$

for if $\gamma \neq 0$ we only need write

$$w = \frac{\alpha}{\gamma} + w_1, \quad w_1 = \frac{1}{w_2}, \quad w_2 = \frac{-\gamma\,(\gamma\, z + \delta)}{\alpha\, \delta - \beta\, \gamma}. \tag{26.5}$$

27. We note next that each of the two transformations (26.1) transforms the straight lines of the complex z-plane into straight lines of the w-plane, and that the first of these transformations maps the circle

$$|z - a| = R \tag{27.1}$$

onto the circle

$$|w - \alpha\, a| = |\alpha|\, R, \tag{27.2}$$

while the second maps the circle (27.1) onto the circle

$$|w - (a + \beta)| = R. \tag{27.3}$$

Now the transformation (26.4) has similar properties. For if we replace the number z in equation (23.3) by $1/w$, and $\bar{z}$ by $1/\bar{w}$, then w and $\bar{w}$ satisfy the relation

$$A\,(w + \bar{w}) - i\, B\,(\bar{w} - w) - C\,(w\,\bar{w} - 1) + D\,(w\,\bar{w} + 1) = 0, \tag{27.4}$$

which is quite analogous to (23.3). One easily verifies that (26.4) maps the straight lines of the z-plane onto the circles through $w = 0$ of the w-plane, and that it maps the circles through $z = 0$ of the z-plane onto the straight lines of the w-plane; also, that the remaining circles of the z-plane are mapped onto circles of the w-plane.

Now the result of § 26 serves to prove that the most general Moebius transformation (24.2) likewise maps every straight line and every circle of the z-plane either onto a straight line or onto a circle of the w-plane.

28. A further elementary transformation that maps the straight lines and circles of the z-plane onto the straight lines and circles of the w-plane, is given by

$$w = \bar{z}. \qquad (28.1)$$

By combining this latter with the general Moebius transformation (24.2), one obtains a new class of transformations,

$$w = \frac{\alpha \bar{z} + \beta}{\gamma \bar{z} + \delta} \qquad (\alpha \delta - \beta \gamma \neq 0), \qquad (28.2)$$

which also map straight lines and circles onto straight lines and circles.

The geometric property of mapping the straight lines and circles of the z-plane onto the straight lines and circles of the w-plane actually *characterizes* the totality of Moebius transformations enlarged by the transformations (28.2); that enlarged totality is also called, for this reason, the totality of *circle-preserving transformations*. This very remarkable result can even be generalized in a certain direction; we may state the following theorem: Let the interior of a circle κ_0 of the z-plane be mapped one-to-one onto a certain set A of points of the w-plane, in such a way that every circle κ contained in the interior of κ_0 is mapped onto a circle $\bar{\kappa}$ contained in A. Then the mapping can be represented either by a Moebius transformation or by a transformation of type (28.2), and must therefore be a circle-preserving mapping.

This purely geometric theorem, in which one need not even assume the given mapping to be continuous, can be proved by quite elementary means;[1] but we shall not concern ourselves with the proof here. Rather we shall concentrate on those properties of circle-preserving mappings which are of importance for the Theory of Functions.

---

[1] C. Carathéodory, *The most general transformations of plane regions which transform circles into circles*, Bull. Amer. Math. Soc. 43, pp. 573-579 (1937).

Isogonality (§ 29)

29. The transformations (26.1), and the transformation (28.1) as well, map two straight lines of the z-plane that intersect at an angle ϑ onto two straight lines of the w-plane that intersect at the same angle. The transformation (26.4) transforms every straight line g of the z-plane that does not pass through $z = 0$, onto a circle through $w = 0$ of the w-plane having its tangent at $w = 0$ parallel to g. Thus two straight lines of the z-plane that intersect at an angle ϑ are mapped onto circles intersecting at the same angle.

Since the most general circle-preserving transformations can be built up by compounding the types just discussed, one concludes readily that they must be *isogonal* (or *angle-preserving*), which means that the following statement is true: Let two arbitrary curves of the z-plane intersect at a point where both have tangents, forming an angle ϑ; any circle-preserving transformation then maps these curves onto two curves of the w-plane that intersect at the same angle ϑ.

However, there is a fundamental difference between the Moebius transformations (24.2) on the one hand and the transformations (28.2), which we shall also call *circle-preserving mappings of the second kind*, on the other hand. For, let us consider the point of intersection of the two curves in the z-plane, as well as the first curve itself as being fixed, while we rotate the second curve, along with its tangent, about this fixed point. The corresponding tangent of the second curve in the w-plane will then also rotate. Now if the mapping is represented by a Moebius transformation, then the two rotating tangents will rotate in the *same sense* (i.e. either both clockwise, or both counter-clockwise); but if the mapping is given by (28.1)—and therefore, also, if the mapping is *any* circle-preserving mapping (28.2), of the second kind—the two tangents will rotate in *opposite senses*.

The Number Infinity (§ 30)

30. We recall the minor nuisance one runs into when studying Moebius transformations with $\gamma \neq 0$ (see § 25 above), because of the fact that the point $z_0 = -\delta/\gamma$ does not have an image point while the point $w_0 = \alpha/\gamma$ does not belong to the set of image points. The following device serves to remove this complication.

In every complex plane, we shall adjoin to the complex numbers an "improper number" (or "improper point," also "ideal" number or point), which we shall call the *point at infinity* and denote by ∞. We then agree that the image point of $z_0 = - \delta/\gamma$ under the Moebius transformation just considered shall be the point $w = \infty$, and that the point $w_0 = \alpha/\gamma$ shall be the image point of $z = \infty$.

It is easy to verify that the above extension of the complex plane by an improper number leaves intact the group property of Moebius transformations under the operation of composition; the only additional requirement is that we agree that $z = \infty$ is to correspond to $w = \infty$ under Moebius transformations of the type

$$w = \alpha z + \beta \qquad (\alpha \neq 0) \qquad (30.\,1)$$

(so-called *integral linear* transformations).

The above agreements can also be rephrased in the form of rules of operation with the number infinity, as follows:

First, if a is any complex number other than ∞, we agree that

$$a + \infty = \infty, \qquad \frac{a}{\infty} = 0. \qquad (30.\,2)$$

Second, if b is any complex number $\neq 0$ (but b may be ∞), we agree that

$$b \cdot \infty = \infty, \qquad \frac{b}{0} = \infty \quad (b \neq 0 \text{ complex}). \qquad (30.\,3)$$

On the other hand, to the combinations

$$\infty + \infty, \qquad 0 \cdot \infty, \qquad \frac{\infty}{\infty}, \qquad \frac{0}{0} \qquad (30.\,4)$$

we shall not assign any meaning whatsoever (*cf.*, however, §§ 160, 161, concerning calculations with meromorphic functions).

The first of the two relations (30.2) is simply another way of expressing the above agreement to the effect that under the Moebius transformation $w = z + a$, the points $z = \infty$ and $w = \infty$ are to correspond to each other. The remaining relations in (30.2) and (30.3) can be interpreted similarly.

The rules expressed by (30.2) and (30.3) are very convenient for determining, among other things, the values taken on by rational functions of z at the point $z = \infty$. This we can also accomplish by first noting that the transformation

$$z = 1/t$$

interchanges the points 0 and ∞, then expressing the given function $f(z)$ as a rational function $g(t)$ of t, and finally calculating the value of this $g(t)$ at $t = 0$.

A complex plane to which the point at infinity has been adjoined will be called, in the sequel, a *complete*, or *extended*, *complex plane*.

The Riemann Sphere (§§ 31-33)

31. It is often useful to consider the complex plane as the stereographic projection of a sphere, as was first done by B. Riemann (1826-1865). In particular, the circle-preserving mappings of the plane correspond to very simple transformations of the sphere. To see this, let us consider a sphere of radius unity (*cf.* Fig. 5) and whose center is coincident with the origin of the

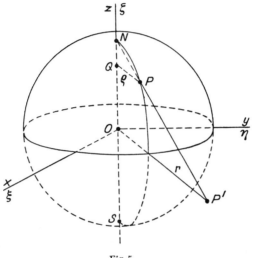

Fig. 5

complex plane (which we visualize here as a horizontal plane). The equator of the sphere then coincides with the unit circle $|z| = 1$. Every point P' of the z-plane may be connected to the north pole N of the sphere by means of a line-segment NP' that intersects the sphere at the point P. We then assign to the point P the number $z = x + iy$ which corresponds to the point P' in the complex plane. Thus the number $z = 0$ is assigned to the south pole S of the sphere. It is easy to see that to the north pole N—the only point of the "Riemann sphere" to which there does not correspond any point of the z-plane in the above arrangement—we must assign the number ∞.

This stereographic projection, which was used as far back as Ptolemy (?-161 A.D.) for celestial maps, has the remarkable property of being isogonal. For, a straight line in the plane of projection is the image of a circle through N on the sphere, and the tangent at N of this circle is parallel to the given line in the plane. Therefore two straight lines in the plane that intersect at P' at an angle ϑ must be the images of two circles passing through P and N on the sphere, and by what has just been said before, these two circles must intersect at N, and hence at P also, at the same angle ϑ.

32. Let us introduce a system of cartesian coordinates ξ, η, ζ, having its origin at the center of the sphere and such that the ξ-axis and η-axis coincide respectively with the x-axis and y-axis of the z-plane, while $\zeta = 1$ at the north pole N.

The equation of the sphere is then as follows:

$$\xi^2 + \eta^2 + \zeta^2 = 1 \quad \text{or} \quad \xi^2 + \eta^2 = 1 - \zeta^2. \tag{32.1}$$

By Fig. 5, however, we have

$$\frac{\varrho}{r} = \frac{1-\zeta}{1}, \tag{32.2}$$

and we have the equations

$$\frac{x}{\xi} = \frac{y}{\eta} = \frac{r}{\varrho} = \frac{1}{1-\zeta}. \tag{32.3}$$

From these it follows that

$$x = \frac{\xi}{1-\zeta}, \quad y = \frac{\eta}{1-\zeta}, \quad z = \frac{\xi + i\eta}{1-\zeta}, \quad \bar{z} = \frac{\xi - i\eta}{1-\zeta}, \tag{32.4}$$

$$z\bar{z} = \frac{\xi^2 + \eta^2}{(1-\zeta)^2} = \frac{1+\zeta}{1-\zeta}, \tag{32.5}$$

$$z\bar{z} - 1 = \frac{2\zeta}{1-\zeta}, \quad z\bar{z} + 1 = \frac{2}{1-\zeta}. \tag{32.6}$$

The coordinates ξ, η, ζ of the point P are then expressed in terms of z as follows:

$$\xi = \frac{2x}{z\bar{z}+1} = \frac{z+\bar{z}}{z\bar{z}+1}, \quad \eta = \frac{i(\bar{z}-z)}{z\bar{z}+1}, \quad \zeta = \frac{z\bar{z}-1}{z\bar{z}+1}. \tag{32.7}$$

33. Now it is easy to derive the various properties of stereographic projection from the above formulas.

Assume, for instance, that z and w are two points of the complex plane that correspond to two diametrically opposite points of the Riemann sphere. From (32.4) we obtain in this case that

$$\bar{z} = \frac{\xi - i\eta}{1-\zeta}, \quad w = -\frac{\xi + i\eta}{1+\zeta}, \quad w\bar{z} = -\frac{\xi^2 + \eta^2}{1-\zeta^2} = -1, \tag{33.1}$$

which implies that

$$w = -\frac{1}{\bar{z}}, \quad w\bar{z} + 1 = 0. \tag{33.2}$$

Hence the mapping of the sphere that sends each point P onto its diametrically opposite point P^* corresponds in the z-plane to a circle-preserving mapping of the second kind (*cf.* §§ 28, 29 above).

As a second example, let us consider equation (23.3) above, which represents an arbitrary circle (or straight line) in the complex plane. By (32.7) and (32.6), this equation is transformed into

$$A\,\xi + B\,\eta + C\,\zeta + D = 0. \tag{33.3}$$

This proves the well-known theorem to the effect that stereographic projection maps the circles on the sphere onto circles (or straight lines) of the plane of projection. The second of the relations (23.5) above now states that the distance of the plane (33.3) from the center of the Riemann sphere is less than unity, i.e. that this plane cuts the sphere in a circle.

The most general circle-preserving transformations of the z-plane also correspond to simple mappings of the sphere, namely to collineations of the (ξ, η, ζ)-space that leave the sphere invariant.

Cross-Ratios (§§ 34-37)

34. Let the four finite numbers w_1, w_2, w_3, w_4 be the images under the Moebius transformation (24.2) of the four finite numbers z_1, z_2, z_3, z_4. The equations

$$w_i - w_k = \frac{\alpha\,\delta - \beta\,\gamma}{(\gamma\,z_i + \delta)\,(\gamma\,z_k + \delta)}\,(z_i - z_k) \qquad (i, k = 1, 2, 3, 4) \tag{34.1}$$

along with the abbreviation

$$A = \frac{(\alpha\,\delta - \beta\,\gamma)^2}{(\gamma\,z_1 + \delta)\,(\gamma\,z_2 + \delta)\,(\gamma\,z_3 + \delta)\,(\gamma\,z_4 + \delta)} \tag{34.2}$$

yield

$$(w_1 - w_2)\,(w_3 - w_4) = A\,(z_1 - z_2)\,(z_3 - z_4).$$

Since A is symmetric in $z_1, \ldots, z_4$, we also have

$$(w_1 - w_3)\,(w_2 - w_4) = A\,(z_1 - z_3)\,(z_2 - z_4).$$

Dividing this last equation into the preceding one, we obtain

$$\frac{(w_1 - w_2)\,(w_3 - w_4)}{(w_1 - w_3)\,(w_2 - w_4)} = \frac{(z_1 - z_2)\,(z_3 - z_4)}{(z_1 - z_3)\,(z_2 - z_4)}. \tag{34.3}$$

The right-hand side of (34.3) is called the *cross-ratio* of the four numbers z_1, z_2, z_3, and z_4, and is denoted by (z_1, z_2, z_3, z_4).

The relation (34.3) does not contain the coefficients $\alpha, \beta, \gamma, \delta$ of the Moebius transformation. We may re-write (34.3) in the form

$$(w_1, w_2, w_3, w_4) = (z_1, z_2, z_3, z_4) \tag{34.4}$$

and express the content of this by saying that *the cross-ratio of any four given points is an invariant under every Moebius transformation.*

To render this statement valid in full generality, we must define the cross-ratio also for the case where one of the points is ∞. This is done as follows: If $z_1 \neq 0$, we may write

$$(z_1, z_2, z_3, z_4) = \frac{\left(1 - \frac{z_2}{z_1}\right)(z_3 - z_4)}{\left(1 - \frac{z_3}{z_1}\right)(z_2 - z_4)},$$

which leads to

$$(\infty, z_2, z_3, z_4) = \frac{z_3 - z_4}{z_2 - z_4}. \tag{34.5}$$

Similar expressions are obtained if one of z_2, z_3, or z_4 coincides with ∞.

35. The cross-ratio

$$\lambda = (z_1, z_2, z_3, z) = \frac{(z_1 - z_2)(z_3 - z)}{(z_1 - z_3)(z_2 - z)} \tag{35.1}$$

can be written as

$$\lambda = \frac{\alpha z + \beta}{\gamma z + \delta}, \tag{35.2}$$

where

$$\alpha = z_2 - z_1, \quad \beta = z_3(z_1 - z_2), \quad \gamma = z_3 - z_1, \quad \delta = z_2(z_1 - z_3), \tag{35.3}$$

$$\alpha \delta - \beta \gamma = (z_1 - z_2)(z_2 - z_3)(z_3 - z_1). \tag{35.4}$$

Hence if the three points z_1, z_2, z_3 are distinct, then (35.2) represents a Moebius transformation, and the fourth point z can always be chosen in such a way that the cross-ratio λ assumes an arbitrarily assigned value (including the value ∞).

We have at the same time obtained the following result: *For the cross-ratio (z_1, z_2, z_3, z_4) of four points to have a well-determined value, it is necessary and sufficient for at least three of the four points to be distinct.*

If we substitute z_1, z_2, and z_3, one after another for z in (35.1), we obtain $\lambda_1 = 1$, $\lambda_2 = \infty$, $\lambda_3 = 0$. Since the cross-ratio is invariant, it follows that

$$(1, \infty, 0, \lambda) = \lambda, \tag{35.5}$$

which can also be verified directly.

The three points 1, ∞, 0 lie on the real axis; so does the fourth point λ, provided that λ is real. From this we can easily deduce the following theorem:

Four points z_1, z_2, z_3, z_4 lie on the same circle if and only if their cross-ratio (z_1, z_2, z_3, z_4) is a real number or ∞.

This theorem may be used to derive once more the representation (15.3) of the unimodular numbers. In fact, (15.3) is equivalent to

$$(i, -1, 1, u) = t, \qquad (35.6)$$

which expresses the fact that the point u lies on the circle determined by the three points $1, i, -1$.

36. If z_1, z_2, z_3 and w_1, w_2, w_3 are two triples of distinct points, then the equation

$$(w_1, w_2, w_3, w) = (z_1, z_2, z_3, z), \qquad (36.1)$$

when solved for w, represents a Moebius transformation that maps each of the points z_i onto the corresponding point w_i. Hence a Moebius transformation is determined uniquely whenever the images of three given points are assigned.

If the three points w_i are all assigned to lie on the circle determined by the three points z_i, then this circle is mapped onto itself. For example, equations (14.2) represent a transformation under which the unit circle is mapped onto itself.

37. If we calculate in addition to the cross-ratio (35.1) the cross-ratios of the same numbers z_i taken in a different order—or if (which amounts to the same) we form all possible cross-ratios of the four numbers 0, 1, ∞, λ— then we obtain the six numbers

$$\lambda, \quad \frac{1}{\lambda}, \quad 1-\lambda, \quad \frac{1}{1-\lambda}, \quad \frac{\lambda}{\lambda-1}, \quad \frac{1-\lambda}{\lambda} \qquad (37.1)$$

(each occurring four times), and no others.

In general, these six numbers are distinct. But we may equate any two of the six numbers in (37.1) and solve the resulting equations for λ, thus finding special values of λ to which correspond very particular configurations of the points z_1, z_2, z_3, z_4. In this way we are led to the following results:

First, if $\lambda = 0$ or 1 or ∞, then (37.1) contains only three distinct numbers, *viz.* 0, 1, ∞, each of which then occurs twice in (37.1). In this case, the point z_4 must coincide with one of the points z_1, z_2, z_3.

Second, if $\lambda = -1$ or 1/2 or 2, then (37.1) contains only the three distinct numbers -1, 1/2, and 2, each occuring twice. The four points z_1, z_2, z_3, z_4 must in this case lie on a circle (or on a straight line) and form a *harmonic set*. If one pair and one point of the other pair of such a set are given, it is possible to construct the fourth point by elementary-geometric constructions.

Finally, if

$$\lambda = \frac{1+i\sqrt{3}}{2} \quad \text{or} \quad \lambda = \frac{1-i\sqrt{3}}{2}, \qquad (37.2)$$

then (37.1) contains only the numbers (37.2), each occurring three times. The four points z_1, z_2, z_3, z_4 are in this case said to be in *equi-anharmonic position*. Here too it is possible to find the fourth point z_4 by elementary-geometric constructions if the points z_1, z_2, z_3 and one of the two numbers (37.2) are assigned. For example, if the points z_1, z_2, z_3 are the vertices of an equilateral triangle, then z_4 must be either the center of the triangle or the point at infinity, depending on the choice of λ.

These symmetries can also be made to show up in the formulas. If, for instance, the two pairs of points z_1, z_4 and z_2, z_3 form a harmonic set, then we must have

$$(z_1, z_2, z_3, z_4) = -1, \tag{37.3}$$

which can also be written in the form

$$2 (z_1 z_4 + z_2 z_3) = (z_1 + z_4) (z_2 + z_3). \tag{37.4}$$

In the special case $z_2 = 0$, $z_3 = \infty$, we find similarly that

$$z_1 + z_4 = 0. \tag{37.5}$$

Finally, if the three points z_1, z_2, z_3 are given, then there exist two points z_4 which complete an equi-anharmonic quadruple. They can be calculated from

$$z_4 = \frac{z_1^2 (z_2 + z_3) + z_2^2 (z_3 + z_1) + z_3^2 (z_1 + z_2) - 6 z_1 z_2 z_3 \pm i \sqrt{3} (z_3 - z_2) (z_1 - z_3) (z_2 - z_1)}{2 (z_1^2 + z_2^2 + z_3^2 - z_2 z_3 - z_3 z_1 - z_1 z_2)} \tag{37.6}$$

and any interchange of two of the points z_1, z_2, z_3 also leads to an interchange of the two points (37.6).

Reflection in a Circle (§§ 38-40)

38. If we plot the point z and its image point w under a given Moebius transformation in the same complex plane, it will be clear what is meant by a *fixed point* of the transformation. We shall see in § 52 below that every Moebius transformation other than the identity transformation $w = z$ has exactly two fixed points, which may or may not coincide.

For the general circle-preserving mapping of the second kind,

$$w = \frac{\alpha \bar{z} + \beta}{\gamma \bar{z} + \delta} \qquad (\alpha \delta - \beta \gamma \neq 0), \tag{38.1}$$

we obtain an equation for the position of the fixed points by eliminating $\bar{z}$ from the two equivalent equations

$$\frac{|\alpha\,\bar{\beta}-\beta\,\bar{\alpha}|}{|\alpha\,\delta-\beta\,\gamma|+|\alpha\,\bar{\delta}-\beta\,\bar{\gamma}|} \leqq \left|\frac{\alpha\,t+\beta}{\gamma\,t+\delta}\right| \leqq \frac{|\alpha\,\delta-\beta\,\gamma|+|\alpha\,\bar{\delta}-\beta\,\bar{\gamma}|}{|\gamma\,\bar{\delta}-\delta\,\bar{\gamma}|} \left.\right\} \quad (42.4)$$

$$t \text{ real}, \quad \alpha\,\delta-\beta\,\gamma \neq 0,$$

obtained in this manner would not have been easy to establish without the above geometric considerations. We note that the first one of the inequalities in (42.4) remains valid even if the circle κ degenerates into a straight line, i.e. even if $\gamma\,\bar{\delta}-\delta\,\bar{\gamma}=0$.

43. The Moebius transformation (41.1) maps the unit circle

$$|t| = 1, \quad t = e^{i\vartheta} \qquad (\vartheta \text{ real}) \quad (43.1)$$

onto a circle κ* whose equation is obtained by eliminating t from

$$z = \frac{\alpha\,t+\beta}{\gamma\,t+\delta}, \quad \bar{z} = \frac{\bar{\alpha}+\bar{\beta}\,t}{\bar{\gamma}+\bar{\delta}\,t}. \quad (43.2)$$

This yields

$$(\gamma\,\bar{\gamma}-\delta\,\bar{\delta})\,z\,\bar{z} - (\bar{\alpha}\,\gamma-\bar{\beta}\,\delta)\,z - (\alpha\,\bar{\gamma}-\beta\,\bar{\delta})\,\bar{z} + (\alpha\,\bar{\alpha}-\beta\,\bar{\beta}) = 0, \quad (43.3)$$

from which we obtain, by the method of the last two sections,

$$\frac{|\alpha\,\bar{\alpha}-\beta\,\bar{\beta}|}{|\alpha\,\delta-\beta\,\gamma|+|\alpha\,\bar{\gamma}-\beta\,\bar{\delta}|} \leqq \left|\frac{\alpha\,e^{i\vartheta}+\beta}{\gamma\,e^{i\vartheta}+\delta}\right| \leqq \frac{|\alpha\,\delta-\beta\,\gamma|+|\alpha\,\bar{\gamma}-\beta\,\bar{\delta}|}{|\gamma\,\bar{\gamma}-\delta\,\bar{\delta}|} \left.\right\} \quad (43.4)$$

$$\vartheta \text{ real}, \quad \alpha\,\delta-\beta\,\gamma \neq 0.$$

44. The various formulas developed above make it easy to calculate the center and radius of a circle that is to pass through three given points z_1, z_2, z_3. For by § 35, we obtain the equation of this circle by equating the cross-ratio (z_1, z_2, z_3, z) to a real number t, thus:

$$\frac{(z_1-z_2)\,(z_3-z)}{(z_1-z_3)\,(z_2-z)} = t. \quad (44.1)$$

In order to be able to make use of equations (41.1), we must write

$$\alpha = (z_1-z_3)\,z_2, \quad \beta = (z_2-z_1)\,z_3, \quad \gamma = z_1-z_3, \quad \delta = z_2-z_1. \quad (44.2)$$

From this we calculate

$$\left. \begin{aligned} \alpha\,\delta-\beta\,\gamma &= (z_1-z_2)\,(z_2-z_3)\,(z_3-z_1), \\ \alpha\,\bar{\delta}-\beta\,\bar{\gamma} &= z_1\,\bar{z}_1\,(z_3-z_2) + z_2\,\bar{z}_2\,(z_1-z_3) + z_3\,\bar{z}_3\,(z_2-z_1), \\ \gamma\,\bar{\delta}-\delta\,\bar{\gamma} &= (z_2\,\bar{z}_3-z_3\,\bar{z}_2) + (z_3\,\bar{z}_1-z_1\,\bar{z}_3) + (z_1\,\bar{z}_2-z_2\,\bar{z}_1), \\ \alpha\,\bar{\beta}-\beta\,\bar{\alpha} &= z_1\,\bar{z}_1\,(z_3\,\bar{z}_2-z_2\,\bar{z}_3) + z_2\,\bar{z}_2\,(z_1\,\bar{z}_3-z_3\,\bar{z}_1) + z_3\,\bar{z}_3\,(z_2\,\bar{z}_1-z_1\,\bar{z}_2), \end{aligned} \right\} \quad (44.3)$$

whence we can immediately write down the final formulas for a and R, which turn out to be symmetrical in z_1, z_2, z_3, as of course they ought to be.

Pencils of Circles (§§ 45-50)

45. Our results concerning circle-preserving transformations imply that every such transformation maps any two circles that intersect each other at right angles onto a like pair of circles. We also note, for use below, that if a circle has a pair z, $\bar{z}$ of complex conjugates as two of its points, then it must be orthogonal to the real axis, and that, conversely, every circle that is orthogonal to the real axis must contain $\bar{z}$ if it contains z.

Now let κ_1 be an arbitrary circle (or straight line), let z_0 be any point not lying on κ_1, and let z_1 be the point obtained from z_0 by inversion in κ_1. Then every circle containing both z_0 and z_1 must intersect the circle κ_1 at right angles, and every circle through z_0 and orthogonal to κ_1 must contain the point z_1.

Let us consider also a second circle κ_2 and the point z_2 obtained from z_0 by inversion in κ_2. Then the circle determined by the three points z_0, z_1, and z_2 must be orthogonal to each of the two circles κ_1 and κ_2.

We define a *pencil of circles* to be the totality of all circles orthogonal to two given circles κ_1 and κ_2. The discussion above shows that every point z_0 lying neither on κ_1 nor on κ_2 must lie on at least one circle of the pencil. We also see that every Moebius transformation maps a pencil of circles onto another pencil of circles. We shall make use of this invariance under Moebius transformations of the set of pencils of circles for a classification of such pencils.

46. Let us consider first the case of two circles κ_1 and κ_2 that intersect at two points P and Q. In this case we can find a Moebius transformation that maps the points P and Q onto $z = 0$ and $z = \infty$ respectively, and that therefore maps κ_1 and κ_2 onto two straight lines passing through $z = 0$. The pencil of circles determined by κ_1 and κ_2 must here be mapped onto the totality of circles having the two straight lines as diameters, i.e. onto the totality of concentric circles with center at $z = 0$. The only points of the extended complex plane that are not contained on any of the circles of the transformed pencil are the two points $z = 0$ and $z = \infty$; these we shall call the *limiting points* of the pencil. Every other point of the plane is contained on exactly one circle of the transformed pencil.

For the original configuration, consisting of all the circles orthogonal to both κ_1 and κ_2, the situation is quite analogous; there passes through every point of the extended plane other than P and Q exactly one circle of the pencil, and no two of these circles have a point in common. Pencils of this kind are called *hyperbolic pencils* of circles.

47. The second case to be considered is that of two circles κ_1 and κ_2 having no point in common. Here we first use a Moebius transformation that maps κ_1 and κ_2 onto a straight line κ_1' and a circle κ_2' respectively; the line κ_1' will of course be entirely on the outside of the circle κ_2' (see Fig. 6). Let us

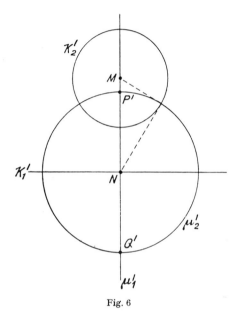

Fig. 6

denote by μ_1' the straight line MN that passes through the center of κ_2' and is perpendicular to κ_1', and by μ_2', the circle with center at N that is orthogonal to κ_2'. Let P' and Q' be the two points of intersection of μ_1' and μ_2'. Now we use a second Moebius transformation to map P' and Q' onto $z = 0$ and $z = \infty$, respectively. As we saw in the preceding section, this transformation maps κ_1' and κ_2' onto two concentric circles κ_1'' and κ_2'' that are orthogonal to every straight line through $z = 0$ but not, both simultaneously, to any other straight line or circle. This implies that the only circles that are orthogonal to both κ_1' and κ_2' are those that pass through P' and Q'.

Hence there are two points P and Q such that the circles through P and Q are the only ones that are orthogonal to the two given circles κ_1 and κ_2. These two points P and Q are the only pair of points having the property of being the images of each other both under inversion in κ_1 and under inversion in κ_2. We shall call these two points the *common points* of the pencil. A pencil consisting of all the circles passing through two fixed points P and Q is called an *elliptic pencil* of circles.

48. A pencil of circles is called *parabolic* if it consists of all the circles orthogonal to two mutually tangent circles. If the point P of tangency of κ_1 and κ_2 is mapped onto the point $z = \infty$ by a suitable Moebius transformation, then the circles κ_1 and κ_2 are mapped onto two parallel straight lines κ_1' and κ_2', and the parabolic pencil defined above is mapped onto a family of parallel straight lines orthogonal to κ_1' and κ_2'. Hence the original parabolic pencil consists of all circles that are orthogonal at P to both κ_1 and κ_2.

49. Two pencils of circles having the property that each circle of one pencil is orthogonal to each circle of the other pencil, are called *conjugate pencils* of circles. Every elliptic pencil has exactly one conjugate pencil, which turns out to be hyperbolic; conversely, the unique conjugate of any given hyperbolic pencil is always an elliptic pencil. The parabolic pencils can be paired off into pairs of conjugates.

The above implies that for any two given circles κ_1 and κ_2, there exists exactly one pencil of circles that contains both of them. This pencil will be elliptic, parabolic, or hyperbolic, according to whether the two circles have two, one, or no points in common.

We have obtained all these results as simple applications of the following theorem: Two circles that intersect or are mutually tangent can always be mapped, by means of a suitable Moebius transformation, onto two intersecting straight lines or onto two parallel straight lines, respectively; and two circles that have no point in common can be similarly mapped onto two concentric circles.

We also note the following fact: Among the members of a pencil of circles, there always exists exactly one straight line, except in the degenerate case of a pencil consisting of concentric circles or of parallel straight lines. This straight line, in fact, is the locus of the centers of the circles that form the pencil conjugate to the given pencil.

50. The families of circles on the Riemann sphere that are mapped onto planar pencils of circles, under stereographic projection, can be described in very simple terms.

For if we consider a circle κ on the sphere and pass through its points Q the tangents to the sphere that are orthogonal to κ, then all these tangents will meet at a point P in space (which may be at infinity). Conversely, every tangent through P to the sphere meets the sphere at a point Q of κ. But the point P is the pole (relative to the sphere) of the plane of κ. Therefore, two circles on the sphere are mutually orthogonal if and only if the plane of one circle passes through the pole of the plane of the other circle and *vice versa*, that is if and only if their planes are conjugates of each other.

Now consider two circles κ_1 and κ_2 on the sphere, and let the poles of their planes be P_1 and P_2 respectively. Let g be the straight line joining P_1 and P_2. The pencil of planes through g intersects the sphere in a family of circles whose stereographic projection onto the plane yields a pencil of circles. This pencil of circles will be elliptic, parabolic, or hyperbolic, according to whether g has two, one, or no points in common with the sphere. The locus of the poles of the planes that make up a pencil with the axis g, is a straight line g', and it is the line g' that can be used to construct the pencil of circles conjugate to the one just obtained from g itself.

Moebius Transformations Generated by Two Reflections (§ 51)

51. Under reflection (i.e., inversion) in a circle κ_1, every circle κ orthogonal to κ_1 is mapped onto itself. If the reflection in κ_1 is followed by a second reflection, in a circle κ_2, then the resulting composition of the two reflections represents a conformal[1] circle-preserving transformation that leaves invariant (i.e., maps onto itself) every circle κ of the pencil consisting of all the circles orthogonal to both κ_1 and κ_2.

Conversely, consider a Moebius transformation that leaves invariant each circle of a given pencil of circles. We shall prove that any transformation of this kind can be broken down into two successive reflections in two circles κ_1 and κ_2 belonging to the pencil of circles conjugate to the given pencil, and that, moreover, one of these two circles can be chosen at random among the circles of its pencil.

Let us assume first that the pencil of invariant circles is hyperbolic. Since a hyperbolic pencil can always be transformed into the pencil of concentric circles $|z| = r$ by means of a suitable Moebius transformation, it suffices to prove the above statement for the case that the invariant circles are the circles $|z| = r$. Now if a Moebius transformation leaves these circles invariant, it must map every straight line g through $z = 0$ onto some straight line g^* also through $z = 0$. If $z_0 \neq 0$ is a point on g, then a reflection in one of the two angle bisectors h of g and g^* maps z_0 onto the same image point z_0^* on g^* as does our Moebius transformation (since the latter shares with the reflection the property of leaving $|z|$ unchanged, for all z). Hence the Moebius transformation in question differs from the reflection in h by a circle-preserving transformation with the fixed points $z = 0$, $z = z_0^*$, and $z = \infty$. By § 40, the only such circle-preserving transformation is a reflection in g^*. We now

---

[1] That is, of the first kind (see § 29 above). A mapping is said to be *conformal* if it preserves the magnitude and the sign (sense) of every angle [*Trans.*].

write the equations of h and of g^* in the forms

$$z\,e^{-i\,\varphi} - \bar{z}\,e^{i\,\varphi} = 0, \qquad z\,e^{-i\,\psi} - \bar{z}\,e^{i\,\psi} = 0.$$ (51.1)

By reflection in h, a point z is mapped on the point

$$z^* = e^{2\,i\,\varphi}\,\bar{z}, \qquad \bar{z}^* = e^{-2\,i\,\varphi}\,z.$$ (51.2)

By reflection in g^*, the point z^* is mapped onto

$$w = e^{2\,i\,\psi}\,\bar{z}^*.$$ (51.3)

The composition of the last two operations yields

$$w = e^{2\,i\,(\psi - \varphi)}\,z.$$ (51.4)

This Moebius transformation is a rotation through the angle $\vartheta = 2(\psi - \varphi)$, and we see that φ (or ψ), hence also h (or g^*), can be chosen arbitrarily.

We are led, by similar reasoning, to analogous conclusions if the pencil of invariant circles is elliptic. After transforming this pencil into the pencil of straight lines through $z = 0$ by means of a suitable preliminary Moebius transformation, we find in this case that any Moebius transformation leaving each of these lines invariant must be the resultant of two successive reflections in two concentric circles

$$z\,\bar{z} = a^2, \qquad z\,\bar{z} = b^2.$$ (51.5)

This time, we have to compound the two transformations $z^*\bar{z} = a^2$ and $w\bar{z}^* = b^2$, and we obtain

$$w = \frac{b^2}{a^2}\,z.$$ (51.6)

Since the Moebius transformation (51.6) depends only on the ratio of the radii of the two circles (51.5), we may once more assign the first (or the second) of these two radii arbitrarily.

In the third case, that of a parabolic pencil of invariant circles, we are similarly led to reflections in two parallel straight lines. The composition (product) of these reflections is a translation of the complex plane. This translation depends only on the direction of the two parallels and on their distance from each other, but not on the position in the plane of each of them. Thus we have proved the statement set forth above, in all of its parts.

Representation of the General Moebius Transformation
as a Product of Inversions in Circles (§§ 52-55)

52. Every Moebius transformation

$$w = \frac{\alpha z + \beta}{\gamma z + \delta} \qquad (\alpha \delta - \beta \gamma \neq 0) \qquad (52.1)$$

can be written as the product of two or of four inversions, as we shall now prove.

We begin by considering the fixed points of the transformation (52.1), which we can obtain by setting $w = z$; thus the fixed points—to be denoted by z_i—are the roots of the equation

$$\gamma z^2 + (\delta - \alpha) z - \beta = 0, \qquad (52.2)$$

and if $\gamma \neq 0$, they can be written

$$z_i = \frac{\alpha - \delta \pm \sqrt{\Delta}}{2\gamma}, \qquad \Delta = (\alpha + \delta)^2 - 4(\alpha \delta - \beta \gamma). \qquad (52.3)$$

Therefore if $\gamma \neq 0$, the number of fixed points is either one or two, according to whether $\Delta = 0$ or $\Delta \neq 0$.

If $\gamma = 0$, we have to count the point $z = \infty$ as a fixed point. Since $\Delta = (\alpha - \delta)^2$ in this case, we once more have one or two fixed points, according to whether $\Delta = 0$ or $\Delta \neq 0$.

53. Let us deal first with the case that $\Delta = 0$, i.e. that $\alpha \delta - \beta \gamma = (\alpha + \delta)^2/4$. If $\gamma = 0$ also, then we must have $\alpha = \delta$ and

$$w = z + \frac{\beta}{\alpha}. \qquad (53.1)$$

This transformation is a translation of the plane, and can be factored into two successive reflections in two parallel straight lines.

But if $\gamma \neq 0$, then we have

$$z_1 = z_2 = \frac{\alpha - \delta}{2\gamma}, \qquad \gamma z_1 + \delta = \frac{\alpha + \delta}{2}, \qquad (53.2)$$

hence by (34.1):

$$w - z_1 = w - w_1 = \frac{(\alpha \delta - \beta \gamma)(z - z_1)}{(\gamma z + \delta)(\gamma z_1 + \delta)} = \frac{(\alpha + \delta)(z - z_1)}{2(\gamma z + \delta)}. \qquad (53.3)$$

On the other hand,

$$\gamma z + \delta = \gamma (z - z_1) + \frac{\alpha + \delta}{2}, \qquad (53.4)$$

so that we can write

$$\frac{1}{w - z_1} = \frac{1}{z - z_1} + \frac{2\gamma}{\alpha + \delta} \tag{53.5}$$

If we introduce the new parameters

$$\omega = \frac{1}{w - z_1}, \quad t = \frac{1}{z - z_1}, \tag{53.6}$$

then our transformation (53.3) assumes once more the form of a translation,

$$\omega = t + \frac{2\gamma}{\alpha + \delta}, \tag{53.7}$$

and we have proved the following theorem:

Every Moebius transformation for which the discriminant Δ vanishes can be represented as the product of two reflections in two mutually tangent circles (or in two parallel straight lines).

54. If $\Delta \neq 0$ and $\gamma \neq 0$, then by (34.1) we have

$$\frac{w - z_2}{w - z_1} = \frac{w - w_2}{w - w_1} = \frac{\gamma z_1 + \delta}{\gamma z_2 + \delta} \cdot \frac{z - z_2}{z - z_1}. \tag{54.1}$$

The change of variables

$$\omega = \frac{w - z_2}{w - z_1}, \quad t = \frac{z - z_2}{z - z_1} \tag{54.2}$$

brings our Moebius transformation into the simple form

$$\omega = \varrho\, t, \tag{54.3}$$

where

$$\varrho = \frac{\gamma z_1 + \delta}{\gamma z_2 + \delta} = \frac{\alpha + \delta + \sqrt{\Delta}}{\alpha + \delta - \sqrt{\Delta}}. \tag{54.4}$$

But if $\gamma = 0$, $\Delta = (\delta - \alpha)^2 \neq 0$, then we write

$$\omega = w - \frac{\beta}{\delta - \alpha}, \quad t = z - \frac{\beta}{\delta - \alpha}; \tag{54.5}$$

we are once more led to (54.3), with

$$\varrho = \frac{\alpha}{\delta} = \frac{\alpha + \delta + \sqrt{\Delta}}{\alpha + \delta - \sqrt{\Delta}} \qquad (\sqrt{\Delta} = \alpha - \delta). \tag{54.6}$$

Thus the two cases $\gamma \neq 0$ and $\gamma = 0$ lead to the same formulas. The resulting types of transformations of the complex plane depend on the value of ϱ, as follows:

First, if ϱ is real and > 0 but $\neq 1$, then the transformation (54.3), and hence also the transformation (54.1), can be represented by two successive reflections (inversions) in two of the circles of a hyperbolic pencil of circles. Second, if ϱ is unimodular but $\neq 1$, then our transformation can be represented by two successive inversions in two of the circles of an elliptic pencil. Finally, if

$$\varrho = a\, e^{i\,\vartheta}, \quad a > 0, \quad a \neq 1, \quad 0 < \vartheta < 2\pi, \tag{54.7}$$

then the transformation (54.3) can be written as the product of *four* inversions, the first two in two circles of a certain pencil and the last two in two circles of the conjugate pencil. We can then verify easily that if $\vartheta \neq \pi$, no circle and no straight line can be mapped onto itself, and from this it follows that *no less than four* inversions will suffice to represent the given Moebius transformation. A Moebius transformation of this type is called *loxodromic*. We find that if $\vartheta = \pi$, the transformation (54.3) is likewise loxodromic.

55. From (54.4), and then (52.3), we obtain

$$\sqrt{\Delta} = (\alpha + \delta)\, \frac{\varrho - 1}{\varrho + 1}, \quad (\alpha + \delta)^2 - 4\,(\alpha\,\delta - \beta\,\gamma) = \Delta = (\alpha + \delta)^2 \left(\frac{\varrho - 1}{\varrho + 1}\right)^2, \tag{55.1}$$

and from this we obtain the rational invariant

$$\lambda = \frac{(\alpha + \delta)^2}{4\,(\alpha\,\delta - \beta\,\gamma)} = \frac{(\varrho + 1)^2}{4\,\varrho} = 1 + \frac{(\varrho - 1)^2}{4\,\varrho}. \tag{55.2}$$

This invariant λ serves very well to characterize, and distinguish between, the various cases just discussed. For if ϱ is real, positive, and $\neq 1$, then $\lambda > 1$. If ϱ is unimodular, say $\varrho = e^{i\,\vartheta}$, then $\lambda = \cos^2 \vartheta/2$; for $\varrho \neq 1$ we then have $0 \leq \lambda < 1$. Finally, if $\Delta = 0$ then $\lambda = 1$.

In summary, we see that *the Moebius transformation (52.1) is always loxodromic for non-real λ, and for negative real λ. If λ is real and ≥ 0, then the transformation can be represented as a product of inversions in two circles of a pencil of circles that is elliptic, parabolic, or hyperbolic, according to whether $\lambda < 1$, $\lambda = 1$, or $\lambda > 1$.*

CHAPTER THREE

EUCLIDEAN, SPHERICAL, AND NON-EUCLIDEAN GEOMETRY

Bundles of Circles (§§ 56-57)

56. By a *bundle of circles* on the Riemann sphere we shall mean the totality of circles on this sphere whose planes pass through some fixed point M in space. This point M may also be at infinity.

If two circles κ_1 and κ_2 belong to a given bundle, then every circle of the pencil containing κ_1 and κ_2 itself belongs to the bundle.

Any three circles κ_1, κ_2, κ_3 that do not belong to the same pencil of circles uniquely determine a bundle of circles. Every other circle of the bundle belongs to one of the pencils determined by κ_3 and some circle κ' of the pencil containing κ_1 and κ_2.

If M does not lie on the sphere, then on every circle of the bundle corresponding to M there are pairs P, Q of points collinear with M. If a circle of the bundle contains the point P it must also contain the point Q.

A *bundle of circles* is said to be *hyperbolic, parabolic,* or *elliptic,* according to whether the point M lies outside the sphere, on the sphere, or in the interior of the sphere.

57. Stereographic projection maps a bundle of circles on the Riemann sphere onto what we shall call a bundle of circles in the complex plane. The latter bundles, of course, have properties analogous to the properties of bundles on the sphere enumerated in § 56 above.

The following remarks will show how the bundles of circles in the plane can be defined independently of bundles of circles on the sphere:

First, if the point M coincides with the north pole N of the sphere, then the bundle on the sphere is parabolic, and its stereographic image is the totality of all the straight lines in the complex plane.

Second, if M lies in the plane that is tangent to the sphere at the north pole N, then the corresponding bundle in the plane consists of all the circles and straight lines that are orthogonal to a fixed straight line.

In all other cases, the line NM meets the complex plane at a point M_1, and the bundle in the plane contains among its members all the straight lines passing through M_1. Now if M lies outside the sphere, then the bundle is hyperbolic and consists of all the circles orthogonal to a fixed circle. In particular, the straight lines through M_1 must be diameters of this fixed circle; its center is therefore at M_1.

If M lies on the sphere, then the bundle is parabolic and consists of all the circles and straight lines that pass through M_1.

Finally, if M lies inside the sphere, then there exists exactly *one* circle with center at M_1 that belongs to the bundle. This circle is called the "equator" of the elliptic bundle. To construct a diameter AB of the equator, we may proceed as follows (see Fig. 7): Let T be the second point of intersection of the

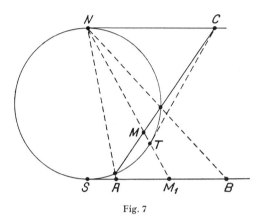

Fig. 7

Riemann sphere and the line NMM_1. The circles on the sphere that project onto circles of the complex plane about M_1 as center, lie in planes that pass through the line of intersection C of the tangent planes at N and at T. Hence the plane through CM perpendicular to the plane in which Fig. 7 is drawn cuts the sphere in a circle whose stereographic projection is the equator of the bundle.

We know from the preceding section that we can find all the circles of an elliptic bundle once we know its equator and two of the diameters of the equator. It is easy to see that such a bundle consists of all the circles that intersect the equator at the end points of one of its diameters.

The Equations of the Circles of a Bundle (§§ 58-59)

58. If we want the plane (33.3) to pass through the point whose coordinates are ξ_0, η_0, ζ_0, we obtain the equation

$$D = -A\,\xi_0 - B\,\eta_0 - C\,\zeta_0. \tag{58.1}$$

To obtain the equations of the circles of an arbitrary bundle, we need only substitute the above value of D into (23.3) and to consider A, B, C as variable parameters.

The set of all great circles on the Riemann sphere is an example of an elliptic bundle. To obtain their equations, we set $\xi_0 = \eta_0 = \zeta_0 = 0$; by (23.3) and (58.1), we find

$$A (z + \bar{z}) + i B (\bar{z} - z) + C (z\bar{z} - 1) = 0. \tag{58.2}$$

The equator of this bundle is the unit circle $z\bar{z} = 1$.

By setting $\xi_0 = \eta_0 = 0$, $\zeta_0 = 1$, we obtain a parabolic bundle. Its equation is

$$A (z + \bar{z}) + i B (\bar{z} - z) - 2 C = 0, \tag{58.3}$$

and it consists of the totality of all straight lines of the complex plane.

By choosing $\xi_0 = \eta_0 = 0$, $\zeta_0 > 1$, we obtain a hyperbolic bundle whose equation is

$$A (z + \bar{z}) + i B (\bar{z} - z) - \frac{D}{\zeta_0} (z\bar{z} - 1) + D (z\bar{z} + 1) = 0.$$

If ζ_0 is made to tend to infinity, the last bundle will become the hyperbolic bundle

$$A (z + \bar{z}) + i B (\bar{z} - z) + D (z\bar{z} + 1) = 0, \tag{58.4}$$

which consists of all the circles orthogonal to the unit circle. As we know from (23.4) above, the additional requirement

$$D^2 < A^2 + B^2 \tag{58.5}$$

must here be satisfied.

Instead of the bundle (58.4), one often uses the bundle

$$A (z + \bar{z}) + C (z\bar{z} - 1) + D (z\bar{z} + 1) = 0 \quad (D^2 < A^2 + C^2), \tag{58.6}$$

which consists of all the circles orthogonal to the real axis.

59. Every circle-preserving transformation maps any given bundle of circles onto another bundle of circles, which must be of the same type as its pre-image. The first part of this statement is an almost obvious consequence of § 56 and of the fact that a circle-preserving transformation maps any given pencil of circles onto another pencil, of the same type. As to the second part of the above statement, it now suffices to note that an elliptic bundle contains none but elliptic pencils, that a parabolic bundle contains both elliptic and parabolic pencils, and that a hyperbolic bundle contains all three types of pencils.

Every elliptic bundle of circles can be mapped onto the bundle (58.2) by means of a suitable Moebius transformation. Every parabolic or hyperbolic bundle can be mapped similarly onto the bundle (58.3) or (58.4), respectively. (Instead of (58.4), we may also use (58.6).)

Products of Inversions in the Circles of a Bundle (§ 60)

60. Let us consider the Moebius transformations that one obtains by performing an even number of successive inversions (reflections) in the circles of a given bundle of circles. The set of all these Moebius transformations has the remarkable property of being a subgroup of the group of all Moebius transformations.

To prove this, it suffices to show that any sequence of *four* inversions may be replaced by *two* inversions in circles of the same bundle. (These two circles may coincide, in which case the mapping leaves each point of the plane fixed.) To this end, let K_1, K_2, K_3, K_4 be the four circles (or straight lines) of the bundle in which the four reflections are carried out, one after the other. We choose an arbitrary point[1] P on K_1. We then replace the reflections in the circles K_2, K_3 by two reflections in circles K_2', K_3' that are chosen such (*cf.* § 51) that the resulting Moebius transformation is the same as that generated by K_2, K_3 and that K_2' passes through the point P. The resultant (product) of the original four reflections is the same as the resultant of the reflections in the four circles K_1, K_2', K_3', K_4. Next we replace the reflections in the circles K_3', K_4 by equivalent reflections in two circles K_3'', K_4', the first of which passes through the point P. We can now consider the sequence of reflections in the circles K_1, K_2', K_3'', K_4'. The first three of these circles pass through one and the same point P and must therefore belong to a pencil of circles, being members of the same bundle. This implies that we can replace the reflections in K_2', K_3'' by a reflection in the circle K_1 followed by a reflection in a circle K_1^*. Denoting the circle K_4' by the new symbol K_2^*, we see that the original four reflections have been replaced by the equivalent two reflections in K_1^*, K_2^*. Incidentally, if K_2' happened to coincide with K_1, or K_3' with K_4, or K_3'' with K_2', then our goal would have been reached in fewer steps.

The theorem stated at the beginning of this section has thus been proved.

---

[1] If the bundle is parabolic, P should not coincide with the common point of intersection of all the circles of the bundle. If the bundle is hyperbolic, P should not lie on its orthogonal circle.

The Rigid Motions of Euclidean, Spherical, and
Non-Euclidean Geometry (§§ 61-62)

61. We turn now to the investigation of those Moebius transformations that are generated by two successive reflections in the circles or straight lines of one of the three "canonical" bundles of circles (58.2), (58.3), (58.4). In each of these three cases, we shall be able to interpret the corresponding group of Moebius transformations as the group of rigid motions of a certain geometry, and we shall therefore refer to these transformations as "rigid motions" (or sometimes just "motions").

We begin by observing that if two given circles have no points in common, then the product of the two reflections in these circles is a Moebius transformation whose fixed points coincide with the points of intersection of the circles orthogonal to the two given circles. Hence if the latter belong to the hyperbolic bundle (58.4), then the fixed points of the resulting rigid motion must lie on the orthogonal circle $z\bar{z} = 1$ of the bundle. The same goes for the fixed point of a motion generated by the two reflections in two mutually tangent circles of the bundle (58.4). Hence if we want the point $z = 0$ to be a fixed point of the rigid motion, then this motion must be obtainable as the product of reflections in two *intersecting* circles of the bundle, both of which must pass through the point $z = 0$. But these circles degenerate into the straight lines

$$A\,(z + \bar{z}) + i\,B\,(\bar{z} - z) = 0$$

of the bundle (58.4). The same result applies also to the other two bundles, (58.3) and (58.2). Hence by § 51 above, a rigid motion that leaves the point $z = 0$ fixed must be, in each of the three cases, of the form

$$w = e^{i\vartheta} z. \tag{61.1}$$

62. Next we shall look for rigid motions that map a given point $z = a$ of the plane onto the point $w = 0$. To this end, we follow up the reflection (39.1), in an arbitrary circle, with a reflection in the real axis, obtaining the Moebius transformation

$$A\,(w + z) - i\,B\,(z - w) + C\,(w\,z - 1) + D\,(w\,z + 1) = 0. \tag{62.1}$$

If this transformation is to map the point $z = a$ onto the point $w = 0$, we must have

$$(A - i\,B)\,a = C - D, \quad (A + i\,B)\,\bar{a} = C - D. \tag{62.2}$$

Solving (62.1) for w, and substituting the values (62.2) into the resulting equation, we obtain

$$w = \frac{\bar{a}}{a} \cdot \frac{(C-D)(a-z)}{(C-D)+(C+D)\,\bar{a}\,z} \cdot \tag{62.3}$$

To obtain the most general rigid motions that can be generated by means of the canonical bundles of § 58, we now need merely follow up a motion that maps $z=a$ onto $z=0$ with an arbitrary motion of the form (61.1).

In particular, we are led to a motion involving the circles of the bundle (58.2) by setting the parameter $D=0$ in (62.3); writing $e^{i\vartheta}\,\bar{a}/a = e^{i\varphi}$, we obtain in this way the Moebius transformations

$$w = e^{i\varphi}\,\frac{a-z}{1+\bar{a}\,z}\,, \tag{62.4}$$

which with the notation

$$a = \frac{\bar{\gamma}}{\delta}\,, \qquad e^{i\varphi} = -\frac{\bar{\delta}}{\delta} \tag{62.5}$$

can also be written in the form

$$w = \frac{\bar{\delta}\,z - \bar{\gamma}}{\gamma\,z + \delta}\,. \tag{62.6}$$

This last formula represents a rigid motion of the group under consideration, provided only that

$$\delta\,\bar{\delta} + \gamma\,\bar{\gamma} \neq 0$$

holds; in particular, for $\delta = 0$ we have the motions

$$w = e^{i\varphi}\,\frac{1}{z} \qquad \left(e^{i\varphi} = -\frac{\bar{\gamma}}{\gamma}\right), \quad (62.7)$$

which interchange the two points $z=0$ and $z=\infty$ with each other. The motions (62.7) must be added separately to the motions (62.4) if one prefers the non-homogeneous notation (62.4), which has certain advantages.

Next we turn to the rigid motions generated by reflections in circles of the *hyperbolic* bundle (58.4), for which $C=0$. The same method as that used above yields, in place of (62.4) and (62.6),

$$w = e^{i\varphi}\,\frac{a-z}{1-\bar{a}\,z}\,, \tag{62.8}$$

$$w = \frac{\bar{\delta}\,z + \bar{\gamma}}{\gamma\,z + \delta} \qquad \left(a = -\frac{\bar{\gamma}}{\delta}\,, \quad e^{i\varphi} = -\frac{\bar{\delta}}{\delta}\right). \quad (62.9)$$

Now (62.2) and $C=0$ imply

$$D^2 = a\,\bar{a}\,(A^2 + B^2)\,.$$

Hence condition (58.5) here becomes

$$a\,\bar{a} < 1,\tag{62.10}$$

or, since $a = -\bar{\gamma}/\bar{\delta}$,

$$\delta\,\bar{\delta} - \gamma\,\bar{\gamma} > 0.\tag{62.11}$$

Incidentally, comparison of (55.2) and (62.9) yields

$$\lambda = \frac{(\delta + \bar{\delta})^2}{4\,(\delta\,\bar{\delta} - \gamma\,\bar{\gamma})}.\tag{62.12}$$

Therefore relation (62.11) may also be considered as being a condition which insures that the Moebius transformation (62.9) is not a loxodromic circle-preserving transformation (see § 55 above).

Thus only interior points of the unit circle can be mapped onto the point $z = 0$ by the transformations (62.8) or (62.9). This fact also becomes evident geometrically by observing that under an inversion in a given circle, the interior of every circle orthogonal to the circle of inversion is mapped onto itself.

Finally, for the motions generated by reflections in the straight lines of the bundle (58.3), we find the formula

$$w = e^{i\varphi}\,(a - z).\tag{62.13}$$

The three groups (62.4), (62.8), and (62.13) of Moebius transformations have additional properties in common, which we shall study presently.

Distance Invariants (§§ 63-65)

63. The transformation (62.13) is an ordinary rigid motion of the Euclidean plane. Every motion of this kind maps two points z_1, z_2, whose distance from each other is $|z_2 - z_1|$, onto a pair of points w_1, w_2 having the same distance from each other, i.e. such that

$$|w_2 - w_1| = |z_2 - z_1|.\tag{63.1}$$

A similar formula holds for the motions (62.4). For let us suppose that a motion (62.4) maps the points z_1, z_2 onto the points w_1, w_2 respectively, and let us introduce the notation

$$\zeta = \frac{z_2 - z}{1 + \bar{z}_2\,z}, \qquad \omega = \frac{w_2 - w}{1 + \bar{w}_2\,w}.\tag{63.2}$$

Since the motions (62.4) constitute a group, elimination of w and z from (63.2) and (62.4) leads to another motion $\omega = \omega(\zeta)$ of the same group, which maps the point $\zeta = 0$ onto the point $\omega = 0$. This last motion must be—as we know from § 61 above—of the form $\omega = e^{i\vartheta}\zeta$, from which it follows that

$$\left| \frac{w_2 - w_1}{1 + \overline{w}_2\, w_1} \right| = \left| \frac{z_2 - z_1}{1 + \overline{z}_2\, z_1} \right|, \tag{63.3}$$

which is a relation of the same type as (63.1).

It follows similarly that for every motion (62.8), the relation

$$\left| \frac{w_2 - w_1}{1 - \overline{w}_2\, w_1} \right| = \left| \frac{z_2 - z_1}{1 - \overline{z}_2\, z_1} \right| \tag{63.4}$$

is satisfied, where the pair of points w_1, w_2 denotes the image under (62.8), of the pair of points z_1, z_2.

We may summarize the results of this section as follows: *The three expressions*

$$\tau(z_1, z_2) = |z_2 - z_1|, \quad \tau'(z_1, z_2) = \frac{|z_2 - z_1|}{|1 + \overline{z}_2\, z_1|}, \quad \tau''(z_1, z_2) = \frac{|z_2 - z_1|}{|1 - \overline{z}_2\, z_1|} \tag{63.5}$$

are invariants of the three groups of motions (62.13), (62.4), and (62.8), respectively.

64. The invariant $\tau(z_1, z_2)$ coincides with the distance invariant of the Euclidean plane. Hence it satisfies an addition theorem for any three collinear points; in particular, if h and k are positive real numbers, then we have the equation

$$\tau(0, h + k) = \tau(0, h) + \tau(h, h + k). \tag{64.1}$$

No addition theorem analogous to the above exists for the invariant $\tau'(z_1, z_2)$. However, consider the fact that an inversion in a circle of the elliptic bundle (58.2) corresponds on the Riemann sphere to an inversion in a great circle of the sphere, and that two consecutive inversions of this kind are equivalent to a rotation of the sphere about its center. This fact leads to the surmise that the invariant $\tau'(z_1, z_2)$ is somehow connected with the spherical distance of the stereographic pre-images of the points z_1 and z_2. We shall therefore try to find a function $f(u)$ which is such that the spherical distance $E_s(z_1, z_2)$ just mentioned is given by the formula

$$E_s(z_1, z_2) = f\big(\tau'(z_1, z_2)\big). \tag{64.2}$$

A first requirement on $f(u)$ is that for any two positive numbers h and k, there should hold an equation analogous to (64.1) above, thus:

$$E_s(0, h + k) = E_s(0, h) + E_s(h, h + k). \tag{64.3}$$

Now we have

$$\tau'(0, h + k) = h + k, \quad \tau'(0, h) = h, \quad \tau'(h, h + k) = \frac{k}{1 + (h + k)\,h}. \quad (64.4)$$

Hence the function $f(u)$ must satisfy the functional equation

$$f(h + k) = f(h) + f\left(\frac{k}{1 + (h + k)\,h}\right) \quad (h \geq 0,\ k \geq 0). \quad (64.5)$$

For $h = k = 0$, this implies that

$$f(0) = 0. \quad (64.6)$$

Moreover, introducing the abbreviations

$$v = \frac{k}{1 + (h + k)\,h}, \quad k = \frac{v\,(1 + h^2)}{1 - v\,h}, \quad (64.7)$$

we may re-write (64.5) in the form

$$\frac{f(h + k) - f(h)}{k} = \frac{f(v)}{v} \cdot \frac{1 - v\,h}{1 + h^2}. \quad (64.8)$$

Now if we let v tend to zero and denote the derivative of $f(u)$ at $u = 0$ by c, we obtain—noting that k must tend to zero if v does—

$$\frac{d}{dh}\,f(h) = c\,\frac{1}{1 + h^2}, \quad (64.9)$$

and from this equation it follows by integration that

$$f(u) = c\,\text{arctg}\,u, \quad u = \text{tg}\,\frac{f(u)}{c}. \quad (64.10)$$

Up to this point, the choice of a value for c is arbitrary. But if we wish the distance invariant just obtained to coincide with arc length on the Riemann sphere of radius unity, in order to obtain agreement with the usual formulas of Spherical Trigonometry, we must set $c = 2$. Comparison of (63.5), (64.2), (64.10) then yields, as the defining equation for $E_s(z_1, z_2)$,

$$\text{tg}\,\frac{E_s(z_1, z_2)}{2} = \frac{|z_1 - z_2|}{|1 + \bar{z}_2\,z_1|}. \quad (64.11)$$

We can verify, as an afterthought, the general validity of the functional equation (64.5) for the functions $f(u) = c\,\text{arctg}\,u$ by means of the addition theorem of the tangent function.

65. Guided by the similarity of the expressions for $\tau'(z_1, z_2)$ and $\tau''(z_1, z_2)$, let us try next to replace equations (64.2) and (64.3) by the following:

$$E_n(z_1, z_2) = g(\tau''(z_1, z_2)),$$

$$E_n(0, h + k) = E_n(0, h) + E_n(h, h + k).$$

(65.1)

Here, $g(u)$ denotes a function to be determined, and $E_n(z_1, z_2)$ denotes a new invariant which can, as we shall show, be interpreted as the distance invariant of a non-Euclidean plane (see § 80 below). In place of the functional equation (64.5), we now obtain

$$g(h + k) = g(h) + g\left(\frac{k}{1 - (h + k)h}\right).$$

(65.2)

Here we must keep in mind that because of (62.10), we need consider the Moebius transformation (62.8) only in the interior $|z| < 1$ of the unit circle, so that (65.2) need be verified only for values of h and k satisfying the conditions

$$h \geq 0, \quad k \geq 0, \quad h + k < 1.$$

(65.3)

From (65.2) we obtain, by a calculation similar to the one in § 64 above,

$$g(0) = 0, \quad \frac{d}{du}g(u) = c\frac{1}{1 - u^2} = \frac{c}{2} \cdot \frac{d}{du}\left(l\frac{1 + u}{1 - u}\right);$$

(65.4)

if we make use of the hyperbolic functions (cf. §§ 240, 243 below), this may also be written in the form

$$u = \left(\frac{e^{\frac{2g}{c}} - 1}{e^{\frac{2g}{c}} + 1}\right) = \operatorname{tgh}\frac{g(u)}{c}.$$

(65.5)

In order to preserve the analogy to the formulas of Spherical Geometry, we again set $c = 2$ and finally obtain

$$\operatorname{tgh}\frac{E_n(z_1, z_2)}{2} = \frac{|z_1 - z_2|}{|1 - \bar{z}_2 z_1|}.$$

(65.6)

By (14.11) above, the right-hand side of (65.6) always represents a number < 1, so that the last equation always yields a finite real value for $E_n(z_1, z_2)$.

Spherical Trigonometry (§§ 66-72)

66. We consider three points z_1, z_2, z_3 of the complex plane. We shall denote arbitrary re-arrangements of these points by z_i, z_j, z_k, and we introduce the notation

$$a_i = E_s(z_j, z_k) \qquad (i = 1, 2, 3). \qquad (66.1)$$

Here the meaning of $E_s(z_j, z_k)$ is that given in § 64 above, so that

$$\operatorname{tg} \frac{a_i}{2} = \frac{|z_j - z_k|}{|1 + \bar{z}_j z_k|} \qquad (i = 1, 2, 3). \qquad (66.2)$$

Let us assume, in what follows, that all the numbers $|z_j - z_k|$ and all the numbers $|1 + \bar{z}_j z_k|$ are different from zero, i.e. that the three numbers z_1, z_2, z_3 are distinct and that no two of them are the stereographic projections of two diametrically opposite points of the Riemann sphere (cf. § 33 above). Then we may always assume that the three numbers a_i satisfy the inequalities

$$0 < a_i < \pi. \qquad (i = 1, 2, 3) \qquad (66.3)$$

These numbers remain invariant under every Moebius transformation of the form (62.4) or (62.6); as we shall see later, they may be regarded as the spherical lengths of the sides of a triangle of circular arcs.

67. We define the angles of the triangle just mentioned as follows. We first note that among the circles of the bundle (58.2), there is exactly one that passes through the points z_1 and z_3, and exactly one that passes through z_2 and z_3; for each of these two circles must also pass through the point $z_3^* = -1/\bar{z}_3$, which by assumption is distinct from both z_1 and z_2. The two circles, incidentally, may coincide. On the first of these circles (the one through z_3, z_1, and z_3^*), consider the arc that joins z_3 to z_3^* and contains z_1. On the second circle, mark the arc joining z_3 to z_3^* and containing z_2. The two arcs just constructed form at the point z_3 an angle α_3 that is uniquely determined by the additional condition

$$0 \leqq \alpha_3 \leqq \pi. \qquad (67.1)$$

The angle α_3 is invariant under every spherical motion (i.e., Moebius transformation generated by inversions in circles of the elliptic bundle (58.2)). It is easy to determine it; to this end, we consider the spherical motion

$$Z = e^{i\varphi} \frac{z_3 - z}{1 + \bar{z}_3 z} \qquad (67.2)$$

and introduce the notation

$$Z_i = e^{i\varphi} \frac{z_3 - z_i}{1 + \bar{z}_3 z_i} \qquad (i = 1, 2, 3). \qquad (67.3)$$

We also choose a value of the parameter φ that makes Z_1 real and positive. Then if we set

$$Z_2 = |Z_2| e^{i\vartheta}, \qquad (-\pi \leqq \vartheta < \pi) \qquad (67.4)$$

it follows that $\vartheta = \pm \alpha_3$. We also have the equation

$$Z_1 \bar{Z}_2 + Z_2 \bar{Z}_1 = 2 |Z_1| |Z_2| \cos \vartheta = 2 |Z_1| |Z_2| \cos \alpha_3, \qquad (67.5)$$

from which $\cos \alpha_3$, and hence by (67.1) also the angle α_3 itself, can be determined uniquely. A similar procedure leads to α_1 and α_2.

In what follows, we shall use in our formulas not the angles α_i themselves but rather the exterior angles

$$A_i = \pi - \alpha_i \qquad (i = 1, 2, 3) \quad (67.6)$$

of the triangle, which has certain advantages. The numbers A_i also lie in the interval

$$0 \leqq A_i \leqq \pi \qquad (i = 1, 2, 3). \quad (67.7)$$

Equation (67.5) now becomes

$$Z_1 \bar{Z}_2 + Z_2 \bar{Z}_1 = - 2 |Z_1| |Z_2| \cos A_3. \qquad (67.8)$$

68. The angles A_i are invariant under every spherical motion, since these motions are conformal circle-preserving transformations (*cf.* § 29 above). Another verification of this invariance is implied by the fact that the A_i can be expressed as functions of the sides a_i, a_j, a_k, as follows. First, (67.3) implies that $z_3 = 0$, so that

$$|Z_1| = \text{tg} \, \frac{a_2}{2}, \qquad |Z_2| = \text{tg} \, \frac{a_1}{2}, \qquad (68.1)$$

$$\frac{|Z_2 - Z_1|}{|1 + \bar{Z}_2 Z_1|} = \text{tg} \, \frac{a_3}{2}. \qquad (68.2)$$

Now the last equation yields

$$|Z_2 - Z_1|^2 \cos^2 \frac{a_3}{2} - |1 + \bar{Z}_2 Z_1|^2 \sin^2 \frac{a_3}{2} = 0. \qquad (68.3)$$

But

$$|Z_2 - Z_1|^2 = |Z_2|^2 + |Z_1|^2 - (Z_1 \bar{Z}_2 + Z_2 \bar{Z}_1),$$

$$|1 + Z_1 \bar{Z}_2|^2 = 1 + |Z_1|^2 |Z_2|^2 + (Z_1 \bar{Z}_2 + Z_2 \bar{Z}_1).$$

Combining the last equation with (68.3) and (67.8), we obtain

$$2 |Z_1| |Z_2| \cos A_3 = (1 + |Z_1|^2 |Z_2|^2) \sin^2 \frac{a_3}{2} - (|Z_1|^2 + |Z_2|^2) \cos^2 \frac{a_3}{2}. \quad (68.4)$$

It is convenient to transform this relation by using the identities

$$\cos A_3 = 2 \cos^2 \frac{A_3}{2} - 1 = 1 - 2 \sin^2 \frac{A_3}{2}.$$

This yields the two mutually equivalent relations

$$4 |Z_1| |Z_2| \cos^2 \frac{A_3}{2} = (1 + |Z_1| |Z_2|)^2 \sin^2 \frac{a_3}{2} - (|Z_1| - |Z_2|)^2 \cos^2 \frac{a_3}{2}, \quad (68.5)$$

$$4 |Z_1| |Z_2| \sin^2 \frac{A_3}{2} = (|Z_1| + |Z_2|)^2 \cos^2 \frac{a_3}{2} - (1 - |Z_1| |Z_2|)^2 \sin^2 \frac{a_3}{2}. \quad (68.6)$$

Now we use equations (68.1) and multiply through by the denominators $\cos^2 a_1/2$, $\cos^2 a_2/2$, obtaining

$$\sin a_1 \sin a_2 \cos^2 \frac{A_3}{2} = \cos^2 \frac{a_1 - a_2}{2} \sin^2 \frac{a_3}{2} - \sin^2 \frac{a_1 - a_2}{2} \cos^2 \frac{a_3}{2}, \quad (68.7)$$

$$\sin a_1 \sin a_2 \sin^2 \frac{A_3}{2} = \sin^2 \frac{a_1 + a_2}{2} \cos^2 \frac{a_3}{2} - \cos^2 \frac{a_1 + a_2}{2} \sin^2 \frac{a_3}{2}. \quad (68.8)$$

69. We now set, for short,

$$s_0 = \frac{a_1 + a_2 + a_3}{2}, \quad (69.1)$$

$$s_i = s_0 - a_i = \frac{a_j + a_k - a_i}{2} \quad (i = 1, 2, 3), \quad (69.2)$$

which, by the way, implies

$$s_0 = s_1 + s_2 + s_3. \quad (69.3)$$

With this new notation, equations (68.7) and (68.8), as well as all the equations resulting from these two by cyclic permutations of the a_i and of the A_i, can be written in the form

$$\sin a_j \sin a_k \cos^2 \frac{A_i}{2} = \sin s_j \sin s_k, \quad (69.4)$$

$$\sin a_j \sin a_k \sin^2 \frac{A_i}{2} = \sin s_0 \sin s_i. \quad (69.5)$$

From these equations, all the formulas of Spherical Trigonometry can now be obtained easily and without recourse to geometric arguments of any sort. We first derive from the inequalities (66.3) above, using (69.1) and (69.2), the following relations:

$$\sin a_i > 0, \qquad (i = 1, 2, 3), \quad (69.6)$$

$$0 < s_0 < \frac{3\pi}{2}, \qquad (69.7)$$

$$-\frac{\pi}{2} < s_i < \pi \qquad (i = 1, 2, 3), \quad (69.8)$$

$$s_0 - \pi < s_i < s_0 \qquad (i = 1, 2, 3). \quad (69.9)$$

By (69.6), the left-hand side of (69.5) is always ≥ 0. Now if $s_0 < \pi$, then (69.7) implies $\sin s_0 > 0$, and by (69.5) we must therefore have

$$\sin s_i \geqq 0 \qquad\qquad (i = 1, 2, 3).$$

By (69.8), we therefore have

$$s_i \geqq 0 \qquad\qquad (i = 1, 2, 3); \qquad (69.10)$$

since these last relations are by (69.9) also valid for $s_0 \geqq \pi$, they must therefore always hold.

Now it is never possible that $s_0 > \pi$, since (69.9) and (69.8) would then imply $s_i > 0$ and $s_i < \pi$, respectively, which in turn would imply the inequalities

$$\sin s_0 < 0, \quad \sin s_i > 0$$

which are incompatible with (69.5). Therefore inequalities (69.7) through (69.9) may be replaced by the inequalities

$$0 \leqq s_i < s_0 \leqq \pi \qquad\qquad (i = 1, 2, 3), \qquad (69.11)$$

which are sharper.

70. It remains to discuss the limiting cases. For $s_0 = \pi$, it follows from (69.9) that all three s_i are > 0, and by (69.4) and (69.5) we must then also have

$$A_1 = A_2 = A_3 = 0. \qquad\qquad (70.1)$$

Next, if one of the $s_i = 0$, then by what has been said above we must have $s_0 < \pi$; and we must also have $s_k > 0$ and $s_j > 0$, since $s_i = s_k = 0$ would imply, by (69.3), that $s_0 - s_j = a_j = 0$, which would contradict our assumption that the three sides a_1, a_2, a_3 are different from zero. Hence the assumption that $s_i = 0$ implies, by (69.5) and (69.4), that

$$\sin^2 \frac{A_i}{2} = 0, \quad \cos^2 \frac{A_j}{2} = \cos^2 \frac{A_k}{2} = 0,$$

and hence that $A_i = 0, A_j = A_k = \pi$.

In each of these two limiting cases, the three points z_1, z_2, z_3 lie on one and the same circle of the bundle (58.3). If each of the three arcs into which the z_i divide this circle is less than π, then $s_0 = \pi$ and the exterior angles A_i all vanish. But if one of the three arcs is $> \pi$, then one of the exterior angles equals zero while the other two each equal π. In either case, the triangle degenerates.

Except in these limiting cases, we are dealing with an actual (non-degenerate) triangle of circular arcs, since none of the exterior angles A_i and none of the angles a_i of the triangle can then be equal to either 0 or π. As for the corresponding spherical triangle, the lengths a_i of its sides are, because of $s_0 < \pi$ and $s_i > 0$, subject to the restrictions

$$a_1 + a_2 + a_3 < 2\pi, \qquad 0 < a_i < a_j + a_k. \qquad (70.2)$$

Spherical triangles that satisfy relations (70.2) are called *Eulerian triangles*. We shall deal with triangles of this kind only. For more general triangles, some of the formulas we are about to derive must be modified suitably.[1]

For every triple of numbers a_1, a_2, a_3 satisfying conditions (70.2), there exists exactly one Eulerian triangle whose sides have (spherical) lengths a_1, a_2, a_3. For if we use (69.4), (69.5) to calculate the number A_3, and construct any triangle of circular arcs with a_1, a_2 as two of its sides, and having the angle $a_3 = \pi - A_3$, then the third side of this triangle must have a_3 as its spherical length.

71. We shall now replace formulas (69.4), (69.5) by equivalent formulas of as symmetrical a structure as possible. To this end, we first multiply (69.4), term by term, by the following equations, which are actually identical, except for notation, with the first equation of (69.4) :

$$\sin s_j \sin s_i = \sin a_j \sin a_i \cos^2 \frac{A_k}{2},$$

$$\sin s_k \sin s_i = \sin a_k \sin a_i \cos^2 \frac{A_j}{2}.$$

After cancelling the common factors introduced on both sides, we obtain

$$\sin^2 s_i \cos^2 \frac{A_i}{2} = \sin^2 a_i \cos^2 \frac{A_k}{2} \cos^2 \frac{A_j}{2}. \qquad (71.1)$$

Noting that for Eulerian triangles the factors $\sin s_i$, $\sin a_i$, $\cos A_i/2$ etc. occurring in this equation are all ≥ 0, we further obtain from (71.1) that

$$\sin s_i \cos \frac{A_i}{2} = \sin a_i \cos \frac{A_j}{2} \cos \frac{A_k}{2}. \qquad (71.2)$$

Similar calculations yield

$$\sin s_0 \cos \frac{A_i}{2} = \sin a_i \sin \frac{A_j}{2} \sin \frac{A_k}{2}, \qquad (71.3)$$

$$\sin s_j \sin \frac{A_i}{2} = \sin a_i \sin \frac{A_j}{2} \cos \frac{A_k}{2}, \qquad (71.4)$$

$$\sin s_k \sin \frac{A_i}{2} = \sin a_i \cos \frac{A_j}{2} \sin \frac{A_k}{2}. \qquad (71.5)$$

---

[1] *Cf.* F. Klein, *Vorlesungen über die hypergeometrische Funktion*, p. 138 ff. (Springer, Berlin 1932). Also H. Weber and J. Wellstein, *Enzyklopädie der Elementarmathematik*, Vol. 2, p. 340 ff. (Teubner, Leipzig 1905).

We now form the sum and the difference of the two equations (71.3) and (71.2), and we then do the same for the two equations (71.4) and (71.5). In each of the four relations thus obtained, we transform the expressions $(\sin s_0 \mp \sin s_i)$ and $(\sin s_j \pm \sin s_k)$, using, for instance,

$$\sin s_0 - \sin s_i = 2 \sin \frac{s_0 - s_i}{2} \cos \frac{s_0 + s_i}{2} = 2 \sin \frac{a_i}{2} \cos \frac{a_j + a_k}{2}.$$

In this way we finally obtain the following system of formulas:

$$\cos \frac{a_j + a_k}{2} \cos \frac{A_i}{2} + \cos \frac{A_j + A_k}{2} \cos \frac{a_i}{2} = 0, \tag{71.6}$$

$$\sin \frac{a_j + a_k}{2} \cos \frac{A_i}{2} - \cos \frac{A_j - A_k}{2} \sin \frac{a_i}{2} = 0, \tag{71.7}$$

$$\cos \frac{a_j - a_k}{2} \sin \frac{A_i}{2} - \sin \frac{A_j + A_k}{2} \cos \frac{a_j}{2} = 0, \tag{71.8}$$

$$\sin \frac{a_j - a_k}{2} \sin \frac{A_i}{2} + \sin \frac{A_j - A_k}{2} \sin \frac{a_i}{2} = 0. \tag{71.9}$$

These formulas were published in 1807 by the astronomer J. B. J. Delambre (1749-1822). A few months later they were discovered independently by Mollweide (1774-1825) and eventually also by Gauss. They are named sometimes for one, sometimes for another of these men.

An outstanding feature of Delambre's formulas is their symmetry; the first terms on the left-hand sides in the four equations are quite similar to each other and can easily be memorized. In the first equation, and in the fourth as well, the second term may be obtained from the first by simply interchanging the lower-case letters with the corresponding capital letters. The same interchange applied to the first term of the second (third) equation yields the second term of the third (second) equation, with its sign reversed.

72. From Delambre's formulas, we can again obtain relations (69.4) and (69.5), by simply eliminating $\cos (A_j + A_k)/2$, $\sin (A_j + A_k)/2$ from (71.6) and (71.8). They, too, may therefore serve as a starting point from which all the remaining formulas of Spherical Trigonometry can be derived. From their above-mentioned symmetry it follows that for every triangle with sides a_i and exterior angles A_i, there is a triangle with sides A_i and exterior angles a_i. This is the relation, on the sphere, between a spherical triangle and its polar triangle.

Delambre's formulas imply also that the size and form of an Eulerian triangle are uniquely determined once its angles a_i (or its exterior angles A_i) are given; but the A_i must be subject to the following restrictions, analogous to (70.2):

$$A_1 + A_2 + A_3 < 2\pi, \quad 0 < A_i < A_j + A_k. \tag{72.1}$$

From this we obtain the following conditions on the angles α_i of the triangle:

$$\alpha_1 + \alpha_2 + \alpha_3 > \pi, \quad \alpha_j + \alpha_k < \pi + \alpha_i < 2\pi. \tag{72.2}$$

If we set, for short,

$$
\left.
\begin{aligned}
S_0 &= \frac{A_1 + A_2 + A_3}{2} = \frac{3\pi - (\alpha_1 + \alpha_2 + \alpha_3)}{2}, \\
S_i &= \frac{A_j + A_k - A_i}{2} = \frac{\pi - (\alpha_j + \alpha_k - \alpha_i)}{2},
\end{aligned}
\right\}
\tag{72.3}
$$

then the equations analogous to (69.4) and (69.5) become

$$
\left.
\begin{aligned}
\sin A_j \sin A_k \cos^2 \frac{a_i}{2} &= \sin S_j \sin S_k, \\
\sin A_j \sin A_k \sin^2 \frac{a_i}{2} &= \sin S_0 \sin S_i.
\end{aligned}
\right\}
\tag{72.4}
$$

From these we derive the relation

$$
\operatorname{tg}^2 \frac{a_i}{2} = - \frac{\cos \dfrac{\alpha_1 + \alpha_2 + \alpha_3}{2} \cos \dfrac{\alpha_j + \alpha_k - \alpha_i}{2}}{\cos \dfrac{\alpha_k + \alpha_i - \alpha_j}{2} \cos \dfrac{\alpha_i + \alpha_j - \alpha_k}{2}}, \tag{72.5}
$$

of which occasional use is made in Function Theory.

Non-Euclidean Trigonometry (§§ 73-75)

73. Let us choose three points z_1, z_2, z_3 in the interior of the unit circle, and let us assign to each pair of two of these points its non-Euclidean distance

$$a_i = E_n(z_j, z_k) \qquad (i = 1, 2, 3)$$

(cf. § 65 above). Then by (65.6),

$$\operatorname{tgh} \frac{a_i}{2} = \frac{|z_j - z_k|}{|1 - \bar{z}_j z_k|} \tag{73.1}$$

These numbers are invariant under every Moebius transformation of the form (62.8). Hence if in analogy to § 67 we set

$$Z = \frac{z_3 - z}{1 - \bar{z}_3 z}, \quad Z_i = \frac{z_3 - z_i}{1 - \bar{z}_3 z_i}, \tag{73.2}$$

then $Z_3 = 0$, and

$$\text{tgh } \frac{a_1}{2} = |Z_2|, \quad \text{tgh } \frac{a_2}{2} = |Z_1|, \tag{73.3}$$

$$\text{tgh } \frac{a_3}{2} = \frac{|Z_1 - Z_2|}{|1 - \overline{Z}_2 Z_1|} \tag{73.4}$$

Consider the triangle whose vertices are the z_i and whose sides are arcs of circles of the bundle (58.4); the angle α_3 and the exterior angle A_3 of this triangle are again determined uniquely by the relations

$$0 \leq \alpha_3 \leq \pi, \quad 0 \leq A_3 \leq \pi, \atop Z_1 \overline{Z}_2 + Z_2 \overline{Z}_1 = 2 |Z_1| |Z_2| \cos \alpha_3 = - 2 |Z_1| |Z_2| \cos A_3. \tag{73.5}$$

Using the relations

$$|Z_1 - Z_2|^2 = |Z_1|^2 + |Z_2|^2 - (Z_1 \overline{Z}_2 + Z_2 \overline{Z}_1),$$

$$|1 - \overline{Z}_2 Z_1|^2 = 1 + |Z_1|^2 + |Z_2|^2 - (Z_1 \overline{Z}_2 + Z_2 \overline{Z}_1),$$

we obtain the equation

$$2 |Z_1| |Z_2| \cos A_3 = (1 + |Z_1|^2 |Z_2|^2) \sinh^2 \frac{a_3}{2} - (|Z_1|^2 + |Z_2|^2) \cosh^2 \frac{a_3}{2}, \tag{73.6}$$

whose structure is analogous to that of (68.4).

We now introduce once more the abbreviations s_0 and s_i, defined by (69.1), (69.2) and first used in § 69 above. Using this time the addition theorems of the hyperbolic functions (cf. § 240) rather than those of the trigonometric functions, we obtain the equations

$$\sinh a_j \sinh a_k \cos^2 \frac{A_i}{2} = \sinh s_j \sinh s_k, \tag{73.7}$$

$$\sinh a_j \sinh a_k \sin^2 \frac{A_i}{2} = \sinh s_0 \sinh s_i. \tag{73.8}$$

Here we are spared the complications which in Spherical Geometry arose out of the fact that the function $\sin u$ can be negative not only for negative values of u but for positive u as well. For equations (73.7) and (73.8) to be valid, it is necessary and sufficient that the relations

$$s_0 \geq 0, \quad s_i \geq 0 \qquad (i = 1, 2, 3) \tag{73.9}$$

hold true, and these relations are in turn equivalent to the following:

$$0 < a_i \leqq a_j + a_k \qquad (i = 1, 2, 3). \qquad (73.10)$$

74. The remaining calculations follow the pattern of §§ 71-72. The Delambre formulas for the present case are

$$\cosh \frac{a_j + a_k}{2} \; \cos \frac{A_i}{2} + \cos \frac{A_j + A_k}{2} \; \cosh \frac{a_i}{2} = 0, \qquad (74.1)$$

$$\sinh \frac{a_j + a_k}{2} \; \cos \frac{A_i}{2} - \cos \frac{A_j - A_k}{2} \; \sinh \frac{a_i}{2} = 0, \qquad (74.2)$$

$$\cosh \frac{a_j - a_k}{2} \; \sin \frac{A_i}{2} - \sin \frac{A_j + A_k}{2} \; \cosh \frac{a_i}{2} = 0, \qquad (74.3)$$

$$\sinh \frac{a_j - a_k}{2} \; \sin \frac{A_i}{2} + \sin \frac{A_j - A_k}{2} \; \sinh \frac{a_i}{2} = 0. \qquad (74.4)$$

This system of formulas again enables us to calculate the remaining parts of a non-Euclidean triangle if we know its exterior angles A_i. But since these formulas are not as symmetric as the corresponding formulas of Spherical Trigonometry, it is not sufficient simply to transform equations (73.7) and (73.8); here we must actually carry out the calculations. For instance, by eliminating the quantities $\cosh (a_j + a_k)/2$, $\sinh (a_j + a_k)/2$ from (74.1) and (74.2) we find

$$\cos^2 \frac{A_i}{2} = \cos^2 \frac{A_j + A_k}{2} \; \cosh^2 \frac{a_i}{2} - \cos^2 \frac{A_j - A_k}{2} \; \sinh^2 \frac{a_i}{2}. \qquad (74.5)$$

Using the abbreviations

$$S_0 = \frac{A_1 + A_2 + A_3}{2}, \qquad S_i = \frac{A_j + A_k - A_i}{2} = S_0 - A_i \qquad (74.6)$$

we obtain from (74.5) the system of equations

$$\sin A_j \sin A_k \cosh^2 \frac{a_i}{2} = \sin S_j \sin S_k, \qquad (74.7)$$

$$\sin A_j \sin A_k \sinh^2 \frac{a_i}{2} = - \sin S_0 \sin S_i. \qquad (74.8)$$

These formulas serve to establish necessary and sufficient conditions characteristic of the angles of a non-Euclidean triangle. Let us first consider the relations

$$0 \leqq A_i \leqq \pi \qquad (i = 1, 2, 3), \qquad (74.9)$$

which imply

$$0 \leqq S_0 \leqq \frac{3\pi}{2}, \qquad -\frac{\pi}{2} \leqq S_i \leqq \pi \quad (i = 1, 2, 3). \qquad (74.10)$$

Now $S_0 = 0$ is impossible, since this would not only imply that all $A_i = 0$ but also, because of (73.8), that all $a_i = 0$, and this would be incompatible with our initial assumptions. To assume that

$$0 < S_0 < \pi$$

likewise leads to a contradiction; for since the right-hand side of equation (74.8) is non-negative, all the sin S_i and hence all the S_i would have to be $\leqq 0$, which is incompatible with $S_0 = S_1 + S_2 + S_3 > 0$.

If $S_0 = \pi$, then by (74.8) we must have sin A_j sin $A_k = 0$ for all combinations of j and k, and from this we conclude that two of the exterior angles are equal to π while the third one equals zero. By (73.8), the resulting non-Euclidean triangle is degenerate.

Therefore we obtain a non-degenerate non-Euclidean triangle only if

$$S_0 > \pi \tag{74.11}$$

holds. Since $S_i \leqq \pi$, we must have $A_i = S_0 - S_i > 0$ in this case, and since $A_i \leqq \pi$, we similarly find that $S_i > 0$. Now if one of the A_i were $= \pi$, then the equations sin $S_j = 0$, sin $S_k = 0$ would have to hold, as we may easily deduce by calculation from (74.8). This would lead to the equations

$$S_i = S_0 - \pi, \quad S_j = \pi, \quad S_k = \pi,$$

which are incompatible with $S_0 = S_1 + S_2 + S_3$. Therefore in the non-degenerate case we must have

$$0 < A_i < \pi \qquad (i = 1, 2, 3), \tag{74.12}$$

and since the right-hand side of (74.8) can then not vanish, we also have

$$0 < S_i < \pi \qquad (i = 1, 2, 3). \tag{74.13}$$

All of these conditions will be satisfied if for the angles $\alpha_i = \pi - A_i$ of the triangle, the relations

$$0 < \alpha_i < \alpha_1 + \alpha_2 + \alpha_3 < \pi \qquad (i = 1, 2, 3) \tag{74.14}$$

hold true.

75. If we introduce the α_i into (74.7) and (74.8) and then divide the first of these equations into the second, we obtain the relation

$$\text{tgh}^2 \frac{a_i}{2} = \frac{\cos \dfrac{\alpha_1 + \alpha_2 + \alpha_3}{2} \cos \dfrac{\alpha_j + \alpha_k - \alpha_i}{2}}{\cos \dfrac{\alpha_k + \alpha_i - \alpha_j}{2} \cos \dfrac{\alpha_i + \alpha_j - \alpha_k}{2}}, \tag{75.1}$$

which is the analogue of equation (72.5) of Spherical Trigonometry.

We are led to an important limiting case by letting one of the angles, say α_3, tend to zero in the last equation. In the resulting triangle, the vertex z_3 will then be at infinity, the two sides a_1 and a_2 will each be of infinite length, and the length a_3 of the third side will be given by the equation

$$\operatorname{tgh} \frac{a_3}{2} = \frac{\cos \dfrac{\alpha_1 + \alpha_2}{2}}{\cos \dfrac{\alpha_1 - \alpha_2}{2}} = \frac{\operatorname{ctg} \dfrac{\alpha_1}{2} \operatorname{ctg} \dfrac{\alpha_2}{2} - 1}{\operatorname{ctg} \dfrac{\alpha_1}{2} \operatorname{ctg} \dfrac{\alpha_2}{2} + 1} . \tag{75.2}$$

Now since

$$\operatorname{tgh} \frac{a_3}{2} = \frac{e^{\frac{a_3}{2}} - e^{-\frac{a_3}{2}}}{e^{\frac{a_3}{2}} + e^{-\frac{a_3}{2}}} = \frac{e^{a_3} - 1}{e^{a_3} + 1} ,$$

equation (75.2) can be written in the simpler form

$$e^{a_3} = \operatorname{ctg} \frac{\alpha_1}{2} \operatorname{ctg} \frac{\alpha_2}{2} . \tag{75.3}$$

We obtain a further specialization by setting

$$\alpha_1 = \frac{\pi}{2}, \qquad \alpha_2 = \frac{\pi}{2} - \varepsilon$$

in formulas (75.2) and (75.3), which yields

$$\operatorname{tgh} \frac{a_3}{2} = \operatorname{tg} \frac{\varepsilon}{2}, \qquad e^{a_3} = \operatorname{ctg} \frac{\alpha_2}{2} = \operatorname{tg} \left(\frac{\pi}{4} + \frac{\varepsilon}{2} \right) \tag{75.4}$$

The first of equations (75.4) can very easily be verified geometrically, as shown in Fig. 8 below.

Spherical Geometry (§ 76)

76. Now that we have derived the formulas of Spherical Trigonometry by algebraic means, we shall add some remarks concerning their geometric significance.

Let us assume first that the three points z_i considered in § 66 above lie in the interior $|z| < 1$ of the unit circle. (Incidentally, every Eulerian triangle can be brought into a position corresponding to this assumption.) Then the antipodal point

$$z_i^* = -\frac{1}{\bar{z}_i}$$

of each of the points z_i must lie outside the unit circle, and the relation

$$s_i = \frac{a_j + a_k - a_i}{2} \geqq 0,$$

established at the end of § 69, simply states that under the above assumptions, the triangle inequality of Euclidean Geometry (*cf.* § 20) also holds for our metric on the sphere.

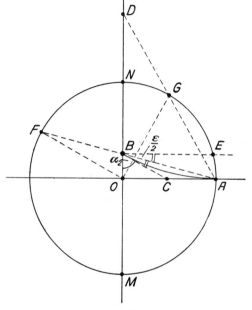

Fig. 8

Note that $\sphericalangle OBC = \alpha_2,$ $\sphericalangle CAB = \sphericalangle CBA = \sphericalangle ABE = \frac{\varepsilon}{2}.$

Moreover, $\operatorname{tgh} \frac{a_3}{2} = \frac{OB}{OA} = \operatorname{tg} \frac{\varepsilon}{2}$ and

$$e^{a_3} = \frac{1 + (\operatorname{tg} \varepsilon/2)}{1 - (\operatorname{tg} \varepsilon/2)} = \operatorname{tg} \left(\frac{\pi}{4} + \frac{\varepsilon}{2} \right).$$

Now if we draw OG perpendicular to OF and extend AG up to the point D, then $OD = e^{a_3}$.

This result enables us to define the spherical length σ of a curve

$$z = z(t) = x(t) + i\, y(t) \qquad (0 \leqq t \leqq 1) \qquad (76.1)$$

that lies in the interior $|z| < 1$ of the unit circle. To this end, we consider partitions

$$0 = t_0 < t_1 < t_2 < \cdots < t_{p-1} < t_p = 1 \tag{76.2}$$

of the interval $0 \leqq t \leqq 1$, and introduce the notation

$$\left. \begin{aligned} z_k &= z(t_k) \quad (k = 0, 1, \ldots, p), \\ S &= \sum_{k=1}^{p} E_s(z_{k-1}, z_k) \,; \end{aligned} \right\} \tag{76.3}$$

we now define σ to be the least upper bound of all the S obtainable in this manner.

We can lift the restriction that the curve (76.1) should lie in the interior $|z| < 1$ of the unit circle. All that is really necessary is that for every one of the partitions (76.3), each of the partial arcs joining two points, such as z_{k-1} and z_k, can be mapped into the interior $|z| < 1$ by means of a suitable spherical motion.

It follows from our definition that the spherical length σ is invariant under any spherical motion (cf. §§ 62-64). If the functions $x(t)$ and $y(t)$ have continuous first derivatives, then by using equation (66.2) and proceeding similarly as in the ordinary Differential Calculus, we obtain the spherical length σ in the form of the integral

$$\sigma = \int \frac{2\,|dz|}{1 + z\,\bar{z}} = \int_0^1 \frac{2\sqrt{x'^2 + y'^2}}{1 + x^2 + y^2}\, dt\,. \tag{76.4}$$

If we interpret the integral in (76.4) as a Lebesgue integral, then formula (76.4) is always meaningful provided only that $\sigma < +\infty$ holds.

The above definition also implies (cf. (76.3)) that the spherical length σ of any curve γ that joins two points z_1 and z_2 must satisfy

$$\sigma \geqq E_s(z_1, z_2)\,.$$

Unless z_1 and z_2 are the stereographic images of two antipodal points of the sphere, there exists exactly one circle of the bundle (58.2) that passes through them. One of the two arcs into which z_1 and z_2 divide this circle is of (spherical) length $\sigma_0 = E_s(z_1, z_2)$. But if $1 + z_1 \bar{z}_2 = 0$, then there exists an infinite number of such arcs, all of which are then of length $\sigma_0 = \pi$.

The circles of the bundle (58.2) are the *geodetic lines*, or *geodesics*, in the spherical metric we have studied. They have many properties in common with the straight lines of Euclidean Geometry. But a basic difference between the two geometries lies in the fact that any two of the geodesics of Spherical Geometry meet in *two* distinct points, just as do any two great circles, the pre-images of the geodesics, on the Riemann sphere.

Elliptic Geometry (§ 77)

77. If we replace the stereographic projection of the Riemann sphere by a central projection, we are led to a geometry that is related to Spherical Geometry and is called "Elliptic Geometry." The geodesics of this geometry are the straight lines of the plane of projection; the point of intersection of any two such lines represents the image of two antipodal points of the sphere. But in this new geometry, as we shall see presently, the formulas for the invariants connected with angle and distance are more complicated than in Spherical

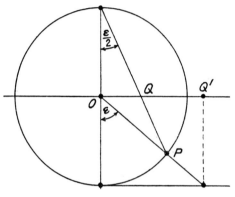

Fig. 9

Geometry.

We set (*cf.* Fig. 9)

$$OQ = r = |z|, \quad OQ' = \varrho = |\zeta|, \qquad (77.1)$$

and obtain

$$r = \operatorname{tg} \frac{\varepsilon}{2}, \quad \varrho = \operatorname{tg} \varepsilon = \frac{2r}{1-r^2}. \qquad (77.2)$$

Using the notation

$$R = \frac{1+r^2}{1-r^2} \qquad (r \neq 1) \quad (77.3)$$

we find

$$R = \pm \sqrt{1+\varrho^2}, \qquad (77.4)$$

where the plus sign applies if $r < 1$, the minus sign if $r > 1$. We then have the relations

$$\zeta = \frac{2z}{1-z\bar{z}}, \quad z = \frac{\zeta}{R+1} = \frac{\zeta}{1 \pm \sqrt{1+\zeta\bar{\zeta}}}; \qquad (77.5)$$

to every value of z satisfying $\bar{z}z \neq 1$, (77.5) assigns a unique value of ζ, and to every value of ζ there correspond two values of z.

These formulas map, as they should, every circle

$$(A - i B) z + (A + i B) \bar{z} - C (1 - z z) = 0 \tag{77.6}$$

of the bundle (58.2) onto a straight line

$$(A - i B) \zeta + (A + i B) \bar{\zeta} - 2 C = 0 \tag{77.7}$$

of the ζ-plane.

The angle formed by two straight lines of the form (77.7) is given by the angle between the corresponding circles (77.6). The calculations to verify this fact are left to the reader. We proceed to set up the distance invariant associated with two points ζ_1 and ζ_2. To this end, we go back to equation (68.4), into which we substitute

$$\left.\begin{aligned}
A_3 = \pi - \alpha, \quad a_3 = a, \quad |Z_1| = r_1, \quad |Z_2| = r_2, \\
2 \sin^2 \frac{a_3}{2} = 1 - \cos a, \quad 2 \cos^2 \frac{a_3}{2} = 1 + \cos a.
\end{aligned}\right\} \tag{77.8}$$

This yields

$$(1 - r_1^2) (1 - r_2^2) + 4 r_1 r_2 \cos \alpha = (1 + r_1^2) (1 + r_2^2) \cos a, \tag{77.9}$$

or, setting

$$\varrho_i = \frac{2 r_i}{1 - r_i^2}, \quad R_i = \frac{1 + r_i^2}{1 - r_i^2}, \quad (i = 1, 2), \tag{77.10}$$

$$1 + \varrho_1 \varrho_2 \cos \alpha = R_1 R_2 \cos a. \tag{77.11}$$

Now note the relations

$$2 \varrho_1 \varrho_2 \cos \alpha = \zeta_1 \bar{\zeta}_2 + \zeta_2 \bar{\zeta}_1, \quad R_i^2 = 1 + \bar{\zeta}_i \zeta_i,$$

which together with (77.11) imply

$$(2 + \zeta_1 \bar{\zeta}_2 + \zeta_2 \bar{\zeta}_1)^2 (1 + \operatorname{tg}^2 a) = 4 (1 + \zeta_1 \bar{\zeta}_1) (1 + \zeta_2 \bar{\zeta}_2),$$

so that we finally obtain

$$(2 + \zeta_1 \bar{\zeta}_2 + \zeta_2 \bar{\zeta}_1)^2 \operatorname{tg}^2 a = 4 (\zeta_2 - \zeta_1) (\bar{\zeta}_2 - \bar{\zeta}_1) - (\zeta_1 \bar{\zeta}_2 - \zeta_2 \bar{\zeta}_1)^2, \tag{77.12}$$

From this we obtain the following expression for the element of arc length ds:

$$(1 + \zeta \bar{\zeta})^2 ds^2 = d\zeta d\bar{\zeta} - \left(\frac{\zeta d\bar{\zeta} - \bar{\zeta} d\zeta}{2} \right)^2, \tag{77.13}$$

or, setting $\zeta = \xi + i \eta$,

$$(1 + \xi^2 + \eta^2)^2 \, ds^2 = d\xi^2 + d\eta^2 + (\eta \, d\xi - \xi \, d\eta)^2$$
$$= (1 + \eta^2) \, d\xi^2 - 2 \, \xi \, \eta \, d\xi \, d\eta + (1 + \xi^2) \, d\eta^2. \qquad (77.14)$$

The metric based on this element of arc length is called an *elliptic metric*. If we set $\zeta_1 = 0$ in (77.12) and let ζ_2 tend to infinity, then a converges to $\pi/2$. From this we conclude that in an elliptic metric, the total length of a geodesic is always finite, and that if the metric is normed as is the particular one we have introduced above, this finite total length is in fact always equal to π.

The "elliptic plane," incidentally, is a one-sided closed surface.

The Rotations of the Sphere (§§ 78-79)

78. Let us turn again to Spherical Geometry, the formulas of which are much easier to manage, and let us find the invariants of the spherical motions (62.6). The fixed points z_0 and $z_0^* = -1/\bar{z}_0$ of these motions are the stereographic images of two antipodal points of the Riemann sphere, and they are the roots of the equation

$$\gamma \, z_0^2 + (\delta - \bar{\delta}) \, z_0 + \bar{\gamma} = 0. \qquad (78.1)$$

The angle ϑ of the corresponding rotation of the sphere can be obtained by noting that, by § 55 and formula (62.6),

$$\cos^2 \frac{\vartheta}{2} = \lambda = \frac{(\delta + \bar{\delta})^2}{4 \, (\delta \, \bar{\delta} + \gamma \, \bar{\gamma})} \qquad (78.2)$$

holds. If we use equation (62.4) to represent the above spherical motion, then it follows from (62.5) that (78.2) may be replaced by

$$\cos \frac{\vartheta}{2} = \frac{\sin \varphi/2}{\sqrt{1 + a \, \bar{a}}}. \qquad (78.3)$$

In this case, we may write, in place of (78.1),

$$\bar{a} \, e^{-\frac{i\varphi}{2}} z_0^2 + 2 \cos \frac{\varphi}{2} \, z_0 - a \, e^{\frac{i\varphi}{2}} = 0, \qquad (78.4)$$

and from this it follows that

$$a \, e^{\frac{i\varphi}{2}} = 2 \cos \frac{\varphi}{2} \cdot \frac{z_0}{1 - z_0 \, \bar{z}_0}. \qquad (78.5)$$

In order to calculate the quantities a and φ from (78.3) and (78.5), we first set

$$\text{tg}\,\frac{\varphi}{2} = u, \quad \text{tg}\,\frac{\vartheta}{2} = v, \quad z_0\,\bar z_0 = N. \tag{78.6}$$

This implies

$$\sin^2\frac{\varphi}{2} = \frac{u^2}{1+u^2}, \quad \cos^2\frac{\vartheta}{2} = \frac{1}{1+v^2}, \quad a = \frac{2\,z_0}{(1-N)\,(1+i\,u)}. \tag{78.7}$$

Hence on the one hand,

$$a\,\bar a = \frac{4\,N}{(1-N)^2\,(1+u^2)},$$

and on the other hand, by (78.3),

$$a\,\bar a = \frac{u^2(1+v^2)}{1+u^2} - 1 = \frac{u^2\,v^2 - 1}{1+u^2},$$

so that

$$\frac{4\,N}{(1-N)^2} = u^2\,v^2 - 1$$

and finally

$$u\,v = \frac{1+N}{1-N}. \tag{78.8}$$

The last equation of (78.7) now yields

$$a = \frac{2\,z_0\,i\,v}{(1-N)\,i\,v - (1+N)}. \tag{78.9}$$

We shall also make use of the relations

$$\cos\vartheta = \frac{1-v^2}{1+v^2}, \quad \sin\vartheta = \frac{2\,v}{1+v^2}, \quad e^{i\vartheta} = \frac{1+i\,v}{1-i\,v}, \quad i\,v = \frac{e^{i\vartheta}-1}{e^{i\vartheta}+1}.$$

These, together with (78.9), yield

$$a = \frac{z_0(1-e^{i\vartheta})}{1+z_0\,\bar z_0\,e^{i\vartheta}}.$$

A similar calculation shows that

$$e^{i\varphi} = \frac{1+i\,u}{1-i\,u} = -\frac{N\,e^{i\vartheta}+1}{N+e^{i\vartheta}}.$$

Now if we substitute the above expressions into (62.4), we finally obtain the rotation of the sphere in the form

$$w = \frac{(z_0\,\bar z_0\,e^{i\vartheta}+1)\,z - z_0(1-e^{i\vartheta})}{-\bar z_0(1-e^{i\vartheta})\,z + (z_0\,\bar z_0 + e^{i\vartheta})}. \tag{78.10}$$

Here, z_0 denotes the fixed point, and ϑ is the angle of rotation of the sphere.

79. If we fix the value of z_0 and allow ϑ to vary, then the images w (under (78.10)) of any given point z of the plane will describe a curve all of whose points are at the same spherical distance from z_0. If $z_0 = 0$ then this curve is evidently a circle of the z-plane, and it must therefore be a circle for any other value of z_0 as well, since every spherical motion (62.6) is a circle-preserving transformation.

Conversely, we may assign an arbitrary circle (23.3) and can then use equation (39.1) to find two points that are related to each other by inversion in the given circle and that are at the same time the stereographic images of two antipodal points of the Riemann sphere. To do this, we merely have to replace $\bar{z}$ and w, in (39.1), by $\overline{z_0}$ and $-1/\overline{z_0}$, respectively, which yields the following equation for z_0:

$$(A - i B)\, z_0^2 - 2 C\, z_0 - (A + i B) = 0.$$

In this way we can calculate the spherical center of any given circle.

Non-Euclidean Geometry (§§ 80-81)

80. As we know from § 62 above, inversions in the circles of the hyperbolic bundle (58.4) map the interior $|z| < 1$ of the unit circle onto itself. We

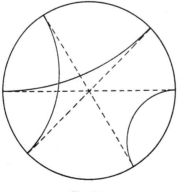

Fig. 10

may therefore consider the interior of this circle to be an image of the *non-Euclidean plane* (Fig. 10). The "straight lines" of the non-Euclidean plane then correspond to arcs of circles orthogonal to the unit circle and lying in its interior. The unit circle $|z| = 1$ itself will be called the *horizon* of the non-Euclidean plane.

For this non-Euclidean geometry, almost all the axioms of Euclidean Geometry are valid: Through any two points there passes exactly one non-Euclidean straight line; therefore two straight lines intersect in no more than one point. The axioms of congruence for triangles likewise remain valid if we interpret the group of transformations (62.8) [or (62.9)] as non-Euclidean motions.

There is, however, the following difference between Euclidean Geometry and the particular Non-Euclidean Geometry we are considering: Every non-Euclidean straight line has two distinct end points, which are improper points of the line and whose images lie on the horizon $|z| = 1$; any given point of the disc $|z| < 1$ can be connected to a point of the horizon by *exactly one non-Euclidean straight line*. Two non-Euclidean straight lines with a common end point are said to be *parallel*.

Therefore if we are given a point P of the non-Euclidean plane, and a non-Euclidean straight line g not passing through P (see Fig. 11), we can

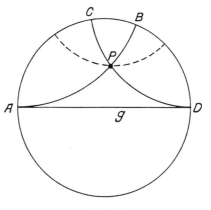

Fig. 11

always draw through P *two* parallels AB and CD to g. If we consider the pencil of non-Euclidean straight lines passing through P, we see that these lines are divided into two classes by the parallels APB and CPD to g; those lines of the pencil that pass from P into the sector APD will meet g at some point, while those that pass from P into the sector APC have neither an ordinary point nor an end point in common with g. Lines of the second class are said to be *ultra-parallel* to g. Hence in the geometry we are here concerned with, *Euclid's postulate to the effect that through a point P not on a* *straight line g, there is at most one straight line not meeting g, is not valid.*[1]

81. The Moebius transformations (62.8) constitute the group of non-Euclidean motions. According to results we obtained earlier, there are therefore two invariants under non-Euclidean motions (just as there are under Euclidean rigid motions), namely the distance invariant $E_n(z_1, z_2)$ given by equation (65.6), and the angle invariant, which in our above mapping of the non-Euclidean plane onto the disc $|z| < 1$ coincides in this disc with the ordinary concept of angle. This last fact may also be expressed by saying that our mapping of the non-Euclidean plane onto the interior $|z| < 1$ of the Euclidean unit circle is a *conformal* mapping.

But we can also map the non-Euclidean plane onto the disc $|z| < 1$ in such a way that every non-Euclidean straight line is transformed into a chord of the unit circle. To this end we merely have to set, very much as in § 77 above,

$$\zeta = \frac{2z}{1 + z\bar{z}}, \qquad z = \frac{\zeta}{1 + \sqrt{1 - \zeta\bar{\zeta}}}. \qquad (81.1)$$

This maps the circles of the bundle (58.4) onto the straight lines

$$(A - iB)\zeta + (A + iB)\bar{\zeta} + 2D = 0 \qquad (D < A^2 + B^2) \qquad (81.2)$$

But the mapping (81.1), which is *not conformal*, leads to rather involved expressions for distance and angle (*cf.* § 77 above).

Relation (73.10) above states that the familiar triangle inequality of Euclidean Geometry holds in a non-Euclidean metric as well. From this fact it follows that in Non-Euclidean Geometry, just as in Euclidean and in Spherical Geometry (*cf.* § 76 for the latter), the length of a rectifiable curve may be defined as the least upper bound of the lengths of inscribed polygons. Instead of the integral (76.4), we here obtain the formula

$$\sigma = \int \frac{2\,|dz|}{1 - z\bar{z}} = \int_0^1 \frac{2\sqrt{x'^2 + y'^2}}{1 - (x^2 + y^2)}\, dt. \qquad (81.3)$$

---

[1] Starting with the geometry of circles in the Euclidean plane, we have found a geometry in which Euclid's Eleventh Postulate is not valid. Hence this postulate can not be a consequence of the remaining axioms of Euclidean Geometry. This result was published by N. J. Lobatchevsky (1793-1856) shortly before 1830, and by J. Bolyai (1802-1860) shortly after 1830. Gauss had discovered it several years earlier but did not publish his discovery. Lobatchevsky later arrived at a much more complete result, which first brought into proper perspective the fundamental significance of Non-Euclidean Geometry. He was able to show that from the remaining Euclidean axioms together with the assumption that there exist at least two intersecting straight lines not meeting a given third line, it is possible to derive all the formulas of Non-Euclidean Trigonometry that we obtained in §§ 73 ff. above. Lobatchevsky thus demonstrated the "uniqueness" of Non-Euclidean Geometry.

The quantity σ is an invariant under all non-Euclidean motions. If z_1, z_2 denote the end points of the arc whose length is σ, then we always have $\sigma \geqq E_n(z_1, z_2)$.

Non-Euclidean Motions (§§ 82-83)

82. The non-Euclidean motion

$$w = e^{i\varphi} \frac{a - z}{1 - \bar{a}\, z} \tag{82.1}$$

can be regarded as the product of two reflections, the first in the circle

$$\bar{a}\, z + a\, \bar{z} - a\, \bar{a}\, (1 + z\, \bar{z}) = 0 \tag{82.2}$$

and the second in the straight line

$$\bar{a}\, z - a\, e^{i\varphi}\, \bar{z} = 0. \tag{82.3}$$

The straight line (82.2) is the non-Euclidean perpendicular bisector of the line segment that joins the two points $z = 0$ and $z = a$ (see Fig. 12). Simi-

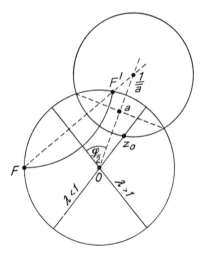

Fig. 12

larly, the straight line (82.3) is the non-Euclidean perpendicular bisector of the line segment that joins $z = a$ and $z = a\, e^{i\varphi}$. The angle formed by the lines (82.3) and $O\,a$ is therefore equal to $\varphi/2$. For the non-Euclidean motion (82.1), the rational invariant (55.2) has the value

$$\lambda = \frac{\sin^2 \varphi/2}{1 - a\,\bar{a}}. \tag{82.4}$$

Now if, first, we have the case $\lambda < 1$, then the two non-Euclidean straight lines (82.2) and (82.3) intersect at some point z_0 of the non-Euclidean plane. In this case, the motion may be regarded as a non-Euclidean rotation about the point z_0. By § 55 above, the angle of rotation ϑ is given by the equation $\lambda = \cos^2 \vartheta/2$, so that

$$\cos^2 \frac{\vartheta}{2} = \frac{\sin^2 \varphi/2}{1 - a\,\bar{a}}. \tag{82.5}$$

Second, if $\lambda > 1$ then the two non-Euclidean straight lines (82.2) and (82.3) have no point in common. In this case, the fixed points F, F' of the non-Euclidean motion (82.1) are the points of intersection of the circle $|z| = 1$ and the (Euclidean) perpendicular through the point $1/\bar{a}$ onto the straight line (82.3). The points F and F' are the end points of the non-Euclidean straight line that cuts each of the two non-Euclidean straight lines (82.2) and (82.3) at a right angle. Hence the motion (82.1) is a translation of the non-Euclidean plane in the direction of the non-Euclidean straight line just described. Let s denote the non-Euclidean length of the line segment through which the translation carries the non-Euclidean plane. To find s, let us consider the non-Euclidean motion

$$w = \frac{z - \operatorname{tgh} s/2}{-z \operatorname{tgh} s/2 + 1}; \tag{82.6}$$

this motion is a non-Euclidean translation of length s in the direction of the real axis. By § 55, the quantity λ for the Moebius transformation (82.6) is given by

$$\lambda = \frac{4}{4\,(1 - \operatorname{tgh}^2 s/2)} = \cosh^2 \frac{s}{2}.$$

If we compare this result with (82.4), we see that for the Moebius transformation (82.1), the (non-Euclidean) length s of the translation along the non-Euclidean straight line FF' is given by the equation

$$\cosh \frac{s}{2} = \frac{\sin \varphi/2}{\sqrt{1 - a\,\bar{a}}}. \tag{82.7}$$

For $\lambda = 1$, finally, we obtain a third and last type of non-Euclidean motion. In this case, we have

$$\sin^2 \frac{\varphi}{2} = 1 - a\,\bar{a}, \tag{82.8}$$

and the Moebius transformation (82.1) is parabolic; it has a single fixed point, located at one of the end points of the non-Euclidean straight line (82.2).

A non-Euclidean motion of this kind is called a *limiting rotation*, because it can be obtained by means of a limiting process from the rotations discussed above. This limiting process consists in making the center z_0 and the angle ϑ of the rotation tend to infinity and to zero, respectively. We would of course be equally justified in using instead, if we wished, the term *limiting translation*.

The limiting rotations can be generated, as we know from § 51 above, as products of two successive reflections in two parallel non-Euclidean straight lines. Since any two given pairs of such straight lines can be mapped, one onto the other, by means of a suitable non-Euclidean motion, it follows that all limiting rotations are equivalent non-Euclidean motions.

By a method similar to that of § 78 above, we find the following formula for the non-Euclidean rotations:

$$w = \frac{(1 - z_0 \bar{z}_0 e^{i\vartheta}) z - z_0(1 - e^{i\vartheta})}{\bar{z}_0(1 - e^{i\vartheta}) z + (e^{i\vartheta} - z_0 \bar{z}_0)} \qquad (|z_0| < 1). \qquad (82.9)$$

For the non-Euclidean translations we obtain, setting tgh $s/2 = \sigma$ and denoting the two fixed points by $e^{i\psi_1}$, $e^{i\psi_2}$,

$$w = \frac{[(e^{i\psi_1} + e^{i\psi_2}) \sigma + (e^{i\psi_1} - e^{i\psi_2})] z - 2\sigma e^{i(\psi_1 + \psi_2)}}{2\sigma z - [(e^{i\psi_1} + e^{i\psi_2}) \sigma - (e^{i\psi_1} - e^{i\psi_2})]} \qquad (-1 < \delta < 1). \qquad (82.10)$$

In order to find a corresponding formula for the limiting rotations, we set $z_0 = \varrho e^{i\psi}$ in (82.9) and we then let ϱ tend to unity and v tend to zero, but in such a way that the value of u in $uv = (1 - N)/(1 + N)$ converges to a finite real number. Then in the limit,

$$a = \frac{e^{i\psi}}{1 + i u},$$

and we obtain the limiting rotation in the form

$$w = \frac{(1 + i u) z - e^{i\psi}}{e^{-i\psi} z - (1 - i u)}, \qquad (-\infty < u < \infty). \qquad (82.11)$$

We can obtain the same formula also from (82.10) by means of a suitable limiting process.

83. Since the non-Euclidean motions (82.1) are generated by reflections in two circles of the complex plane, it follows that each of these Moebius transformations leaves invariant the circles of a certain pencil of circles. To the extent to which they are contained within $|z| < 1$, these circles can be interpreted in very simple terms in the language of Non-Euclidean Geometry.

First, if the non-Euclidean motion is a rotation, then each of these circles is a locus of points z having a constant non-Euclidean distance from the center

z_0 of the rotation. Therefore the circles may be regarded, in this case, as being *non-Euclidean circles*.

Second, if the motion is a translation along a non-Euclidean straight line g, then the above invariant curves are arcs of circles of the complex plane that join the end points F and F' of g to each other; these arcs may be regarded as *lines of constant non-Euclidean distance* from g, and are called *hypercycles*.

Finally, if the motion is a limiting rotation, then the invariant curves are so-called *oricycles* in the non-Euclidean plane. Their Euclidean images in $|z| < 1$ are circles tangent to the horizon $|z| = 1$ from within. The oricycles may be regarded as non-Euclidean circles of infinite radius, or as the loci of points having the same distance from a non-Euclidean line that lies at infinity.

Conversely, every circle of the complex plane that is entirely contained in the interior of $|z| = 1$ is the image of a non-Euclidean circle whose center we can easily construct; and every circle tangent to $|z| = 1$ from within is the image of an oricycle; and finally, every arc of a circle that connects, in $|z| < 1$, two points F, F' of the horizon $|z| = 1$, is the image of a line that maintains a constant distance from the non-Euclidean straight line having F and F' as end points, i.e. the image of a hypercycle.

Poincaré's Half-Plane (§§ 84-85)

84. The first to construct a conformal mapping of the non-Euclidean plane was H. Poincaré (1854-1912). This mapping is especially convenient for many problems of Function Theory, and it consists in identifying the horizon with the real axis, and the non-Euclidean plane with the upper half-plane, of the complex plane.

Under the above mapping, the non-Euclidean straight lines correspond to semi-circles and half-lines contained in the bundle (58.6) (see Fig. 13). The

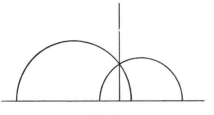

Fig. 13

non-Euclidean motions are represented here by non-loxodromic Moebius transformations of the form

$$w = \frac{a\,z + b}{c\,z + d} \qquad (a, b, c, d \text{ real}) \qquad (84.1)$$

that assign to every real value of z a real value of w (or the value $w = \infty$). It is easy to see that if a Moebius transformation has the property just mentioned, then it is always possible to choose its coefficients a, b, c, d as four *real* numbers. In addition, every point z of the upper half-plane—i.e., every z for which $i(\bar{z} - z) > 0$—must be mapped by (84.1) onto a point w of the upper half-plane, i.e. onto a w for which $i(\bar{w} - w) > 0$. Now since (84.1) implies that

$$- (\bar{z} - z)\,(\bar{w} - w) = \frac{|\bar{z} - z|^2}{|c\,z + d|^2}\,(a\,d - b\,c),$$

we must have

$$a\,d - b\,c > 0. \qquad (84.2)$$

Conversely, every Moebius transformation (84.1) satisfying condition (84.2) represents a rigid motion of the Poincaré half-plane, since a transformation of this kind can be compounded from the following types:

$$w = z + h \qquad (h \text{ real}),$$
$$w = k\,z \qquad (k \text{ real and } > 0), \qquad (84.3)$$
$$w = -\frac{1}{z},$$

and each of these can be generated by two successive reflections in non-Euclidean straight lines of the Poincaré half-plane.

85. If z_1 is a point of the Poincaré half-plane, then the Moebius transformation

$$w = \frac{z_1 - z}{\bar{z}_1 - z} \qquad (85.1)$$

maps this half-plane conformally onto the interior $|w| < 1$ of the unit circle. It is clear that this mapping may be regarded as an *isometric* mapping of the non-Euclidean plane, and that therefore the distance invariant $E_n(z_1, z_2)$ of the Poincaré half-plane can be obtained by writing

$$E_n(z_1, z_2) = E_n(w_1, w_2) = E_n(0, w_2), \qquad (85.2)$$

where $E_n(0, w_2)$ is given by the formulas in § 65 above. In this way we find

$$\operatorname{tgh} \frac{E_n(z_1, z_2)}{2} = \left| \frac{z_1 - z_2}{\bar{z}_1 - z_2} \right|. \qquad (85.3)$$

From this last formula, we obtain the following expression for the element of arc length ds of the Poincaré half-plane:

$$ds = \frac{|dz|}{y} \qquad (z = x + i\,y,\; y > 0). \quad (85.4)$$

It is very easy, incidentally, to verify by direct calculation that the right-hand side of (85.3) is invariant under all transformations (84.3) and is therefore a distance invariant.

Chordal and Pseudo-Chordal Distance (§§ 86-88)

86. We shall denote by $\chi(z_1, z_2)$ one-half the ordinary Euclidean distance (i.e., one-half the length of the straight chord) between the two points of the Riemann sphere that correspond, by § 31, to the two points z_1, z_2 of the complex plane. The quantity $\chi(z_1, z_2)$ is sometimes very convenient as a measure of the distance between z_1 and z_2, and is called the *chordal distance* between z_1 and z_2. If two points of the unit sphere are at spherical distance s from each other, then their straight-line distance is equal to $2 \sin s/2$. Hence the above definition implies that

$$\chi(z_1, z_2) = \sin \frac{E_s(z_1, z_2)}{2}. \quad (86.1)$$

Using (64.11), we may write

$$\sin^2 \frac{E_s(z_1, z_2)}{2} = \frac{\mathrm{tg}^2\,E_s/2}{1 + \mathrm{tg}^2\,E_s/2} = \frac{|z_1 - z_2|^2}{|z_1 - z_2|^2 + |1 + \bar{z}_2 z_1|^2}, \quad (86.2)$$

from which we obtain

$$\chi(z_1, z_2) = \frac{|z_1 - z_2|}{\sqrt{(1 + |z_1|^2)(1 + |z_2|^2)}}. \quad (86.3)$$

If we let z_2 tend to ∞ in (86.3), we find that

$$\chi(z_1, \infty) = \frac{1}{\sqrt{1 + |z_1|^2}}. \quad (86.4)$$

Using the notation of § 66, and relation (70.2), we have

$$a_1 + a_2 + a_3 \leqq 2\pi, \qquad a_3 \leqq a_1 + a_2; \quad (86.5)$$

by having replaced each symbol $<$ in (70.2) with the symbol $\leqq$, we are insuring the validity of relations (86.5) not only under the assumptions of § 66 above, but for entirely arbitrary positions of the three points z_1, z_2, z_3 as well. Now (86.5) implies that

$$0 < \frac{a_3}{2} \le \frac{a_1 + a_2}{2} \le \pi - \frac{a_3}{2} < \pi, \tag{86.6}$$

and from this we obtain

$$\left. \begin{aligned} &\sin \frac{a_3}{2} \le \sin \frac{a_1 + a_2}{2} \\ &= \sin \frac{a_1}{2} \cos \frac{a_2}{2} + \sin \frac{a_2}{2} \cos \frac{a_1}{2} < \sin \frac{a_1}{2} + \sin \frac{a_2}{2}. \end{aligned} \right\} \tag{86.7}$$

Hence if z_1, z_2, z_3 are any three points of the complex plane, we always have the relation

$$\chi(z_1, z_2) < \chi(z_1, z_3) + \chi(z_2, z_3), \tag{86.8}$$

even if one of the numbers z_1, z_2, z_3 equals ∞. This relation is simply the triangle inequality applied to a triangle inscribed in the Riemann sphere. (A triangle of this kind can of course never be degenerate in the sense of having three distinct collinear vertices.)

The use of the chordal distance $\chi(z_1, z_2)$ instead of the ordinary distance $|z_2 - z_1|$ is very advantageous in many investigations, not only because the improper point ∞ is [by (86.4)] on an equal footing, in this metric, with the other points of the complex plane, but also, and mainly, because

$$\chi(z_1, z_2) \le 1$$

always hold true. By (86.2), $\chi(z_1, z_2)$ attains its upper bound unity if and only if $1 + \bar{z}_2 z_1 = 0$, i.e. if and only if z_1 and z_2 correspond to two antipodal points of the Riemann sphere.

87. A distance invariant of Non-Euclidean Geometry that is in some ways similar to the chordal distance $\chi(z_1, z_2)$ is represented by the function

$$\psi(z_1, z_2) = \operatorname{tgh} \frac{E_n(z_1, z_2)}{2} = \frac{|z_2 - z_1|}{|1 - \bar{z}_2 z_1|}, \quad |z_1| < 1, \quad |z_2| < 1, \tag{87.1}$$

which we shall call the *pseudo-chordal distance*[1] between the two points z_1 and z_2. The similarity is explained by the fact that the function tgh x is always monotonically increasing and less than unity (*cf.* § 243 below). With the notation of § 73 above, we also obtain from (73.10) that

$$\operatorname{tgh} a_3 \le \operatorname{tgh} (a_1 + a_2) = \frac{\operatorname{tgh} a_1 + \operatorname{tgh} a_2}{\operatorname{tgh} a_1 \operatorname{tgh} a_2 + 1} < \operatorname{tgh} a_1 + \operatorname{tgh} a_2.$$

---

[1] In the Poincaré half-plane, the formula for pseudo-chordal distance is, by (85.3),

$$\psi(z_1, z_2) = |(z_1 - z_2)/(\bar{z}_1 - z_2)|.$$

From this it follows that

$$\psi(z_1, z_2) < \psi(z_1, z_3) + \psi(z_2, z_3).$$ \hfill (87. 2)

Therefore the pseudo-chordal distances between the vertices of a non-Euclidean triangle can always be used as the lengths of the sides of a Euclidean triangle. On the other hand, it is not possible to map the non-Euclidean plane onto a surface in space in such away—as one might try to do in analogy to Spherical Geometry—that the pseudo-chordal distance between two points is the same as the ordinary Euclidean distance between their image points. This is connected with the fact that the triangle whose sides are the $\psi(z_j, z_k)$ has larger angles than the corresponding non-Euclidean triangle.

88. A last remark: By (86.1) and (86.3), the spherical length of a curve may be defined as double the least upper bound of the "chordal lengths" of all the polygons that can be inscribed in the curve.

Similarly, the non-Euclidean length of a curve lying in $|z| < 1$ may be defined as double the least upper bound of the "pseudo-chordal lengths" of all the polygons that can be inscribed in the curve.

PART TWO

SOME RESULTS FROM POINT SET THEORY
AND FROM TOPOLOGY

CHAPTER ONE

CONVERGENT SEQUENCES OF NUMBERS AND CONTINUOUS COMPLEX FUNCTIONS

Definition of Convergence (§§ 89-90)

89. An infinite sequence $z_1, z_2, \ldots$ of complex numbers is said to converge to zero if the sequence of absolute values of these numbers converges to zero in the ordinary sense (i.e., in the real domain). Similarly, the equations

$$\lim_{n=\infty} z_n = a, \quad \lim_{n=\infty} z_n = \infty \tag{89.1}$$

are to be merely another notation for

$$\lim_{n=\infty} |z_n - a| = 0, \quad \lim_{n=\infty} \frac{1}{|z_n|} = 0. \tag{89.2}$$

If we make use of the concept of chordal distance (*cf.* § 86 above), we can rewrite relations (89.2) in a more symmetric form; for, the equation

$$\lim_{n=\infty} \chi(z_n, a) = 0 \tag{89.3}$$

is equivalent to the second equation of (89.2) if $a = \infty$, and to the first if $a \neq \infty$. It is sufficient to verify this statement for $a \neq \infty$, since

$$\chi(z, \infty) = \chi(\frac{1}{z}, 0) \tag{89.4}$$

holds true.

To this end, assume we have

$$|z_n| \geq 2|a| + 1 \qquad (a \neq \infty) \tag{89.5}$$

this implies that

$$\frac{1}{|z_n|} \leq 1, \quad \left|\frac{a}{z_n}\right| \leq \frac{|a|}{2|a|+1} < \frac{1}{2},$$

$$\left|1 - \frac{a}{z_n}\right| \geq 1 - \left|\frac{a}{z_n}\right| > \frac{1}{2},$$

$$|z_n - a| = |z_n|\left|1 - \frac{a}{z_n}\right| > \frac{1}{2}|z_n|,$$

87

and from these inequalities we obtain, using (86.3),

$$\chi(z_n, a) > \frac{1}{2} \cdot \frac{1}{\sqrt{[1 + (1/|z_n|^2)] (1 + |a|^2)}} > \frac{1}{4\sqrt{1 + |a|^2}} . \tag{89.6}$$

Now if we set

$$\lambda^2 = [1 + (1 + 2|a|)^2] (1 + |a|^2), \tag{89.7}$$

then for

$$|z_n| < 2|a| + 1 \tag{89.8}$$

it follows that

$$|z_n - a| < \lambda \chi(z_n, a). \tag{89.9}$$

These arguments show that the first equation of (89.2) is a consequence of (89.3). Conversely, (89.3) follows from (89.2), since $\chi(z_n, a) \leq |z_n - a|$ always holds.

We may therefore define the equation

$$\lim_{n = \infty} z_n = a$$

to have the meaning

$$\lim_{n = \infty} \chi(z_n, a) = 0 ,$$

and in this definition, both the limit a as well as any of the z_n may assume the value infinity.

90. We can apply to convergent sequences of complex numbers some of the elementary arithmetical operations, as follows: The equations

$$\lim_{n = \infty} z_n = a, \quad \lim_{n = \infty} w_n = b \tag{90.1}$$

imply the further equations

$$\lim_{n = \infty} (z_n + w_n) = a + b, \quad \lim_{n = \infty} z_n w_n = a b , \tag{90.2}$$

provided only that the operations occurring in (90.2) are meaningful (*cf.* § 30 above).

For if, first, the two numbers a and b are finite, then we can obtain (90.2) by using the relations

$$|(z_n + w_n) - (a + b)| \leq |z_n - a| + |w_n - b| ,$$

$$|z_n w_n - a b| \leq |z_n - a| |w_n - b| + |a| |w_n - b| + |b| |z_n - a| .$$

Second, if $a = \infty$ and $b \neq 0$, then we can assume without loss of generality that all the w_n satisfy

$$|w_n| > \frac{|b|}{2}.$$

This implies that

$$\left| \frac{1}{z_n w_n} \right| < \frac{2}{|b| \, |z_n|}, \qquad \lim_{n=\infty} \frac{1}{z_n w_n} = 0,$$

and from this follows the second equation (90.2), with $ab = \infty$.

Third, if $a = \infty$ and $b \neq \infty$, then

$$\lim_{n=\infty} \frac{w_n}{z_n} = 0, \qquad \lim_{n=\infty} \left(1 + \frac{w_n}{z_n} \right) = 1,$$

and hence by the preceding case,

$$\lim_{n=\infty} (z_n + w_n) = \lim_{n=\infty} z_n \left(1 + \frac{w_n}{z_n} \right) = \infty.$$

This completes the proof of the statement at the beginning of this section.

Compact Sets of Points (§ 91)

91. A well-known theorem of the Theory of Sets of Points states that in every bounded infinite set of points there can be found a subset which is a convergent sequence of points. Point sets that have this property are called *compact*. The great advantage of adjoining the number infinity to the finite complex numbers, and of the definition of convergence given at the end of § 89 above, lies mainly in the fact that the (extended) set of all complex numbers is thus made compact.

For if $\mathfrak{M}$ is any infinite set whose elements are finite complex numbers or the number ∞, then we must have one or the other of the following two cases : Either there are, for every given natural number n, infinitely many elements in $\mathfrak{M}$ that lie outside the circle $|z| = n$; in this case, $\mathfrak{M}$ contains sequences of numbers that converge to ∞. Or there exists a natural number N which is such that no more than a finite number of points of $\mathfrak{M}$ lie outside the circle $|z| = N$. In this second case, the existence of a convergent subsequence of $\mathfrak{M}$ is guaranteed by the theorem stated at the beginning of this section. Therefore the set $\mathfrak{M}$ is compact.

This result leads to the following consequences. If $\{z_n\}$ is any given infinite sequence of complex numbers, then among its infinite subsequences there is at least one, say $\{z_n'\}$, that converges to some complex number a. Now if the original sequence $\{z_n\}$ is not itself convergent, then there must exist a positive number ε_0 such that the relations

$$\chi(z_{k_n}, a) > \varepsilon_0 \qquad\qquad (n = 1, 2, \ldots)$$

hold for infinitely many natural numbers k_n. Then if $\{z_n''\}$ is any convergent subsequence of $\{z_{k_n}\}$, the limit b of $\{z_n''\}$ must be different from a.

We therefore have the following theorem: *An infinite sequence of complex numbers converges if and only if all of its convergent subsequences have the same limit.*

This theorem can be substituted to good advantage for the so-called *Cauchy convergence criterion*; incidentally, the latter is an almost immediate consequence of the former.

The Cantor Diagonal Process (§ 92)

92. In many problems it is necessary to select convergent subsequences simultaneously from several, or sometimes even from infinitely many, sequences of numbers. We consider the array

$$
\begin{aligned}
&a_{11}, \quad a_{12}, \quad \ldots, \; a_{1n} \cdots \\
&a_{21}, \quad a_{22}, \quad \ldots, \; a_{2n} \cdots \\
&\ldots\ldots\ldots\ldots\ldots \\
&a_{m1}, \; a_{m2}, \; \ldots, \; a_{mn} \cdots \\
&\ldots\ldots\ldots\ldots\ldots
\end{aligned}
\tag{92.1}
$$

consisting of infinitely many rows and columns, and we select from the first row a convergent subsequence

$$a_{1 j_{11}}, \; a_{1 j_{12}}, \; \ldots, \; a_{1 j_{1n}}, \; \ldots,$$

the limit of which we denote by a_1. For the subscript j_{11} we shall below also write k_1, for short. Next we select from the sequence

$$a_{2 j_{12}}, \; a_{2 j_{13}}, \; \ldots, \; a_{2 j_{1n}} \cdots$$

a convergent subsequence, which we denote by

$$a_{2 j_{22}}, \; a_{2 j_{23}}, \; \ldots, \; a_{2 j_{2n}}, \; \cdots$$

and whose limit we denote by a_2. For j_{22}, we shall write k_2, for short.

Continuing in this way, we obtain for every $i = 1, 2, \ldots$ a convergent sequence of numbers

$$a_{i j_{ii}}, \; a_{i j_{i,\, i+1}}, \; \ldots, \tag{92.2}$$

whose limit is denoted by a_i. Each time, we agree to use k_i to stand for j_{ii}.

Now if we consider the sequences

$$a_{i k_1}, \; a_{i k_2}, \; \ldots, \; a_{i k_n}, \; \ldots, \qquad (i = 1, 2, \ldots) $$

we see that each one of them is, except for a finite number of initial elements, a subsequence of (92.2) (for the same value of i), and must therefore converge to a_i. Thus by crossing out certain of the columns in the array (92.1), we have managed to obtain a new array in which all the rows are convergent infinite sequences. The method of selection that was used here is called the *Cantor diagonal process*.

Classification of Sets of Points (§§ 93-94)

93. The terminology of Point Set Theory is used also in the Theory of Functions. For instance if z_0 is the limit of a convergent sequence of points $z_1, z_2, \ldots$ all of which are distinct from z_0 and are contained in a set A of complex numbers, we shall say that z_0 is a *point of accumulation*[1] of A. We shall similarly call z_0 an *interior point* of A if there exists a positive number ε such that all points z whose chordal distance from z_0 satisfies

$$\chi(z_0, z) < \varepsilon$$

belong to the set A. With these definitions, the concepts of point of accumulation and of interior point are meaningful also if $z_0 = \infty$.

The interior points of the complementary set A' of A are called *exterior points* of A. The points of the (extended) complex plane that are neither interior nor exterior points of A are said to constitute the *frontier* of A. The frontier points belonging to A constitute the *boundary* R_A of A, while the others—those belonging to A'—constitute the *boundary* $R_{A'}$ of A'.

Finally, a point of A is said to be *isolated* if it is not a point of accumulation of points of A.

94. We shall also classify sets of points in a similar way. An *open* set is one that consists entirely of interior points; a *closed* set is one that contains all of its points of accumulation; a set is said to be *dense-in-itself* if each of its points is a point of accumulation of the set. A point set that is both closed and dense-in-itself is said to be *perfect*.

If a set is open, its complementary set is closed, and *vice versa*. The only set of complex numbers that is both open and closed is the extended complex plane itself.

By forming the union $A + H_A$ of a set A and the set H_A of its points of accumulation, we obtain the smallest closed set $\overline{A}$ that contains all the points of A. The point set $\overline{A}$ is called the *closure* of A.

The complementary set A_α of the closure $\overline{A'}$ of the complementary set A' of A is the largest open subset of A. This point set A_α is called the *open kernel* of A.

---

[1] Also called a *limit point* of A.

The union of a finite or of a denumerably infinite number of open point sets is itself an open point set.

The intersection of a denumerable infinity of closed, non-empty, nested point sets

$$A_1 \geqq A_2 \geqq A_3 \geqq \cdots$$

is itself a *closed and non-empty* point set. We can prove this statement as follows: In each of the point sets A_ν we select a point z_ν, and from the sequence $\{z_\nu\}$ we select a convergent subsequence with limit ω, say

$$z_{n_1}, z_{n_2}, \cdots \qquad\qquad (n_1 < n_2 < n_3 < \cdots).$$

Now if m is any given natural number, and if we choose j large enough for $n_j > m$ to hold, then the sequence

$$z_{n_j}, z_{n_{j+1}}, \cdots$$

consists entirely of points of A_m, since the sequence of sets A_ν is nested. Therefore since A_m is closed, the limit ω of the above sequence of points also belongs to A_m. This holds true for $m = 1, 2, \ldots$, so that ω must belong to the intersection D of all the A_ν; hence D is not empty. And since every point of accumulation of D must belong to D, the set D is closed.

Complex Functions (§§ 95-98)

95. By assigning to every point z of a point set A_z of the z-plane a point w of a second complex plane, we define a one-valued (or single-valued) *complex function*

$$w = F(z), \qquad\qquad (95.1)$$

whose *domain of definition* is the point set A_z. Equation (95.1) gives a *single-valued mapping* of the point set A_z of the z-plane onto some point set A_w of the w-plane. To each point of A_z there corresponds a well-defined point of A_w; but every point of A_w may be the image of several points, even of an infinite number of points, of A_z. (We also speak of this as a *many-to-one mapping* of A_z onto A_w.) In extreme cases, all the points of A_z may correspond to a single point w_0 of the w-plane; the function $F(z) = w_0$ is then a constant (or constant function).

If we set $z = x + i y, w = u + i v$, then the one equation (95.1) is equivalent to two equations of the form

$$u = \varphi(x, y), \quad v = \psi(x, y). \qquad\qquad (95.2)$$

But for our purposes, the representation (95.1) of the mapping will be preferable by far to the more explicit description of the same mapping by means of the system of equations (95.2).

96. Let z_0 be a point of accumulation of A_z, but not necessarily a point of A_z itself. Then there exist sequences $\{z_n\}$ of points of A_z that converge to z_0. By means of the equations

$$w_n = F(z_n) \qquad (n = 1, 2, \ldots), \quad (96.1)$$

we determine the sequence $\{w_n\}$ of the image points of the z_n. It may happen (as for instance in the case of the function $F(z) \equiv z$) that the sequence $\{w_n\}$ is convergent whenever the z_n converge to z_0. If so, then the limit $w_0 = \lim w_n$ must be the same for all the possible sequences $\{w_n\}$ that one obtains from (96.1); for if we have

$$\left. \begin{aligned} w_n = F(z_n'), \quad w_n'' = F(z_n'') \qquad (n = 1, 2, \ldots), \\ \lim_{n=\infty} z_n' = \lim_{n=\infty} z_n'' = z_0, \end{aligned} \right\} \quad (96.2)$$

then the sequence

$$z_1', \ z_1'', \ z_2', \ z_2'', \ \ldots$$

also converges to z_0, and the limit w_0 (which exists by hypothesis) of the sequence

$$w_1', \ w_1'', \ w_2', \ w_2'', \ \ldots$$

satisfies the equations

$$\lim_{n=\infty} w_n' = \lim_{n=\infty} w_n'' = w_0. \qquad (96.3)$$

Now assume that the point z_0 belongs to the domain A_z of definition of $F(z)$. Then we must have, in particular,

$$w_0 = F(z_0), \qquad (96.4)$$

since we may set all the $z_n' = z_0$ in the above argument. We say in this case that the function $F(z)$ is *continuous at the point* z_0. But even if z_0 is not a point of A_z, we can *define* $F(z_0)$ by means of equation (96.4), in which we substitute for w_0 its value from (96.3). After this *extension of its domain of definition*, the function $F(z)$ is continuous at the point z_0.

Note that in the above definition of continuity, both z_0 and w_0 may assume the value ∞.

97. Let us assume that every point ζ of some *closed* subset B_ζ of A_z is a point of accumulation of A_z, and that $F(z)$ is continuous at all these points ζ. We assign a positive number δ and consider all the pairs z, ζ of points for which the three relations

$$z \in A_z, \quad \zeta \in B_\zeta, \quad \chi(z, \zeta) < \delta \qquad (97.1)$$

hold true. We then determine the number

$$\varepsilon(\delta) = \sup \chi\big(F(z), F(\zeta)\big), \tag{97.2}$$

where the pair z, ζ is subject to relations (97.1). The (real) function $\varepsilon(\delta)$ is clearly monotonically increasing, which implies the existence of the limit

$$\lim_{\delta=0} \varepsilon(\delta) = \varepsilon_0. \tag{97.3}$$

In order to determine ε_0, we select a sequence of numbers δ_n that satisfies the two conditions

$$\delta_1 > \delta_2 > \delta_3 > \cdots, \quad \lim_{n=\infty} \delta_n = 0, \tag{97.4}$$

and we assign to each of the numbers δ_n a pair z_n, ζ_n of points for which

$$\left.\begin{array}{c} z_n \in A_z, \quad \zeta_n \in B_\zeta, \quad \chi(z_n, \zeta_n) < \delta_n, \\[2mm] \chi\big(F(z_n), F(\zeta_n)\big) \geq \dfrac{\varepsilon(\delta_n)}{2} \geq \dfrac{\varepsilon_0}{2}\,. \end{array}\right\} \tag{97.5}$$

We may assume without loss of generality that the sequence of points ζ_n converges to a point ζ_0 (cf. § 91 above). Since we have assumed B_ζ to be closed, ζ_0 must belong to B_ζ and must therefore be a point of continuity of $F(z)$. Considering that (97.4) and (97.5) imply the relations

$$\lim_{n=\infty} z_n = \lim_{n=\infty} \zeta_n = \zeta_0,$$

we now obtain

$$\lim_{n=\infty} F(z_n) = \lim_{n=\infty} F(\zeta_n) = F(\zeta_0)$$

and finally

$$\frac{\varepsilon_0}{2} \leq \lim_{n=\infty} \chi\big(F(z_n), F(\zeta_n)\big) = 0.$$

Hence we have proved that

$$\lim_{\delta=0} \varepsilon(\delta) = 0. \tag{97.6}$$

98. The importance of this result is pointed up better if we rephrase it somewhat. Equation (97.6) states that to every positive number ε, we can assign at least one number $\delta > 0$ which is such that $\varepsilon(\delta) < \varepsilon$. For every δ selected in this way, the assumptions

$$z \in A_z, \quad \zeta \in B_\zeta, \quad \chi(z, \zeta) < \delta \tag{98.1}$$

lead to the relation

$$\chi\big(F(z), F(\zeta)\big) \leq \varepsilon. \tag{98.2}$$

This result yields us a new insight if B_ζ consists of a single point; it shows that the above definition of continuity is equivalent to the definition given by Cauchy.

If A_z is a closed point set on which $F(z)$ is continuous, then we may set $B_\zeta = A_z$, and the above result therefore contains also the theorem which states that any function defined and continuous on a closed point set must be *uniformly continuous* on that set.

The Boundary Values of a Complex Function (§ 99)

99. If a complex function $F(z)$ is defined on a set A of points of the complex plane and if ζ is a frontier point of A, then we can find sequences of points $z_1, z_2, ..., z_\nu, ...$ that converge to ζ and for which, at the same time,

$$\lim_{\nu = \infty} F(z_\nu) = \alpha \qquad (99.1)$$

exists. A number α of this kind is called a *boundary value* of the function $F(z)$ at the frontier point ζ.

Let us denote by W the set of boundary values of the function $F(z)$ at the point ζ. For W, the following theorem holds:

The set W of boundary values (at ζ) is always a closed point set.

For if α_0 is a point of accumulation of W, and if $\{\alpha_n\}$ is a sequence of boundary values for which $\chi(\alpha_n, \alpha_0) < 1/n$ holds, then in every circle $\chi(z, \zeta) < 1/n$ there exists at least one point z_n for which $\chi(F(z_n), \alpha_n) < 1/n$ From these it follows that $\chi(F(z_n), \alpha_0) < 2/n$, and α_0 is therefore a boundary value of $F(z)$ at the point ζ.

If the point ∞ is not a boundary value of $F(z)$ at ζ, then there is a neighborhood of ζ in which $F(z)$ is bounded. For otherwise, there would be in every circle $\chi(z, \zeta) < 1/n$ at least one point z_n for which $|F(z_n)| > n$, and the value ∞ would then be a boundary value of $F(z)$ after all.

Similar reasoning shows that if $a \neq \infty$ is not a boundary value of $F(z)$ at the point ζ, then the function

$$\frac{1}{F(z) - a}$$

must be bounded in a certain neighborhood of ζ.

CHAPTER TWO

CURVES AND REGIONS

Connected Sets of Points (§§ 100-101)

100. Of special importance in the sequel will be some concepts that have the property of invariance under *topological* mappings (i.e., mappings that are one-to-one and bi-continuous). We shall take up first, among these concepts, that of *connectivity*. If A is a planar set of points that contains the point z_0 but does not contain the point $z = 1$, then the line segment $O1$ contains at least one point of the frontier of A; for this reason, the line segment is said to be *connected*. We are thus led to the following general definition:

A point set E containing at least two distinct points is said to be connected if for every point set A that contains at least one but not all of the points of E, the frontier B of A also contains at least one point of E. Point sets that consist of a single point are also classified as connected sets.

This definition of connectivity immediately implies the following criterion, which is often useful: *A point set E is connected if and only if for any choice of two points P and Q belonging to E, there is at least one connected subset $E(P, Q)$ of E that contains P and Q.* Hence the union E of a denumerable infinity of nested connected sets

$$E_1 \subseteq E_2 \subseteq E_3 \subseteq \ldots$$

is always itself a connected point set. Furthermore, the sum $A + B$ of two open point sets A and B that have no point in common (i.e. that are disjoint) is *not* connected; for, the frontier of A contains no points of $A + B$, while both A and its complementary set A' do contain points of $A + B$.

We shall list here, without proofs, some additional properties of connected sets; for the proofs, we refer the reader to pertinent sources.[1]

A point set A_1 is said to be *open (closed) relative to a second point set A* if A_1 can be represented as the intersection of A with an open (closed) point set. Therefore if A is the sum $A_1 + A_2$ of two disjoint sets one of which is open relative to A, then the other one must be closed relative to A. Now we can state the following *Main Theorem of the Theory of Connectivity*: *A point*

---

[1] C. Carathéodory, *Reelle Funktionen*, Vol. I, pp. 71 ff. (New York, Chelsea 1946).

set E is connected if and only if it does not contain any proper subset E_1 that is both open and closed relative to E.

A different formulation of the same result is as follows: *A point set E is connected if and only if it can not be represented as a sum $E_1 + E_2$ of two non-empty, disjoint sets both of which are open relative to E (or: both of which are closed relative to E).*

A point set that is open and connected is called a *region*. A closed connected point set, or a point set consisting of a single point, is called a *continuum*.

The result just stated now implies the following: An open point set is a region if and only if it can not be represented as a sum of two non-empty, disjoint, open point sets. Similarly, a closed point set containing at least two distinct points is a continuum if and only if it can not be represented as a sum of two non-empty, disjoint, closed point sets.

We note also that every connected point set is dense in itself, and that every continuum containing at least two distinct points is therefore a perfect point set.

If we add to any (non-closed) connected point set any part of its set of points of accumulation, the resulting point set is itself connected.

101. We shall state some additional theorems on connected point sets that follow almost immediately from those listed above:

The union $E_1 + E_2$ of two connected point sets is itself connected if and only if one of the two sets E_1, E_2 has at least one point in common with the closure of the other.

The following theorem belongs to an entirely different order of ideas:

The image of a connected point set under a single-valued, continuous mapping is itself a connected point set.

This last theorem is of special importance, not only because it can often be used to construct particular connected sets, but also, and primarily, because it shows that the property of connectedness is a topological property of point sets.

Curves (§ 102)

102. The simplest type of connected point set in the complex plane is an open straight-line segment. If we add to such a segment one or both of its end points, we obtain a half-open or a closed line-segment, respectively, and these are likewise connected.

The continuous image (i.e., image under a continuous mapping) of a closed line-segment $0 \leq t \leq 1$ is called a *continuous arc* (or *curve*) on the Riemann sphere or in the complex plane. A continuous arc can therefore be represented by an equation of the form

$$z = z(t) = x(t) + i\, y(t), \tag{102.1}$$

where the functions $x(t)$, $y(t)$ are continuous, so that the function $z(t)$ is continuous in the metric of the chordal distance (*cf.* § 86 above). Hence a continuous arc is a closed, connected point set, and therefore it is a continuum.

We shall occasionally make use of *polygonal trains*; these are special continuous arcs in the complex plane, and consist of a finite number of straight-line segments laid off end to end.

Regions (§ 103)

103. An open point set every two of whose points can be joined to each other by a polygonal train within the set, is connected (by § 100), and is therefore a region. From this it follows that the interior and the exterior of a circle in the complex plane, i.e. the point sets

$$|z - a| < r, \quad |z - a| > r \tag{103.1}$$

both are regions. Similarly, the open point sets

$$\chi(z, a) < \varepsilon \leqq 1 \tag{103.2}$$

on the Riemann sphere are connected and hence are regions.

Conversely, it is easy to show (e.g. by means of Lindelöf's Covering Theorem) that any given region in the complex plane or on the Riemann sphere can be covered by a union of at most denumerably many elementary regions

$$E_1, E_2, E_3, \ldots$$

of the form (103.1) or (103.2), and in such a way that each of the regions E_k has a point in common with at least one of the regions that precede it in the above sequence.

It follows from this that any two points of a region of the complex plane can be connected to each other by a polygonal train all of whose points belong to the given region. This last property therefore constitutes a necessary and sufficient condition for an open point set to be a region, and this condition is a very convenient one with which to operate.

Every open point set can be represented as the sum of at most denumerably many disjoint open regions.

A region is also called a *neighborhood* of each of its points.

Neighborhood-Preserving Mappings (§§ 104-105)

104. Except for constant functions, most of the functions that occur in Function Theory are continuous functions

$$w = F(z) \tag{104.1}$$

whose domain of definition is a region G_z and that satisfy the following additional property (*cf.* § 144 below) : Let z_0 be any point of G_z, let $w_0 = F(z_0)$ be the image point of z_0 in the w-plane, and let A_z be any subset of G_z that contains z_0 as an *interior* point; then the image A_w of A_z under the mapping given by the function (104.1) contains w_0 as an *interior* point. A mapping that has this property is said to be *neighborhood-preserving*; and indeed, a mapping of this kind maps any open connected subset of G_z onto an open connected subset of the image G_w of G_z, i.e. it does indeed "preserve" regions (or neighborhoods).

105. If a continuous function $w = F(z)$ defined in a region G_z always maps two distinct points of G_z onto two distinct points of the w-plane, then the mapping represented by the function can be proved to be neighborhood-preserving and bi-continuous (i.e., continuous in both directions). But the proof of this theorem is rather complicated. Fortunately, in the Theory of Functions we can manage without this general theorem, since we will always know in advance that all the mappings to be considered are neighborhood-preserving, so that it only remains to show that the inverse function

$$z = \Phi(w), \tag{105.1}$$

which is defined in the region G_w, is continuous.

To prove continuity of the inverse function under the assumption stated at the beginning of § 105, we consider a point z_0 of G_z and its image point w_0 of G_w, as well as a sequence $\{w_n\}$ of points of G_w converging to w_0. Every point w_n is the image of exactly one corresponding point z_n of G_z. A circular disc $\chi(z, z_0) < \varepsilon$ of the Riemann sphere corresponds under the mapping to a point set E_w that contains w_0 as an interior point. This implies that no more than a *finite* number of the points of $\{w_n\}$ can fail to belong to the point set E_w. Hence all but at most finitely many of the points of $\{z_n\}$ are contained in the above circular disc, and the sequence of points $\{z_n\}$ must therefore converge to z_0.

The mapping given by (105.1) is also *neighborhood-preserving*. To show this, we consider any circular disc $\chi(w, w_0) < \varepsilon$ of G_w and assume that w_0 is the image of the point z_0 of G_z. Since the function $F(z)$ is continuous, it follows that any sufficiently small circular disc $\chi(z, z_0) < \delta$ is mapped onto a point set that is interior to $\chi(w, w_0) < \varepsilon$, and the latter disc is therefore the image of a point set which contains z_0 as an *interior* point.

In particular, therefore, every subregion of G_w is the image of a subregion of G_z.

Jordan Curves (§§ 106-109)

106. If we want the curves with which we shall work to have certain essential properties from among those properties shared by the familiar types of analytic curves, we must add special conditions to the definition of continuous curve (or arc) as given in § 102 above. We shall specialize this definition in two different directions and introduce *Jordan curves* on the one hand, and—in § 114 below—*rectifiable curves* on the other hand.

By a *Jordan arc* we shall mean a continuous arc having no double points (i.e. no points of self-intersection); thus a Jordan arc is not merely a continuous image but a *one-to-one* and continuous image of a closed straight-line segment.

By a *Jordan curve*, or *simple closed curve*, we shall mean a closed Jordan arc, i.e. the one-to-one and continuous image of a circle (e.g. of the circle $|z| = 1$). The main theorem concerning Jordan curves, the so-called *Jordan Curve Theorem*, is not especially easy to prove; probably the shortest proof is the one given by Erhard Schmidt.[1] We can state this theorem as follows:

Every Jordan curve γ is the frontier of two disjoint regions G_1 and G_2 which together with γ fill out the entire Riemann sphere.

The most general Jordan curves have, like the triangle, the property of dividing the plane into two regions.[2] Since we have adjoined the point $z = \infty$ to the other points of the complex plane, we can no longer differentiate *a priori* between the exterior and the interior of a Jordan curve.

The Jordan curve theorem is supplemented by the following observation:
Each of the two regions G_1 and G_2 defines a "side" of the Jordan curve γ. Two points of the complex plane lie on the same side of γ if and only if they can be joined by a continuum that does not meet γ.

107. The following theorem is easy to prove and is very convenient for many applications: If two points z' and z'' lie on the same side G_1 of a Jordan curve γ and if the chordal distance from the curve of each of them is less than a number $\varepsilon > 0$, then the two points can be connected by a polygonal train

---

[1] E. Schmidt, *Über den Jordanschen Kurvensatz*, Sitz.-Ber. Berlin. Akad. Wiss., 1923.

[2] In contrast to this, it should be noted that the most general continuous curves, as defined in § 102 above, may fill out entire regions, even the entire Riemann sphere.

each of whose points is interior to G_1 and at a chordal distance less than ε from γ.

We also note the following generalization of the Jordan curve theorem: Let a Jordan curve γ lie in the interior of a region G, and consider the two open point sets G' and G'' that are the intersections of G with the two sides G_1 and G_2 of the curve; then G' and G'' must each be connected, and therefore must themselves be regions. Hence γ divides G into two subregions.

108. Let $\gamma^{(1)}$ and $\gamma^{(2)}$ be two Jordan curves that have no points in common (see Fig. 14 below). Let $\gamma^{(2)}$ lie on the side $G_2^{(1)}$ of $\gamma^{(1)}$ and let $\gamma^{(1)}$ lie on the side $G_2^{(2)}$ of $\gamma^{(2)}$. The region $G_1^{(1)}$, whose frontier is $\gamma^{(1)}$, contains points of $G_2^{(2)}$ but contains no points of $\gamma^{(2)}$; therefore $G_1^{(1)}$, being a connected point set, can not contain any points of $G_1^{(2)}$. Hence $G_1^{(1)}$ is a subset of $G_2^{(2)}$. Similarly, we find that $G_1^{(2)}$ is a subset of $G_2^{(1)}$. All the other points of the (extended) complex plane are in the intersection $G_2^{(1)} G_2^{(2)}$ of the two regions $G_2^{(1)}$ and $G_2^{(2)}$. By the preceding section, this intersection is itself a region, so that every point of the extended complex plane lies either on one of the two curves or in one of the three regions $G_1^{(1)}$, $G_1^{(2)}$, and $G_2^{(1)} G_2^{(2)}$.

A similar train of reasoning leads to the general result that n mutually disjoint Jordan curves $\gamma^{(1)}, \gamma^{(2)}, \ldots, \gamma^{(n)}$ divide the complex plane into $(n + 1)$ regions.

But for any given $n \geq 3$, there are several topologically different relative positions possible for the n Jordan curves, as may be easily verified, for instance, with circles. The most important case is that of *"complete separation"* of the Jordan curves. We say that the n curves $\gamma^{(\nu)}$ are completely separated if any $(n - 1)$ of them always lie on one and the same side of the n-th curve. Another definition of complete separation of Jordan curves, easily shown to be equivalent to the one

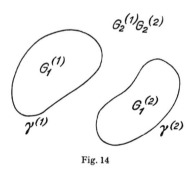

Fig. 14

just given, is the following: Of the $(n + 1)$ regions into which the n curves $\gamma^{(\nu)}$ divide the complex plane, one is bounded by all the curves $\gamma^{(1)}, \ldots, \gamma^{(n)}$, while each of the n remaining regions is bounded by a single curve $\gamma^{(\nu)}$.

109. Let us consider three completely separated curves $\gamma_z^{(1)}, \gamma_z^{(2)}, \gamma_z^{(3)}$ lying in a region G_z (see Fig. 15 below). Then any two of these curves, say $\gamma_z^{(2)}$ and $\gamma_z^{(3)}$, lie on one and the same side of the third curve, $\gamma_z^{(1)}$.

By § 107 above, we can find connected point sets lying *in the interior of G_z* that connect a point of $\gamma_z^{(2)}$ with a point of $\gamma_z^{(3)}$ without meeting $\gamma_z^{(1)}$. *Hence the fact that the three given Jordan curves are completely separated can be* *verified by means of a construction entirely within G_z.*

We now consider a topological mapping of the region G_z onto a region G_w. This mapping transforms the three given Jordan curves $\gamma_z^{(i)}$ into three Jordan curves $\gamma_w^{(i)}$, and it transforms any connected subset of G_z that joins $\gamma_z^{(2)}$ with $\gamma_z^{(3)}$ into a connected subset of G_w that joins $\gamma_w^{(2)}$ with $\gamma_w^{(3)}$.

This implies that the three curves $\gamma_w^{(i)}$ are themselves completely separated. The same result applies to any number of completely separated curves lying in G_z.

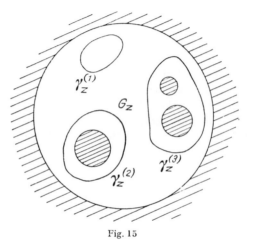

Fig. 15

Therefore *the property of being completely separated within a region is a topological property of Jordan curves.*

Simply and Multiply Connected Regions (§§ 110-113)

110. Let us consider a region G_z that contains not only all the points of a given Jordan curve γ_z but that contains also the set G_z' of all the points of the extended complex plane that lie on one of the two sides of γ_z.

Let (the interior of) G_z be mapped onto a region G_w of the w-plane by means of a topological mapping that transforms γ_z into γ_w and G_z' into G_w'. We shall prove that G_w' must contain all the points of the extended w-plane that lie on one of the two sides of γ_w. For if this were false, then at least one point ω of the frontier of G_w would lie on the same side of γ_w as G_w'. Let $w_1, w_2, \ldots$ be a sequence of points of G_w that converges to ω; we may assume all of them to lie on the same side of γ_w as G_w. Their preimages $z_1, z_2, \ldots$ all lie on the same side of γ_z as G_z', and these must therefore all be themselves contained in G_z'. Hence any point of accumulation ζ_0 of the sequence $z_1, z_2, \ldots$ must itself lie either in G_z' or on γ_z and must therefore be an *interior* point of G_z. Its image point w_0 must therefore be an interior point of G_w and hence cannot be a point of accumulation of the sequence $w_1, w_2, \cdots$. This contradiction yields the truth of the statement that we set out to prove.

We have proved at the same time that if G_z' contains frontier points of G_z, then G_w' must contain frontier points of G_w. For if G_w' contains no frontier points of G_w, then it follows from our above result that all the points of G_z' are interior points of G_z.

111. In considering the above topological mapping of G_z onto G_w, we made no mention of what happens to the frontier points of G_z under the mapping. The frontier points ζ of G_z not only may fail to have an image in the w-plane or on the Riemann w-sphere, but it may actually happen that for every given frontier point ζ there exist sequences $\{z_n\}$ of points G_z that converge to ζ while their images in the w-plane do not converge. This will be the case, for instance, if we map the circular disc $|z| < 1$ topologically onto itself in such a way that each of its radii is mapped onto a spiral that approaches the circle $|z| = 1$ asymptotically (see Fig. 16 below).

It is all the more remarkable that on the basis of the result proved in § 110 above, we can find certain properties of the frontier of G_z that are invariant under topological mappings of (the *interior* of) G_z.

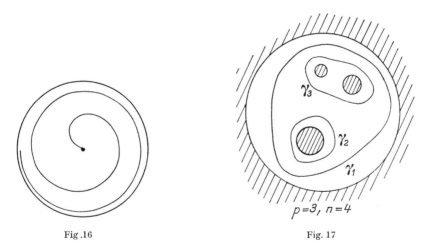

$p=3, n=4$

Fig .16   Fig. 17

The frontier of a region G_z is a *closed* point set. We shall say that a region G_z is *simply connected* if its frontier β_z is a single continuum. Thus if the frontier of a region is a Jordan curve, the region is simply connected. For instance, the circular disc $|z| < 1$ is simply connected, and so is the half-plane $\Re z > 0$.

But a circular disc with a cut along a radius is a simply connected region whose frontier is *not a Jordan curve,* and by piling up cuts of this sort we can construct simply connected regions of a very complicated nature.

We shall see later on that any two simply connected regions can be mapped onto each other topologically, and even conformally, so that the above-mentioned complications of the frontier are not essential features—in the sense of not being invariant under topological mapping of (the interior of) the region.

If G_z is a simply connected region, and γ a Jordan curve entirely contained in G_z, then all the points of the plane lying on one of the two sides of γ must also be contained in G_z, since the frontier of G_z could not otherwise be a continuum. Conversely, if the region G_z is not simply connected—e.g. if its frontier consists of a finite number ≥ 2 of mutually disjoint continua—then it is easy to show (by using the fact that two disjoint continua have a positive minimum distance from each other) that there exist Jordan curves γ lying in G_z that contain frontier points of G_z in *both* of their two sides. These facts lead to a new definition of simple connectedness, entirely in terms of interior points of G_z:

A region G_z is simply connected if, and only if, every Jordan curve γ that lies entirely in G_z has one of its two sides lying entirely in G_z.

112. In Function Theory we have to deal mainly with regions whose frontier consists of a finite number of continua. We shall say that a region is *doubly connected* if its frontier β_z is the sum of two disjoint continua, and more generally we call a region *n-tuply connected* if β_z is the sum of n mutually disjoint continua.

The number n, called the *connectivity* of the region, is invariant under topological mappings of the region. The proof of the fact, for instance, that the topological image G_w of a simply connected region G_z is itself simply connected, follows directly from the discussion in the preceding section and from the theorem proved in § 110 above.

If we want to apply similar arguments to multiply connected regions, we must consider systems of p completely separated Jordan curves lying within an n-tuply connected region G_z and having the property that the "in-between" region whose frontier consists of all the p curves is the only region, among those into which the system of curves divides the Riemann sphere, that contains no points of the frontier of G_z. If

$$2 \leq p \leq n,$$

then we can always find such systems of curves (*cf.* Fig. 17 above); but if $p > n$, the construction can not be carried out.

Under a topological mapping of G_z onto a region G_w, the system of curves $\gamma_z^{(\nu)}$ is mapped onto a similar system of curves $\gamma_w^{(\nu)}$. The connectivity of G_w

must therefore be $\geq n$; but it cannot be $> n$, since we could otherwise find $(n + 1)$ completely separated curves $\gamma_w^{(\nu)}$ which would have as their pre-images $(n + 1)$ completely separated curves $\gamma_z^{(\nu)}$ having the property described above.

113. Thus for determining the connectivity n of a given region G_z of finite connectivity, we have a choice of three mutually equivalent criteria.

First, n equals the number of continua that make up the frontier of G_z.

Second, n is equal to the connectivity of any region G_w that is a topological image of G_z.

Third, n is equal to the maximal number of completely separated Jordan curves that can be drawn in G_z and that have the additional property described in the preceding section.

We shall state a fourth criterion, based on a definition we shall give presently.

A Jordan arc that connects an interior point of a region G with a frontier point of G, all of its points except for this frontier point being interior points of G, is called a *free cut* of the region G. A Jordan arc both of whose end points (which may coincide) are frontier points of G, and all of whose remaining points are within G, is called a *cross cut* of G. It is easy to prove that a cross cut of a simply connected region G divides G into two simply connected regions G' and G''.

Now to give the fourth criterion for the connectivity n. We may characterize n in terms of the maximal number N of cross cuts that can be applied to G without disconnecting G into more than one connected component; it can be proved that $n = N + 1$.

In conclusion, we note the fact that the complementary set of any continuum in the complex plane consists of at most denumerably many regions each of which is simply connected.

CHAPTER THREE

CONTOUR INTEGRATION

Rectifiable Curves (§ 114)

114. We consider a continuous arc γ of the complex plane, as defined in § 102 above, i.e. the continuous image (image under a continuous mapping) $z(t)$ of a straight-line segment

$$t_0 \leq t \leq T \tag{114.1}$$

of the t-axis. Let us subdivide this segment by means of the points

$$t_0 < t_1 < t_2 < \cdots < t_{n-1} < t_n = T \tag{114.2}$$

into a finite number of subintervals. To each of these points t_k there corresponds a point $z_k = z(t_k)$ of the curve. If we connect consecutive points z_k and z_{k+1} by means of line segments (see Fig. 18 below), we obtain a polygonal train inscribed in γ.

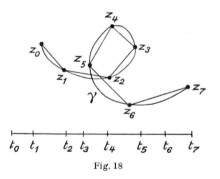

Fig. 18

The length of the inscribed polygonal train is given by the number

$$|z_1 - z_0| + |z_2 - z_1| + \cdots + |z_n - z_{n-1}|. \tag{114.3}$$

We shall say that the continuous arc γ is *rectifiable* if the lengths of all possible inscribed polygonal trains, corresponding to all possible partitions (114.2), have a finite least upper bound. This least upper bound (abbreviated as l.u.b.) is then called the *length of the arc* γ.

Every sub-arc of a rectifiable curve is itself rectifiable. If a rectifiable curve is subdivided into a finite number of sub-arcs, then the length of the whole curve equals the sum of the lengths of the sub-arcs.

Complex Contour Integrals (§§ 115-119)

115. Let us consider a continuous and bounded complex function $F(z)$ that is defined at all the points $z(t)$ of a rectifiable curve γ. With every partition (114.2) of the interval (114.1) we associate, just as in the preceding section, the points $z_i = z(t_i)$, and we form the number

$$\left. \begin{aligned} S &= F(z_0)(z_1 - z_0) + F(z_1)(z_2 - z_1) + \cdots + F(z_{n-1})(z_n - z_{n-1}) \\ &= \sum_{k=1}^{n} F(z_{k-1})(z_k - z_{k-1}). \end{aligned} \right\} \tag{115.1}$$

Let us also consider a second partition

$$t_0 = t'_0 < t'_1 < \cdots < t'_m = T \tag{115.2}$$

of the same interval (114.1), obtained by adding further points of division to those of (114.2), and let us compare the corresponding new sum

$$S' = \sum_{j=1}^{m} F(z'_{j-1})(z'_j - z'_{j-1}) \tag{115.3}$$

with S.

Now we assign to each number t'_j of the system (115.2) the largest of the numbers $t'_1 < t'_2 < \ldots < t'_j$ that belongs at the same time to the system (114.2), and we denote the latter number by t_j^*. Then if we set $z_j^* = z(t_j^*)$, we can re-write the sum (115.1) in the form

$$S = \sum_{j=1}^{m} F(z_{j-1}^*)(z'_j - z'_{j-1}). \tag{115.4}$$

Equations (115.3) and (115.4) imply that

$$S' - S = \sum_{j=1}^{m} [F(z'_{j-1}) - F(z_{j-1}^*)](z'_j - z'_{j-1}). \tag{115.5}$$

We denote by δ the largest of the differences

$$(t_1 - t_0), \quad (t_2 - t_1), \quad \ldots, \quad (t_n - t_{n-1}),$$

and we determine the number

$$\varepsilon(\delta) = \text{l.u.b. of } \left| F\big(z(t')\big) - F\big(z(t'')\big) \right| \Big\}$$
$$\text{for } |t'' - t'| \leq \delta, \quad t_0 \leq t' < t'' \leq T. \quad\Big\} \tag{115.6}$$

For each of the terms occurring in (115.5), we now must have

$$\left| F(z_j') - F(z_j^*) \right| \leq \varepsilon(\delta),$$

since $|t_j' - t_j^*| < \delta$ always holds.

This implies that

$$|S' - S| \leq \sum_{j=1}^{m} \left| F(z_j') - F(z_j^*) \right| \, |z_j' - z_{j-1}'| \Big\}$$
$$\leq \varepsilon(\delta) \sum_{j=1}^{m} |z_j' - z_{j-1}'|. \quad\Big\} \tag{115.7}$$

Hence if we denote the length of the given curve γ by L_γ, we may write

$$|S' - S| \leq \varepsilon(\delta) \, L_\gamma. \tag{115.8}$$

A similar inequality can be obtained even in the case that the points of division (115.2) do not contain among them all the points of division (114.2). In order to obtain this inequality, we consider the new partition

$$t_0' = t_0'' < t_1'' < t_2'' < \cdots < t_p'' = T,$$

consisting of all the points t_k and all the points t_j', and we compute the sum S'' that corresponds to this partition. By (115.8), we then have

$$|S'' - S| \leq \varepsilon(\delta) \, L_\gamma, \quad |S'' - S'| \leq \varepsilon(\delta') \, L_\gamma,$$

where δ' denotes the largest of the numbers $(t_j' - t_{j-1}')$. Hence we have, in any case,

$$|S' - S| \leq |S'' - S| + |S'' - S'| \leq [\varepsilon(\delta) + \varepsilon(\delta')] \, L_\gamma. \tag{115.9}$$

116. Let us now consider an infinite sequence of partitions

$$t_0 = t_0^{(k)} < t_1^{(k)} < \cdots < t_{n_k}^{(k)} = T \tag{116.1}$$

of the interval (114.1), and let us denote by $\delta^{(k)}$ the largest of the differences $(t_j^{(k)} - t_{j-1}^{(k)})$ for $j = 1, 2, \ldots, n_k$. Let us also denote by $S^{(k)}$, in analogy to (115.1), the sums

$$S^{(k)} = \sum_{j=1}^{n_k} F(z_{j-1}^{(k)}) \, (z_j^{(k)} - z_{j-1}^{(k)}). \tag{116.2}$$

If we set

$$\varepsilon^{(k)} = \varepsilon(\delta^{(k)}), \tag{116.3}$$

then by (115.9), we have the relations

$$\left| S^{(k)} - S^{(k+p)} \right| \leqq [\varepsilon^{(k)} + \varepsilon^{(k+p)}] \, L_\gamma. \tag{116.4}$$

Now if we assume the sequence of partitions (116.1) to be so chosen that

$$\lim_{k=\infty} \delta^{(k)} = 0, \tag{116.5}$$

then because of the continuity of the functions $z(t)$ and $F(z)$ it follows that

$$\lim_{k=\infty} \varepsilon^{(k)} = 0 \tag{116.6}$$

must also hold. By (116.4) and by Cauchy's Convergence Criterion, the sequence of sums $S^{(1)}, S^{(2)}, \ldots$ must therefore converge to a number J. This number is called the *contour integral of $F(z)$ along the curve* (or *contour*, or *path*) γ, and is denoted by

$$J = \int_\gamma F(z) \, dz. \tag{116.7}$$

The justification of this terminology, and of the notation (116.7) as well, will be substantiated by the following arguments. First, it follows from (116.4), by passing to a limit, that

$$\left| S^{(k)} - J \right| = \lim_{p=\infty} \left| S^{(k)} - S^{(k+p)} \right| \leqq \varepsilon^{(k)} \, L_\gamma. \tag{116.8}$$

Hence the degree of approximation of J by the sums $S^{(k)}$ depends only on $\delta^{(k)}$ and can be estimated uniformly for all the partitions for which $\delta^{(k)}$ does not exceed a fixed number δ. Hence every choice of a sequence of partitions satisfying condition (116.5) leads to one and the same limit.

Moreover, the method of evaluating the integral J can be modified in various ways, and the modified procedures may be used for deriving the main properties of the contour integral.

117. The possibility of modifications in the evaluation is based on the following argument. We associate with each of the sums (116.2) a new sum

$$T^{(k)} = \sum_{j=1}^{n_k} \varphi_{j-1}^{(k)}, \tag{117.1}$$

consisting of the same number of terms, where the terms $\varphi_j^{(k)}$ are so chosen that we may write

$$\left| F(z_{j-1}^{(k)}) - \frac{\varphi_{j-1}^{(k)}}{z_j^{(k)} - z_{j-1}^{(k)}} \right| < \eta^{(k)} \qquad (j = 1, 2, \ldots, n_k), \quad (117.2)$$

where

$$\lim_{k=\infty} \eta^{(k)} = 0. \tag{117.3}$$

Then we have

$$|S^{(k)} - T^{(k)}| \leqq \eta^{(k)} \sum_{j=1}^{n_k} |z_j^{(k)} - z_{j-1}^{(k)}| \leqq \eta^{(k)} L_\gamma,$$

which implies

$$\left. \begin{aligned} \lim_{k=\infty} |S^{(k)} - T^{(k)}| &= 0, \\ |T^{(k)} - J| \leqq |S^{(k)} - J| + |T^{(k)} - S^{(k)}| &\leqq (\varepsilon^{(k)} + \eta^{(k)}) L_\gamma, \end{aligned} \right\} \quad (117.4)$$

and hence also

$$J = \lim_{k=\infty} T^{(k)}. \tag{117.5}$$

118. A first method for defining the numbers $\varphi_j^{(k)}$ in such a way that conditions (117.2) and (117.3) hold simultaneously, is to write

$$\left. \begin{aligned} \varphi_{j-1}^{(k)} &= F(\zeta_{j-1}^{(k)}) \, (z_j^{(k)} - z_{j-1}^{(k)}), \\ \zeta_j^{(k)} &= z(\tau_j), \quad t_{j-1}^{(k)} \leqq \tau_j \leqq t_j^{(k)}, \end{aligned} \right\} \quad (118.1)$$

i.e. to replace the numbers $F(z_{j-1}^{(k)})$ in the sum (116.8) by the numbers $F(\zeta_{j-1}^{(k)})$, where $\zeta_{j-1}^{(k)}$ denotes any point whatsoever of that sub-arc of γ which connects the points $z_{j-1}^{(k)}$ and $z_j{}^{(k)}$ with each other.

If $F(z)$ is defined not only on the curve γ but also in a region G that contains γ, then one may sometimes replace the number $\zeta_j^{(k)}$ in the first of equations (118.1) by the number $(\zeta' + \zeta'')/2$, where ζ' and ζ'' are any two points of the above-mentioned sub-arc of γ.

By way of giving examples of such calculations, let us first set $F(z) = 1$, then $F(z) = z$, and finally $F(z) = z^2$. If we denote the initial point of γ by z_0 and the end point of γ by Z, we obtain for $F(z) = 1$ that

$$S^{(k)} = \sum_{j=1}^{n_k} (z_j^{(k)} - z_{j-1}^{(k)}) = Z - z_0, \tag{118.2}$$

so that, in the limit,

$$J = \int_\gamma dz = Z - z_0. \tag{118.3}$$

For $F(z) = z$, we consider the sums

$$S^{(k)} = \sum_{j=1}^{n_k} z_{j-1}^{(k)} \, (z_j^{(k)} - z_{j-1}^{(k)}), \quad T^{(k)} = \sum_{j=1}^{n_k} z_j^{(k)} \, (z_j^{(k)} - z_{j-1}^{(k)}), \tag{118.4}$$

and find that

$$S^{(k)} + T^{(k)} = Z^2 - z_0^2.$$

This implies

$$\int_\gamma z \, dz = \lim_{k=\infty} \frac{S^{(k)} + T^{(k)}}{2} = \frac{Z^2 - z_0^2}{2}. \tag{118.5}$$

Finally, if $F(z) = z^2$ we set

$$\left. \begin{aligned} S^{(k)} &= \sum_{j=1}^{n_k} (z_{j-1}^{(k)})^2 \, (z_j^{(k)} - z_{j-1}^{(k)}), \\[2mm] T^{(k)} &= \sum_{j=1}^{n_k} (z_j^{(k)})^2 \, (z_j^{(k)} - z_{j-1}^{(k)}), \\[2mm] U^{(k)} &= \sum_{j=1}^{n_k} \left(\frac{z_j^{(k)} + z_{j-1}^{(k)}}{2} \right)^2 (z_j^{(k)} - z_{j-1}^{(k)}). \end{aligned} \right\} \tag{118.6}$$

From this we obtain that

$$S^{(k)} + T^{(k)} + 4 \, U^{(k)} = 2 \, (Z^3 - z_0^3), \tag{118.7}$$

and, by passing to the limit, that

$$\int_\gamma z^2 \, dz = \frac{Z^3 - z_0^3}{3}. \tag{118.8}$$

119. Let us now assume that the curve

$$z(t) = x(t) + i \, y(t) \qquad (t_0 \leq t \leq T) \tag{119.1}$$

is continuously differentiable, i.e. that the two real functions $x(t)$, $y(t)$ have continuous first derivatives. Then if we set

$$F\big(z(t)\big) \, z'(t) = A(t) + i \, B(t), \tag{119.2}$$

where $A(t)$ and $B(t)$ denote real functions continuous in the interval $t_0 \leq t \leq T$, the integral of $F(z) z'$ over the interval $t_0 \leq t \leq T$, defined by the equation

$$J^* = \int_{t_0}^{T} F(z) \, z' \, dt = \int_{t_0}^{T} A(t) \, dt + i \int_{t_0}^{T} B(t) \, dt, \tag{119.3}$$

is meaningful. The integral (116.7) is also meaningful, since the curve (119.1) will presently be shown to be rectifiable. We shall then proceed to prove that the two integrals (116.7) and (119.3) *have the same value.*

We denote the maximum of $|z'(t)|$ on the curve γ by μ; then $|x'(t)| \leq \mu$ and $|y'(t)| \leq \mu$. For any subinterval $t_{j-1} \leq t \leq t_j$ it then follows that

$$z_j - z_{j-1} = \int_{t_{j-1}}^{t_j} x'(t)\, dt + i \int_{t_{j-1}}^{t_j} y'(t)\, dt, \tag{119.4}$$

which implies that

$$|z_j - z_{j-1}| \leq 2\,\mu\,(t_j - t_{j-1}). \tag{119.5}$$

The length of any polygonal train inscribed in γ is therefore at most equal to $2\mu(T-t_0)$, and the curve γ is therefore rectifiable.

Arguments involving inequalities of a very similar nature will now make it possible for us to compare the integrals J and J^* with each other. We introduce the notation

$$\varkappa(\delta) = \quad \text{l.u.b.} \quad |F(z(t_1))\, z'(t_1) - F(z(t_2))\, z'(t_2)| \quad \text{for } |t_2 - t_1| < \delta, \tag{119.6}$$

$$\lambda(\delta) = \quad \text{l.u.b.} \quad |z'(t_1) - z'(t_2)| \qquad\qquad\qquad \text{for } |t_2 - t_1| < \delta, \tag{119.7}$$

where t_1 and t_2 are any two points of the interval $t_0 \leq t \leq T$. Now for any partition of the interval of integration into subintervals $t_{j-1} \leq t \leq t_j$ satisfying $|t_j - t_{j-1}| < \delta$, we have

$$\left| \int_{t_{j-1}}^{t_j} F(z(t))\, z'(t)\, dt - F(z_{j-1})\, z'(t_{j-1})\, (t_j - t_{j-1}) \right| \leq \varkappa(\delta)\, (t_j - t_{j-1}). \tag{119.8}$$

On the other hand,

$$|(z_j - z_{j-1}) - z'(t_{j-1})\, (t_j - t_{j-1})| \leq \lambda(\delta)\, (t_j - t_{j-1}). \tag{119.9}$$

Therefore if M denotes the maximum of $|F(z)|$ on the curve γ, then

$$|F(z_{j-1})\, (z_j - z_{j-1}) - F(z_{j-1})\, z'(t_{j-1})\, (t_j - t_{j-1})| \leq M\, \lambda(\delta)\, (t_j - t_{j-1}),$$

and hence, by (119.8),

$$\left| \int_{t_{j-1}}^{t_j} F(z(t))\, z'(t)\, dt - F(z_{j-1})\, (z_j - z_{j-1}) \right| \leq [\varkappa(\delta) + M\, \lambda(\delta)]\, (t_j - t_{j-1}). \tag{119.10}$$

From this, considering on the one hand the sum S defined by (115.1) and on the other hand the integral J^* defined by (119.3), follows the inequality

$$|J^* - S| \leqq [\varkappa(\delta) + M \lambda(\delta)] (T - t_0),$$

and from this combined with inequality (116.8) we finally obtain

$$|J^* - J| \leqq \varepsilon(\delta) L_\gamma + [\varkappa(\delta) + M \lambda(\delta)] (T - t_0). \tag{119.11}$$

The left-hand side of this last relation does not depend on δ, while the right-hand side must converge to zero if δ does. From this follows the equation we wanted to prove, namely,

$$J^* = J. \tag{119.12}$$

The Main Properties of Contour Integrals (§§ 120-122)

120. Let us subdivide the curve γ into sub-arcs $\gamma_1, \gamma_2, \cdots, \gamma_m$, each oriented so as to have the same sense of traversal as γ itself. We denote the integral of $F(z)$ along γ and γ_k by J_γ and J_{γ_k} respectively. From the fact that all of these integrals may be regarded as limits of sums of the form (116.2), it follows that

$$J_\gamma = J_{\gamma_1} + J_{\gamma_2} + \cdots + J_{\gamma_m}. \tag{120.1}$$

If we associate with γ the sense of traversal opposite to the one originally given, we shall regard the resulting curve as a new curve and denote it by γ^{-1}. In this connection, we have the identity

$$J_\gamma + J_{\gamma^{-1}} = 0, \tag{120.2}$$

which we can prove by first approximating J_γ and $J_{\gamma^{-1}}$ by sums S and T, respectively, for which $S + T = 0$.

Finally, from the calculation of the contour integral J as the limit of approximating sums $S^{(k)}$ we derive the formula

$$\int_\gamma [F(z) + G(z)] \, dz = \int_\gamma F(z) \, dz + \int_\gamma G(z) \, dz. \tag{120.3}$$

121. If the function $F(z)$ is defined and continuous throughout a certain neighborhood of the curve γ, then all polygonal trains inscribed in γ and having sides of sufficiently small lengths will also lie within this neighborhood. Let us consider a sequence of such inscribed polygons, whose lengths we denote by π_n and which we assume to have been chosen in such a way that the lengths of their longest sides tend to zero as n runs through the sequence of the natural numbers. We denote the value of the integral taken along the polygon π_n by J_{π_n}. Using inequalities established earlier for contour integrals, we can now easily verify that the following relation holds true:

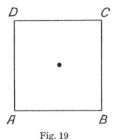

Fig. 19

$$J_\gamma = \lim_{n=\infty} J_{\pi_n}. \qquad (121.1)$$

122. We denote by Q a square $ABCD$ of the complex plane, with sides parallel to the coordinate axes and of lengths $2a$, and having its center at the origin (see Fig. 19). We propose to evaluate the integral

$$J = \int_Q \frac{dz}{z}, \qquad (122.1)$$

where the square Q is to be traversed in the sense $ABCDA$. By § 119 above, we may write

$$J = \int_{-a}^{a} \frac{dt}{t - ia} + \int_{-a}^{a} \frac{i\,dt}{a + it} - \int_{-a}^{a} \frac{dt}{t + ia} - \int_{-a}^{a} \frac{i\,dt}{-a + it}. \qquad (122.2)$$

In the sum on the right-hand side, we combine the first term with the third, and the second term with the fourth, and we find, upon setting $t = as$, that

$$J = \int_{-1}^{1} \frac{2i\,ds}{s^2 + 1} + \int_{-1}^{1} \frac{-2i\,ds}{-(s^2 + 1)} = 8i \int_{0}^{1} \frac{ds}{s^2 + 1}.$$

As is well known, the integral on the right-hand side equals $\pi/4$ (*cf.* § 237 below), so that we finally obtain

$$\int_Q \frac{dz}{z} = 2\pi i. \qquad (122.3)$$

The Mean-Value Theorem (§ 123)

123. Let us denote by M the maximum of the modulus $|F(z)|$ of $F(z)$ on the curve γ. By (116.2) above, we may write

$$|S^{(k)}| \leq M \sum_{j=1}^{n_k} |z_j^{(k)} - z_{j-1}^{(k)}| \leq M L_\gamma. \qquad (123.1)$$

Passing to the limit (as $k \to \infty$, *cf.* § 116 above) in (123.1), we obtain the general formula

$$\left| \int_\gamma F(z)\,dz \right| \leq M L_\gamma. \qquad (123.2)$$

If $|F(z_0)| < M$ at some point z_0 of γ, then there is a sub-arc γ_1 of γ on which $|F(z)| \leq M - \varepsilon$ holds, so that

$$\left| \int_\gamma F(z)\, dz \right| \leq (M - \varepsilon)\, L_{\gamma_1} + M\, (L_\gamma - L_{\gamma_1}) < M\, L_\gamma. \qquad (123.3)$$

Hence the equality sign will hold in relation (123.2) only if $|F(z)|$ equals the constant M everywhere on the curve γ.

In the case that the curve γ is a segment of the real axis, or more generally, any straight-line segment, the necessary (but of course not sufficient) condition $|F(z)| \equiv M$ for equality in (123.2) may be replaced by a stronger condition. For in this case, relation (123.2) becomes

$$\left| \int_{t_0}^{T} F(t)\, dt \right| \leq M\, (T - t_0). \qquad (123.4)$$

Now note that any two complex numbers a and b satisfying

$$|a| \leq M, \quad |b| \leq M, \quad a \neq b$$

must satisfy

$$|a + b| < 2\, M.$$

Hence if the interval $t_0 < t < T$ contains two interior points t_1 and t_2 (with $t_1 < t_2$) for which $F(t_1) \neq F(t_2)$, then we must have

$$|F(t_1) + F(t_2)| = 2\, M - 2\, \varepsilon \qquad (\varepsilon > 0). \quad (123.5)$$

Then there must exist a positive number h for which, on the one hand,

$$t_0 < t_1 < t_1 + h < t_2 < t_2 + h < T, \qquad (123.6)$$

and on the other hand, for $0 < s < h$,

$$|F(t_1 + s) + F(t_2 + s)| < 2\, M - \varepsilon. \qquad (123.7)$$

We may write

$$\int_{t_0}^{T} F(t)\, dt = \int_{t_0}^{t_1} F\, dt + \int_{t_1 + h}^{t_2} F\, dt + \int_{t_2 + h}^{T} F\, dt + \int_{0}^{h} [F(t_1 + s) + F(t_2 + s)]\, ds. \qquad (123.8)$$

If we now apply inequality (123.3) to the various integrals on the right-hand side of (123.8), we obtain

$$\left| \int_{t_0}^{T} F(t)\, dt \right| \leqq M\,(T - t_0 - 2\,h) + (2\,M - \varepsilon)\, h = M\,(T - t_0) - \varepsilon\, h. \quad (123.9)$$

Thus unless the function $F(t)$ is actually a constant in the entire interval $t_0 \leqq t \leqq T$, the relation $|F(t)| \leqq M$ implies that

$$\left| \int_{t_0}^{T} F\, dt \right| < M\,(T - t_0), \quad (123.\,10)$$

with the equality sign excluded.

PART THREE

ANALYTIC FUNCTIONS

CHAPTER ONE

FOUNDATIONS OF THE THEORY

The Derivative of a Complex Function (§ 124)

124. A one-valued complex function $f(z)$ defined in a region G is said to be *differentiable* at a point z_0 of this region if there exists a finite function $\varphi(z; z_0)$ that is continuous at the point $z = z_0$ and satisfies the relation

$$f(z) = f(z_0) + (z - z_0)\, \varphi(z; z_0) \tag{124.1}$$

at all points z of G.

The conditions on $\varphi(z; z_0)$ imply that if $f(z)$ is differentiable at the point z_0, then $f(z)$ must also be continuous at z_0. Furthermore, the assumption that $\varphi(z; z_0)$ is continuous at $z = z_0$ means that the limit

$$\varphi(z_0; z_0) = \lim_{z = z_0} \varphi(z, z_0) \tag{124.2}$$

exists; we shall denote this limit by $df(z_0)/dz$ or by $f'(z_0)$, and we shall call it the *derivative* of $f(z)$ at the point z_0.

Equation (124.1) determines the function $\varphi(z; z_0)$ uniquely at all those points $z \neq z_0$ at which $f(z)$ is defined.

Hence if $f(z)$ is differentiable at the point z_0, then the value $f'(z_0) = \varphi(z_0; z_0)$ of the derivative of $f(z)$ at z_0 is also determined uniquely. We shall find it convenient, in what follows, to write

$$\varphi(z_0, z_0) = f'(z_0), \qquad \varphi(z; z_0) = f'(z_0) + R(z; z_0). \tag{124.3}$$

In this notation, the condition that $f(z)$ be differentiable at the point z_0 can be expressed by means of the formulas

$$\left. \begin{aligned} f(z) &= f(z_0) + (z - z_0)\, f'(z_0) + (z - z_0)\, R(z; z_0) \\ \lim_{z = z_0} R(z; z_0) &= 0. \end{aligned} \right\} \tag{124.4}$$

Most of the arguments of the ordinary Differential Calculus can be applied to the differentiation of complex functions and lead to the same formulas for calculating the derivative of the sum, of the product, and of the quotient of differentiable functions. The same holds true for the "chain rule" for differentiating a composite function $g(f(z))$.

Integrable Functions (§§ 125-127)

125. Let γ be a rectifiable curve with z_0 as its initial point and z as its end point. In § 118 above, we arrived at the following formulas:

$$\int_\gamma d\zeta = z - z_0, \quad \int_\gamma \zeta\, d\zeta = \frac{z^2}{2} - \frac{z_0^2}{2}, \quad \int_\gamma \zeta^2\, d\zeta = \frac{z^3}{3} - \frac{z_0^3}{3}. \quad (125.1)$$

Thus the value of these contour integrals depends only on the choice of the end points, and does not depend on the particular curve γ chosen to connect these end points.

We shall say that a function $f(z)$ defined and continuous in a region G is *integrable* in G if the value of the contour integral

$$\int_\gamma f(\zeta)\, d\zeta \qquad\qquad (125.2)$$

is the same for all rectifiable curves γ that lie entirely in G and have the same initial point z_0 and end point z.

Thus if z_0 is held fixed and if the end point z of γ is allowed to vary, then the contour integral (125.2) represents a one-valued function $F(z)$ of z, called an *integral* of $f(z)$.

Let z and $z + h$ be two points of G and let γ_1 be any rectifiable curve that lies in G and joins z to $z + h$. Then every integral $F(z)$ of $f(z)$ must satisfy the relation

$$F(z + h) - F(z) = \int_{\gamma_1} f(\zeta)\, d\zeta. \qquad\qquad (125.3)$$

If $|h|$ is sufficiently small, then the two points z and $z + h$ may be joined by a straight-line segment lying within G. This segment can be represented in terms of a real parameter t by means of the equation

$$z + h t \qquad\qquad (0 \leq t \leq 1). \quad (125.4)$$

Equation (125.3) can in this case be written in the form

$$F(z + h) = F(z) + \int_0^1 f(z + h t)\, h\, dt \qquad\qquad (125.5)$$

$$= F(z) + h\, f(z) + h\, R(z; z + h),$$

where

$$R(z; z + h) = \int_0^1 [f(z + h\,t) - f(z)]\, dt.$$ (125.6)

Since the function $f(z)$ is continuous in the region G, the above $R(z; z+h)$ must converge to zero if h does. Hence $F(z)$ is differentiable in G, and specifically, $F(z)$ is a function defined in G whose derivative

$$F'(z) = f(z)$$ (125.7)

equals the given (integrable) function $f(z)$ (see also § 146 below).

126. We found earlier (*cf.* § 120 above) that the value of the contour integral of a function $f(z)$ taken along a curve γ is the negative of the value of the contour integral of $f(z)$ taken along the curve γ^{-1} obtained by re-orienting γ so that the sense of traversal is opposite to that of γ. From this fact it now follows that for $f(z)$ to be integrable in a region G, it is necessary and sufficient that the integral of $f(z)$ along every *closed* curve in G be zero.

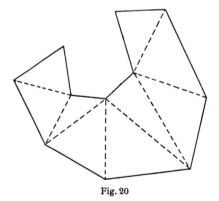

Fig. 20

We now introduce the following definition: A function $f(z)$ will be called *integrable in the small* in the region G if the integral of $f(z)$ is zero whenever it is taken along the boundary of any triangle that is contained, with its interior, in G.

Now we shall prove that if a region G is *simply connected*, then any function $f(z)$ that is integrable in the small in G must also be integrable *in the large* in G (i.e. must be integrable in G in the sense of § 125 above).

To this end, we shall first prove that any simple closed polygon $\mathfrak{P}$ can be *triangulated*, i.e. that each of the two regions into which $\mathfrak{P}$ divides the Riemann sphere (or the extended complex plane) can be represented as the union of a finite number of triangles whose interiors are mutually disjoint and which are obtained by drawing a certain number of the diagonals of $\mathfrak{P}$ (see Fig. 20 above).

Assume we had proved this last fact for all n-gons (i.e., polygons having n sides). Consider any given $(n + 1)$-gon; through at least one of its vertices, say through A, we can pass a line of support[1] to the $(n + 1)$-gon. For convenience, we shall call the *interior of the polygon* that one of the two regions bounded by the polygon (*cf.* § 106 above) which has no points in common with the line of support. Now if BA and AC are the two sides of the polygon that meet at A, then either the line segment BC is a diagonal of the polygon and interior to the polygon, or there exists at least one vertex V of the polygon that lies on BC or in the interior of triangle ABC. Among these vertices V, there must be at least one for which the diagonal AV lies in the interior of the polygon, and a diagonal like AV divides the $(n + 1)$-gon into two polygons of at most n sides each; these two polygons can be triangulated by the induction hypothesis, and therefore so can the $(n + 1)$-gon.

Now let $\mathfrak{P}$ be any closed simple polygon all of whose points belong to G; since G is simply connected, the interior of $\mathfrak{P}$ must also belong to G, and therefore so must the interior of each of the triangles occurring in a triangulation of the interior of $\mathfrak{P}$. If $f(z)$ is integrable in the small, then its contour integral along each of the triangles of the triangulation must be equal to zero. Let us traverse each of these triangles in the positive sense, i.e. in such a way that the exterior normal to any side of the triangle has the same relative position to this side as the positive x-axis of the complex plane has to the positive y-axis, and let us form the sum of the contour integrals along all the triangles of the triangulation; this is a sum of zeros. But the contour integrals along the diagonals used in the triangulation will also cancel out in pairs, since each of the diagonals is traversed twice—namely, once in each of its two (opposite) directions. Thus there remains in the sum only the contour integral along the polygon $\mathfrak{P}$ itself, and hence this contour integral equals zero.

Any (not necessarily simple) closed polygonal train π, whose sides may cross each other or may partly coincide, can be regarded as being composed of a finite number of simple closed polygons $\mathfrak{P}$ and of line segments, each of the latter being traversed twice (in opposite directions) as π is traversed once. Therefore the contour integral of $f(z)$ along π must equal zero. Finally, if γ is any closed rectifiable curve lying in G, then the integral of $f(z)$ along γ may be considered as the limit of the integrals of $f(z)$ along any sequence $\pi_1, \pi_2, \ldots$ of approximating polygonal trains inscribed in γ, and must there-

---

[1] I.e., a straight line through A which is such that the interior of one of the two half-planes bounded by the line is free of points of the polygon.

fore also be equal to zero. Thus we have proved the result stated earlier in this section, since we have shown that $f(z)$ is indeed integrable in the large in G.

127. If G is not simply connected, then there may very well exist functions $f(z)$ that are integrable in the small in G but whose contour integrals along certain closed rectifiable curves lying in G are not equal to zero. For example, we shall soon see (*cf.* § 129 below) that the function $1/z$ is integrable in the small in the region $0 < |z| < 1$, while according to § 122 above, there exist closed curves γ in this region along which the integral of $1/z$ does not vanish. But even in this case, we can arrive at a general result along the lines of the result of § 126 above.

Let us consider a finite number of *completely separated* simple closed polygons $\pi_0, \pi_1, \ldots, \pi_m$ (*cf.* § 108 above) lying in G, and let us assume that these polygons are the frontier of a subregion $\mathfrak{P}$ of G that is confined to some finite part of the complex plane. We may assume that every point of $\mathfrak{P}$ is inside the polygon π_0 and outside each of the polygons $\pi_1, \ldots, \pi_m$. It is then possible to triangulate $\mathfrak{P}$, each of the triangles of the triangulation lying in G, along with its interior. The sum of the integrals of $f(z)$ along all of these triangles will then be equal, by the same reasoning as was used in § 126 above, to the integral of $f(z)$ along the frontier of $\mathfrak{P}$ traversed in a certain sense; π_0 must be traversed in the positive sense, and each of $\pi_1, \ldots, \pi_m$ in the negative sense. From this and from the assumption that $f(z)$ is integrable in the small, it follows that the integral of $f(z)$ along π_0 is equal to the sum of the integrals of $f(z)$ along $\pi_1, \pi_2, \ldots, \pi_m$, provided that all of these $(m + 1)$ polygons are traversed in the same sense.

In this result, the $(m + 1)$ polygons may be replaced by $(m + 1)$ rectifiable Jordan curves; the details of the proof of this, by means of a limiting process, will not be set down here.

But we shall prove the following theorem, which will be very useful to us in the sequel. *Let G be a region obtained from a simply connected region G' by removing from G' a finite number of points $\xi_1, \xi_2, \ldots, \xi_p$. Then every continuous and bounded function $f(z)$ defined in G that is integrable in the small in the region G is also integrable in the large in this region.*

To prove this, consider any simple closed polygon π_0 lying in G (and therefore lying in G'). The formula

$$\int_{\pi_0} f(z)\, dz = 0, \qquad (127.1)$$

which is what we have to prove, will certainly hold true if none of the points ξ_j lies in the interior of π_0. If some of the points ξ_j do lie in the interior of π_0, then we surround these by squares $\pi_{m_1}, \pi_{m_2}, \ldots, \pi_{m_k}, (k \leq p)$, also interior to π_0, and by the preceding result we then have

$$\int\limits_{\pi_0} f(z)\ dz = \int\limits_{\pi_{m_1}} f(z)\ dz + \cdots + \int\limits_{\pi_{m_k}} f(z)\ dz. \qquad (127.2)$$

(To insure that the squares π_{mj} are all inside π_0, we merely have to choose the length ε of their sides smaller than a suitable positive ε_0.) If M is an upper bound of $|f(z)|$ in G, then by the inequality (123.2) for contour integrals, we have

$$\left| \int\limits_{\pi_{mj}} f(z)\ dz \right| \leq 4\ M\ \varepsilon \qquad (j=1,\ldots,k), \qquad (127.3)$$

and (127.2) together with (127.3) now yields

$$\left| \int\limits_{\pi_0} f(z)\ dz \right| \leq 4\ k\ M\ \varepsilon. \qquad (127.4)$$

Since this last relation holds for any $\varepsilon < \varepsilon_0$, it follows that (127.1) must hold, and the theorem is proved.

Definition of Regular Analytic Functions (§ 128)

128. A complex function that is differentiable at every point of a region G is called a *regular analytic function*[1] *in* G. We shall see later that the same concept can also be defined in terms of other properties. For instance, the property of being representable by power series (*cf.* § 208 below) is one that many authors use to define regular analytic functions. Other basic properties that might be used for the same purpose are the fact that these functions can be represented as contour integrals (see § 131 below), or the fact that they are integrable in the small (see § 129 below). The definition which we have adopted here is not only the simplest in concept, but it also allows for the fastest development of the theory of analytic functions.

Thus the results of § 124 above show immediately that the totality of analytic functions regular in a region G constitutes a "field" of functions, i.e. that the sum, difference, product, and quotient (if the denominator is $\neq 0$ throughout G) of two analytic regular functions are themselves analytic regular functions in G. The composite function $g(f(z))$ formed from two analytic regular functions $g(u)$ and $f(z)$ is also regular in G, provided that the substitution of $f(z)$ for u in $g(u)$ is meaningful whenever z is in G.

---

[1] Sometimes just *analytic function*, or just *regular function*.

Every constant may be considered as an analytic function (in any region) with an identically vanishing derivative. The function $f(z) = z$ is a regular analytic function (in any region), having as its derivative the constant 1. From this and from the preceding paragraph it follows that any polynomial

$$P(z) = a_0 + a_1 z + a_2 z^2 + \cdots + a_n z^n$$

is an analytic function regular in the whole plane. Similarly, any rational function

$$\frac{P(z)}{Q(z)}$$

is a regular analytic function in any region of the complex plane throughout which $Q(z) \neq 0$ holds true. For example, the fractional linear function

$$\frac{\alpha z + \beta}{\gamma z + \delta} \qquad (\alpha \delta - \beta \gamma \neq 0, \ \gamma \neq 0),$$

which we used earlier in the theory of Moebius transformations (*cf.* § 24 above), is regular in the whole complex plane except at the point $z = -\delta/\gamma$.

Cauchy's Theorem (§ 129)

129. We shall now prove the theorem to the effect that every function that is regular in a region G must also be integrable in the small in this region. This theorem was discovered[1] by A. L. Cauchy (1789-1857) in the year 1814, and forms one of the foundation stones on which Function Theory rests.

What we must show is that for every complex function $f(z)$ which is differentiable in the interior and on the boundary of a triangle Δ, the integral

$$J = \int_{\Delta} f(z) \, dz \qquad (129. 1)$$

has the value zero. To this end, we connect the mid-points of the sides of the triangle Δ, obtaining in this way four new triangles which we denote by Δ', Δ'', Δ''', and $\Delta^{(IV)}$ (see Fig. 21). We denote by $J', \ldots, J^{(IV)}$ the

---

[1] Cauchy proved the theorem only under the assumption that the derivative $f'(z)$ be continuous in G. It was not until around 1900 that É. Goursat made the discovery— which created quite a stir—that the theorem remains valid even if any assumption of *continuity* or even of *boundedness* of $f'(z)$ is dropped, as long as $f'(z)$ is just assumed to be *finite* in G. For this reason, some authors nowadays call the theorem, justifiably, the *Cauchy-Goursat* theorem. On the other hand, almost all the applications of the theorem in question were found by Cauchy himself, so that the historical inaccuracy attaching to our above designation of the theorem is quite defensible. The proof used in the text is a little simpler than Goursat's original proof, and is due to A. Pringsheim (1850-1941).

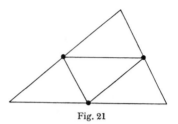

Fig. 21

integrals of $f(z)$ along these four triangles, each traversed in the same sense as was the original triangle in (129.1), and we then have

$$J = J' + J'' + J''' + J^{(\text{IV})}. \qquad (129.2)$$

Since this implies that

$$|J| \leq |J'| + |J''| + |J'''| + |J^{(\text{IV})}|, \qquad (129.3)$$

there must be among the numbers $J', \ldots, J^{(\text{IV})}$ at least one whose modulus is not less than $|J|/4$. We denote by Δ_1 the *first* one of the triangles $\Delta', \ldots, \Delta^{(\text{IV})}$ for which the corresponding contour integral has the property just mentioned. Thus if we denote this contour integral by J_1, then

$$|J| \leq 4 |J_1|.$$

Similarly, we can determine a triangle Δ_2 lying in the triangle Δ_1 and coinciding with one of the four congruent triangles into which Δ_1 can be decomposed, and being such that the contour integral J_2 of $f(z)$ along Δ_2 satisfies

$$|J_1| \leq 4 |J_2|.$$

Continuing in this way, we obtain a sequence

$$\Delta \geq \Delta_1 \geq \Delta_2 \geq \cdots \qquad (129.4)$$

of nested triangles which is such that the corresponding contour integrals $J, J_1, J_2, \ldots$ of $f(z)$ along these triangles satisfy the relations

$$|J| \leq 4 |J_1| \leq 4^2 |J_2| \leq \cdots \leq 4^n |J_n| \qquad (129.5)$$

for every natural number n.

Let L be the perimeter of the triangle Δ and let L_n be the perimeter of Δ_n. We note that

$$L_n = \frac{L}{2^n}, \qquad (129.6)$$

which follows directly from our construction of the sequence of triangles. The triangles of the nested infinite sequence (129.4) have a common point z_0, and by hypothesis $f(z)$ is differentiable at z_0, so that equations (124.4) hold. We can therefore write

$$J_n = \int_{\Delta_n} f(z)\, dz$$

$$= \int_{\Delta_n} [f(z_0) + (z - z_0)\, f'(z_0)]\, dz + \int_{\Delta_n} (z - z_0)\, R(z; z_0)\, dz.$$

By § 125, the linear function which forms the first integrand in the last line is integrable, and hence

$$J_n = \int_{\Delta_n} (z - z_0)\, R(z; z_0)\, dz. \tag{129.7}$$

Let η_n be the least upper bound of $|R(z; z_0)|$ for z ranging over (the interior of) the circular region

$$|z - z_0| < L_n. \tag{129.8}$$

Then by the second relation of (124.4), we must have

$$\lim_{n=\infty} \eta_n = 0. \tag{129.9}$$

On the other hand, the triangle Δ_n lies within the circular region (129.8), so that equation (129.7), together with (123.2) and (129.6), yields the inequality

$$|J_n| \leq L_n \eta_n L_n = \frac{L^2}{4^n} \eta_n. \tag{129.10}$$

By (129.5), this implies the inequality

$$|J| \leq L^2 \eta_n \tag{129.11}$$

for all values of n, and thus we see from (129.9) that we must have $J = 0$, which is what we had to show. Hence Cauchy's Theorem is proved. It may be rephrased as follows: *Every complex function $f(z)$ that is differentiable at every point of a region G must be integrable in the small in G.*

Cauchy's Integral Formula (§§ 130-131)

130. Let G be a simply connected region with z_0 as one of its points, and let G^* be the region consisting of all the points of G other than z_0. If $f(z)$ is a function that is bounded and regular in G, then the function

$$g(z) = \frac{f(z) - f(z_0)}{z - z_0} \tag{130.1}$$

is regular *and bounded* in G^*, since $f(z)$ is differentiable at the point z_0, so that for z close to z_0, the function $g(z)$ assumes values close to $f'(z_0)$. By Cauchy's Theorem, $g(z)$ is integrable in the small in G^*, and hence by § 127, $g(z)$ is also integrable in the large in G^*.

Therefore if γ is a rectifiable (closed) Jordan curve lying in G^*, then we have

$$\int_\gamma \frac{f(z) - f(z_0)}{z - z_0}\, dz = 0, \tag{130.2}$$

which may also be written in the form

$$f(z_0) \int_\gamma \frac{dz}{z - z_0} = \int_\gamma \frac{f(z)\, dz}{z - z_0}. \tag{130.3}$$

Let us now make the additional assumption that the point z_0 lies in the *finite region* G_γ, bounded by γ, the "interior" of γ. Then Cauchy's Theorem and the result of § 127 yield

$$\int_\gamma \frac{dz}{z - z_0} = \int_\varkappa \frac{dz}{z - z_0}, \tag{130.4}$$

where $\varkappa$ is a square with z_0 at its center, with its sides parallel to the coordinate axes, and lying entirely in the interior of γ. By § 122 above, the right-hand side of (130.4) equals $2\pi i$, so that (130.3) may be replaced by

$$f(z_0) = \frac{1}{2\pi i} \int_\gamma \frac{f(z)\, dz}{z - z_0}. \tag{130.5}$$

We now consider the curve γ as fixed and the point z_0 as a variable point in the interior of γ. With a slight change of notation (writing z instead of z_0 and ζ instead of z), we may re-write (130.5) in the form

$$f(z) = \frac{1}{2\pi i} \int_\gamma \frac{f(\zeta)\, d\zeta}{\zeta - z}. \tag{130.6}$$

This relation was discovered by Cauchy and is called the *Cauchy Integral Formula*. Before discussing it in greater detail, we shall study some general properties of the integral on the right-hand side of (130.6).

131. To this end, we consider a rectifiable curve $\overline{\gamma}$, not necessarily a Jordan curve nor even closed, and a finite region G whose closure $\overline{G}$ contains none of the points of $\bar{\gamma}$. We consider also a complex function $\varphi(\zeta)$ defined and sectionally continuous on $\bar{\gamma}$ and satisfying $|\varphi(\zeta)| < M$ on $\bar{\gamma}$. (We use ζ here as a generic notation for points of $\bar{\gamma}$.) *We shall show that the function $f(z)$ defined by the equation*

$$f(z) = \int_{\bar{\gamma}} \frac{\varphi(\zeta)}{\zeta - z} \, d\zeta \tag{131.1}$$

is a regular analytic function in G, whose derivative $f'(z)$ is likewise analytic in G.

To prove this, we note first that there must be a positive number $\delta > 0$ such that for *every* point ζ of $\bar{\gamma}$ and for *every* point z of $\overline{G}$ the relation

$$|\zeta - z| > \delta \tag{131.2}$$

holds.

Then if z and $z + h$ are any two points of $\overline{G}$, we have

$$\left. \begin{array}{l} \dfrac{1}{\zeta - (z + h)} - \dfrac{1}{\zeta - z} = \dfrac{h}{(\zeta - z)\,[\zeta - (z + h)]} \\[2mm] \qquad = \dfrac{h}{(\zeta - z)^2} + \dfrac{h^2}{(\zeta - z)^2\,[\zeta - (z + h)]} \, . \end{array} \right\} \tag{131.3}$$

From this and from (131.1) above, it follows that

$$f(z + h) = f(z) + h \int_{\bar{\gamma}} \frac{\varphi(\zeta)}{(\zeta - z)^2} \, d\zeta + h \, R(z; z + h). \tag{131.4}$$

Here,

$$R(z; z + h) = h \int_{\bar{\gamma}} \frac{\varphi(\zeta) \, d\zeta}{(\zeta - z)^2\,[\zeta - (z + h)]} \,, \tag{131.5}$$

so that, by the Mean Value Theorem of § 123 above,

$$|R(z; z + h)| < \frac{h \, M}{\delta^3} \, L_{\bar{\gamma}} \tag{131.6}$$

holds. These formulas imply that $f(z)$ is differentiable at every point of G and has the function

$$f'(z) = \int_{\bar{\gamma}} \frac{\varphi(\zeta)}{(\zeta - z)^2} \, d\zeta \tag{131.7}$$

as its derivative.

We can show similarly that the derivative $f'(z)$ of $f(z)$ is likewise a regular analytic function in G, by using instead of (131.3) the identity

$$\frac{1}{[\zeta-(z+h)]^2}-\frac{1}{(\zeta-z)^2}=\frac{2\,h}{(\zeta-z)^3}+\frac{h^2\,[3\,(\zeta-z)-2\,h]}{(\zeta-z)^3\,[\zeta-(z+h)]^2}\cdot \quad (131.8)$$

Hence the function $f(z)$ has a second derivative $f''(z)$ which is given by the contour integral

$$f''(z)=2\int_{\overline{\gamma}}\frac{\varphi(\zeta)}{(\zeta-z)^3}\,d\zeta. \qquad (131.9)$$

Thus we have proved the theorem stated earlier in this section.

Some Basic Properties of Analytic Functions (§ 132)

132. The fact expressed by relation (130.6) above is in a certain sense the converse of the result we proved in the preceding section. For, (130.6) shows that if a function $f(z)$ is regular in a region that contains a rectifiable Jordan curve along with the interior of this curve, then $f(z)$ can be represented by an integral of the form (131.1).

By § 131 above, any function $f(z)$ represented by a Cauchy Integral (130.6) has a derivative that is itself differentiable; also, any analytic function can be represented, in some neighborhood of every point of its region of regularity, by Cauchy Integrals; hence it follows that *the derivative of a regular analytic function is itself a regular analytic function.*

This implies immediately that *every regular analytic function has derivatives up to any order, and that all of these derivatives are themselves regular analytic functions.*

Now by § 125 above, every function $f(z)$ that is *integrable* in a region G is the derivative of at least one function $F(z)$, and $F(z)$ is thus a regular analytic function in G. Hence by the last theorem above, the function $f(z)$ is itself differentiable and is therefore an analytic function in G.

Moreover, we know from § 126 that any function that is integrable in the small is also integrable in the large in any circular disc that lies within the domain of definition of the function, and we are thus led to the following general theorem, called *Morera's Theorem*:

If a function $f(z)$ is single-valued, continuous, and integrable in the small in a region G, then $f(z)$ is a regular analytic function in G.

Riemann's Theorem (§§ 133-134)

133. We are now in a position where we can easily prove an important theorem that was first stated by Riemann (1826-1865) and which we shall therefore call *Riemann's Theorem*. Let G_1 be a region obtained from a region G

by removing from G a single point ξ, and let $f(z)$ be an analytic function that is regular and bounded in G_1. Then if z_0 is any point of G_1, the function

$$g(z) = \frac{f(z) - f(z_0)}{z - z_0} \tag{133.1}$$

is regular and bounded in the region G_2 that is obtained from G by removing from G the two points ξ and z_0. By § 127 above, $g(z)$ is integrable in G_2; hence if γ is a rectifiable Jordan curve whose interior contains the two points z_0 and ξ, then we have

$$\int_\gamma \frac{f(z) - f(z_0)}{z - z_0} \, dz = 0.$$

From this we conclude, like in § 130 above, that the equation

$$f(z_0) = \frac{1}{2 \pi i} \int_\gamma \frac{f(z) \, dz}{z - z_0} \tag{133.2}$$

holds true for all those points z_0 of G_1 that lie in the interior of γ. Now the right-hand side of the last equation represents an analytic function that is regular in the region interior to γ, hence also at the point $z = \xi$ which was excluded up to now. The result implied by this may be put as follows: *Let $f(z)$ be an analytic function that is regular at all the points of a neighborhood of the point ξ, with the possible exception of ξ itself, and assume that $f(z)$ is bounded in this "punctured" neighborhood. Then there exists one and only one complex number a with the property that the extension of the domain of definition of $f(z)$ produced by setting $f(\xi) = a$ yields a function that is not only continuous at ξ but also regular at ξ.*

134. By way of example, let $f(z)$ be a function that is regular in a neighborhood of z_0 (including z_0 itself); then the function

$$g(z) = \frac{f(z) - f(z_0)}{z - z_0} \tag{134.1}$$

satisfies the hypotheses of the last theorem in a certain neighborhood of z_0, and we can therefore complete the definition of $g(z)$ in such a way as to arrive at a function for which z_0 itself is a point of analyticity. In order to evaluate $g(z_0)$ and the successive derivatives $g'(z_0), g''(z_0), \ldots$, we must differentiate the relation

$$(z - z_0) \, g(z) = f(z) - f(z_0) \tag{134.2}$$

$(n + 1)$ times in succession, and we obtain

$$(z - z_0) \, g^{(n+1)}(z) + (n + 1) \, g^{(n)}(z) = f^{(n+1)}(z).$$

From this we obtain for $n = 0, 1, 2, \ldots$, setting $z = z_0$, that

$$g(z_0) = f'(z_0), \quad g'(z_0) = \frac{1}{2} f''(z_0), \quad \ldots, \quad g^{(n)}(z_0) = \frac{1}{n+1} f^{(n+1)}(z_0). \tag{134.3}$$

CHAPTER TWO

THE MAXIMUM-MODULUS PRINCIPLE

The Mean Value of a Function on a Circle (§ 135)

135. Consider an analytic function $f(z)$ that is regular at every point of the closed circular disc $|z - z_0| \leqq r$. If $\varkappa$ denotes the boundary of this disc, then by the Cauchy Integral Formula we have

$$f(z) = \frac{1}{2\pi i} \int\limits_{\varkappa} \frac{f(\zeta)}{\zeta - z} \, d\zeta \qquad (|z - z_0| < r). \quad (135.1)$$

Now note that

$$\zeta = z_0 + r \, (\cos \vartheta + i \sin \vartheta), \quad\quad\quad\quad (135.2)$$

$$\frac{d\zeta}{d\vartheta} = r \, (-\sin \vartheta + i \cos \vartheta) = i \, (\zeta - z_0), \quad\quad (135.3)$$

so that we may re-write (135.1) in the form

$$f(z) = \frac{1}{2\pi} \int\limits_{\pi}^{\pi} f(\zeta) \, \frac{\zeta - z_0}{\zeta - z} \, d\vartheta. \quad\quad\quad (135.4)$$

If we set $z = z_0$ in this relation, we obtain

$$f(z_0) = \frac{1}{2\pi} \int\limits_{-\pi}^{\pi} f(\zeta) \, d\vartheta, \quad\quad\quad\quad (135.5)$$

and this shows that if $f(z)$ is regular within and on a circle, then its value at the center of the circle equals the *mean value* of the values assumed by $f(z)$ on (the boundary of) the circle.

Hence if we use M_r to denote the maximum of the modulus $|f(\zeta)|$ as ζ ranges over the points of the circle $|z - z_0| = r$, then by the Mean Value Theorem of § 123 we obtain

$$|f(z_0)| \leqq M_r, \quad\quad\quad\quad\quad (135.6)$$

and the results of § 123 also show that *the equality sign applies in* (135.6) *only if the function $f(\zeta)$ is a constant on the boundary of the circle.*

The Maximum-Modulus Principle (§§ 136-139)

136. The last result can be generalized quite considerably; in fact, the following theorem holds true: *If $f(z)$ is an analytic function that is regular and not identically a constant in a region G, and if M denotes the least upper bound of $|f(z)|$ in G, then at every point z_0 of G we have*

$$|f(z_0)| \neq M,$$

hence—equality being explicitly excluded—

$$|f(z_0)| < M. \tag{136.1}$$

To prove this theorem, assign z_0 in G and let G_1 be the subset of G consisting of all the points of G at which

$$f(z) \neq f(z_0) \tag{136.2}$$

holds. Since $f(z)$ is a continuous function, G_1 must be an open subset of G; since $f(z)$ is non-constant in G, the set G_1 is not empty; since z_0 lies in G but not in G_1, the latter set is a proper subset of the former. The region G being connected, it contains at least one frontier point z_1 of G_1 (*cf.* § 100 above). Since the open set G_1 does not contain any of its frontier points, the definition of G_1 implies that at the point z_1 of G,

$$f(z_1) = f(z_0) \tag{136.3}$$

must hold.

Now z_1 is a point of accumulation of G_1; we can therefore find a point z_2 of G_1 such that the closed circular disc

$$|z - z_1| \leq |z_2 - z_1|$$

is entirely contained in G. By (136.2) and (136.3), we have $f(z_2) \neq f(z_1)$. Hence $f(z)$ can not be constant on the circle $\varkappa$ which forms the boundary of the disc (and which contains z_2), since relation (135.5) would otherwise imply that $f(z_1) = f(z_2)$. Thus if M' denotes the maximum of $|f(z)|$ on $\varkappa$, then by the remark at the end of the preceding section,

$$|f(z_1)| < M' \leq M \tag{136.4}$$

must hold, and inequality (136.1) now follows from (136.3) and (136.4), so that the theorem is proved.

137. We shall consider next the boundary values of $f(z)$, as defined in § 99 above. If a is a boundary value of $f(z)$ at a frontier point ζ of G, then the number $|\alpha|$ is of course a boundary value of $|f(z)|$ at ζ. Hence we always have

$$|\alpha| \leq M.$$

Now let M' denote the l.u.b. of the moduli of all the possible boundary values α that may occur as ζ ranges over all the frontier points of G. We certainly have $M' \leq M$.

On the other hand, the region G contains sequences $\{z_k\}$ of points for which the numbers $|f(z_k)|$ converge to M, and without loss of generality we may assume that the sequence $z_1, z_2, \ldots$ itself converges to a point z_0. Except in the case of a constant function $f(z)$, such a point z_0 cannot be an interior point of G, since we would otherwise have

$$f(z_0) = \lim_{n = \infty} f(z_n),$$

which would imply $|f(z_0)| = M$, contrary to the result of § 136 above. Hence z_0 must be a point of the frontier of G, and M is therefore a boundary value of $|f(z)|$ at this point. This shows that $M' = M$.

We note that if $f(z)$ is not only regular in G but is also continuous on the closure $\overline{G}$ of G, then $|f(z)|$ must assume its maximum M at one point, at least, of $\overline{G}$ (cf. § 96), and any such point must lie on the frontier of G (except in the case of a constant function $f(z)$).

138. Now let m denote the greatest lower bound (g.l.b., for short) of the modulus $|f(z)|$ of a function $f(z)$ regular in a region G, and let m' denote the g.l.b. of the moduli of the boundary values α of $f(z)$ on the frontier of G. Let us assume that $m' > 0$. We must then distinguish between two basically different cases.

The first case is that of a function $f(z)$ which does not vanish at any point of G. In this case, $1/f(z)$ is a regular function in G, and the preceding section then applies to show that

$$\frac{1}{m'} = \frac{1}{m} = \text{l.u.b. of } \frac{1}{|f(z)|} \text{ in } G. \qquad (138.1)$$

For non-constant functions $f(z)$, we furthermore have at every point of G that

$$|f(z)| > m = m'. \qquad (138.2)$$

But if there exists at least one interior point z_0 of G at which

$$|f(z_0)| \leq m' \qquad (138.3)$$

holds, then we have

$$m' > m = 0, \qquad (138.4)$$

and in this (second) case, the function $f(z)$ must have zeros in G. Thus we have proved the following theorem:

Let $f(z)$ be an analytic function that is regular and non-constant in a region G, and let m' denote the greatest lower bound of the moduli of the boundary values of $f(z)$. Let m denote the g.l.b. of $|f(z)|$ in the interior of G. Then if $m' > 0$, we have $m' = m$ if and only if $f(z)$ has no zeros in G.

139. This theorem represents a very important criterion for establishing the existence of zeros of $f(z)$—a criterion not only of fundamental importance in theoretical investigations (*cf.* §§ 199, 170 below) but one that can also be used for numerical calculations. The latter use is possible because for a verification of the inequality (138.3), an approximate calculation of m' and of $f(z_0)$ is sufficient.

Schwarz's Lemma (§§ 140-141)

140. A theorem discovered by H. A. Schwarz (1843-1921) yields surprisingly far-reaching results on the behavior of regular analytic functions.

Consider a complex function $f(z)$ that is regular in the interior

$$|z| < 1 \tag{140.1}$$

of the unit circle and for which the l.u.b. of its modulus $|f(z)|$ does not exceed 1 within this circle. Assume further that

$$f(0) = 0.$$

Then by § 134 above, the function $f_1(z)$ defined by the equations

$$f_1(z) = \frac{f(z) - f(0)}{z - 0} = \frac{f(z)}{z} \qquad (0 < |z| < 1),$$
$$f_1(0) = f'(0) \tag{140.2}$$

is regular in the disc (140.1). Let z_0 be any point of this disc and let r be any positive number satisfying the condition

$$|z_0| < r < 1. \tag{140.3}$$

Then by the Maximum-Modulus Principle there is at least one point ζ on the circle $|z| = r$ for which

$$|f_1(z_0)| \leq |f_1(\zeta)| = \frac{|f(\zeta)|}{|\zeta|} = \frac{|f(\zeta)|}{r} \tag{140.4}$$

holds. Now by one of our assumptions, we have $|f(\zeta)| \leq 1$; hence for all values of r satisfying (140.3), we must have

$$|f_1(z_0)| \leqq \frac{1}{r},$$

and hence also

$$|f_1(z_0)| \leqq \lim_{r=1} \frac{1}{r} = 1. \tag{140.5}$$

Therefore unless the function $f_1(z)$ is a constant of modulus unity, we must have $|f_1(z)| < 1$ at every point z in the interior of the unit circle. Hence (140.2) above now implies that

$$|f'(0)| < 1, \quad |f(z)| < |z|.$$

These last relations must therefore always hold true except in the case that $f_1(z) \equiv e^{i\vartheta}$, in which case we have

$$f(z) = e^{i\vartheta} z,$$

and we have therefore proved the following theorem:

SCHWARZ'S LEMMA: *Let* $f(z)$ *be a function that is regular in the unit circle and that satisfies*

$$f(0) = 0, \quad |f(z)| \leqq 1 \quad (0 < |z| < 1). \tag{140.6}$$

Then it follows that

$$|f'(0)| < 1, \quad |f(z)| < |z| \quad (0 < |z| < 1), \tag{140.7}$$

unless $f(z)$ *is a linear function of the form*

$$f(z) = e^{i\vartheta} z. \tag{140.8}$$

In either case, we have the relations

$$|f'(0)| \leqq 1, \quad |f(z)| \leqq |z|, \tag{140.9}$$

and any one of the conditions $|f'(0)| = 1$ or $|f(z_0)| = |z_0|$ (for at least one interior point z_0 of the unit circle) ensures that we have the second case (140.8).

141. Retaining the notation of the preceding section, let us assume that the function $f_1(z)$ defined by equations (140.2) vanishes at the point $z = 0$. Then the arguments of the last section may be applied to the function $f_1(z)$ in place of $f(z)$, and serve to establish the existence of a function $f_2(z)$ that is regular within the unit circle and for which the relations

$$|f_2(z)| \leqq 1, \quad f_1(z) = z f_2(z) \qquad (|z| < 1)$$

both hold. Furthermore, if we also have $f_2(0) = 0$, then there exists a function $f_3(z)$ with similar properties. Let us assume that this process can be repeated n times and that we have found a function $f_n(z)$ for which

$$|f_n(z)| \leqq 1, \quad f(z) = z\,f_1(z) = z^2\,f_2(z) = \cdots = z^n\,f_n(z) \qquad (141.1)$$

holds. Under these assumptions, we obtain

$$|f(z)| \leqq |z|^n \qquad\qquad (|z| < 1). \quad (141.2)$$

The Zeros of Regular Analytic Functions (§§ 142-143)

142. If the function $f(z)$ discussed in the preceding section is not identically equal to zero, then after a finite number of steps we must get to a function $f_n(z)$ for which

$$f_n(0) \neq 0 \qquad (142.1)$$

holds. For if $f(z_0) \neq 0$ at a point z_0 of the disc (140.1) and if

$$|f(z_0)| \leqq |z_0|^k, \qquad (142.2)$$

then we may write

$$\left(\frac{1}{|z_0|}\right)^k \leqq \frac{1}{|f(z_0)|}. \qquad (142.3)$$

Let us set

$$\frac{1}{|z_0|} = 1 + p, \qquad p = \frac{1 - |z_0|}{|z_0|}. \qquad (142.4)$$

As is well known,

$$1 + k\,p < (1 + p)^k, \qquad (142.5)$$

an inequality which can immediately be verified by induction on k; and comparison of (142.3) with (142.4) and (142.5) yields the relation

$$k < \frac{(1 - |f(z_0)|)\,|z_0|}{|f(z_0)|\,(1 - |z_0|)}, \qquad (142.6)$$

from which our statement follows.

Thus for any $f(z)$ that satisfies the same hypotheses as in Schwarz's Lemma, the following additional result holds true: *Either $f(z)$ is identically equal to zero throughout the interior of the unit circle, or there is a natural number $n \geqq 1$ for which*

$$f(z) = z^n\,f_n(z), \qquad f_n(0) \neq 0. \qquad (142.7)$$

143. This result enables us to derive a general property of the zeros of regular analytic functions. Let us consider a region G and a function $f(z)$ that is regular in G. Let A be the set of all those points of G that are *points of accumulation of zeros* of $f(z)$. Since $f(z)$ is continuous, every point of A must itself be a zero of $f(z)$.

Therefore, if $A = G$ then $f(z)$ must vanish at all the points of G. But if $A \neq G$ and if A is not empty, then G contains at least one frontier point z_0 of A. This point z_0, being a point of accumulation of points of A, must itself be a point of A; on the other hand, every neighborhood of z_0 must contain points of G that are not points of accumulation of zeros of $f(z)$, and hence must contain points at which $f(z) \neq 0$. From this it follows that $f(z)$ cannot vanish identically in any neighborhood of z_0.

We choose r small enough for the closed circular disc

$$|z - z_0| \leqq r \qquad (143.1)$$

to be contained within G. The l.u.b. M_r of $|f(z)|$ on this disc is $\neq 0$. The function

$$\varphi(u) = \frac{1}{M_r} f(z_0 + r u) \qquad (143.2)$$

then satisfies all the hypotheses of Schwarz's Lemma in the unit circle $|u| < 1$, and $\varphi(u)$ does not vanish identically within this circle. Therefore by the preceding section, there is a natural number n for which

$$\varphi(u) = u^n \psi(u) \qquad (\psi(0) \neq 0) \qquad (143.3)$$

holds, and hence there is a positive number $\vartheta \leqq 1$ such that for $|u| < \vartheta$, the function $\varphi(u)$ has only the *one* zero $u = 0$. But this means that in the circle $|z - z_0| < r \vartheta$, the function $f(z)$ itself can have no zeros other than the single point z_0, and we have thus arrived at a contradiction to the assumption that z_0 is a point of A. Therefore the assumption that A is neither empty nor identical with G is also untenable, and we therefore have the following theorem:

If a function $f(z)$ is regular and not identically equal to zero in a region G, then the set of zeros of $f(z)$ in G is either empty or consists entirely of isolated points. In proving that G cannot contain any points of accumulation of zeros of $f(z)$, we made essential use of the fact that G is an open point set. It may very well happen that the zeros of $f(z)$ in G have points of accumulation on the frontier of G. Using methods to be developed later, we shall even be able to construct examples of functions $f(z)$ for which *every* frontier point of G is a point of accumulation of zeros of $f(z)$.

As a corollary of our proof, we have also obtained the following important theorem:

If the analytic function $f(z)$ is regular and not constant in the region G, and if z_0 is a zero of $f(z)$ in G, then there exists a natural number n and an analytic function $g(z)$ regular in G for which

$$f(z) = (z - z_0)^n g(z) \qquad (g(z_0) \neq 0). \qquad (143.4)$$

Preservation of Neighborhoods (§ 144)

144. Our results immediately imply that an analytic function regular in a region G cannot be constant throughout a subregion of G without being constant throughout all of G. Now it is not very difficult to establish a much more precise result.

Let $f(z)$ be an analytic function that is regular and not a constant in a region G; also, let z_0 be any point of G. We set

$$w_0 = f(z_0), \quad \varphi(z) = f(z) - w_0 \tag{144.1}$$

and we have thus defined a function $\varphi(z)$ that is regular and not constant in G and that vanishes at the point z_0. Then by § 143 above, there are in G closed discs

$$|z - z_0| \leq r \tag{144.2}$$

on whose boundary the function $\varphi(z)$ has no zeros. We denote by 2ε the minimum of $|\varphi(\zeta)|$, where

$$\zeta = z_0 + r\, e^{i\vartheta}, \tag{144.3}$$

with ϑ varying over all real values. In the same disc (144.2), we form the function

$$\psi(z) = f(z) - w = \varphi(z) - (w - w_0), \tag{144.4}$$

regular in G, and we note that

$$|\psi(\zeta)| \geq |\varphi(\zeta)| - |w - w_0| \geq 2\varepsilon - |w - w_0|.$$

Then for

$$|w - w_0| < \varepsilon, \tag{144.5}$$

we find on the one hand that at every point of the circle (144.3),

$$|\psi(\zeta)| > \varepsilon, \tag{144.6}$$

while on the other hand we have at the center z_0 of the same circle that

$$|\psi(z_0)| = |\varphi(z_0) - (w - w_0)| = |w - w_0| < \varepsilon. \tag{144.7}$$

By § 138 above, the function $\psi(z)$ must have at least one zero in the interior of the disc (144.2), so that there is in the disc

$$|z - z_0| < r \tag{144.8}$$

at least one point for which

$$f(z) = w \tag{144.9}$$

holds. Here, w is any point in the disc (144.5) of the w-plane. This result shows that *the mapping given by equation* (144.9) *is neighborhood-preserving at every point z_0 of the region G* (cf. § 104 above).

This implies the following corollary: *Let $f(z)$ be a function regular in G whose modulus $|f(z)|$, or whose real part $\Re f(z)$, is constant throughout some subregion G_1 of G. Then the mapping* (144.9) *cannot be neighborhood-preserving at the points of G_1, and therefore the function $f(z)$ must itself be a constant throughout the entire region G.*

The Derivative of a Non-Constant Analytic Function Cannot Vanish Identically (§§ 145-146)

145. Consider a function $f(z)$ that is regular and not constant in a region G. For any given point z_0 of G, we may write

$$f(z) = f(z_0) + (z - z_0)^p\, g(z), \quad g(z_0) \neq 0 \quad (p \geq 1). \quad (145.1)$$

Differentiating this, we obtain

$$\left.\begin{aligned} f'(z) &= (z - z_0)^{p-1}\, h(z), \\ h(z) &= p\, g(z) + (z - z_0)\, g'(z). \end{aligned}\right\} \quad (145.2)$$

Thus we have $h(z_0) = p\, g(z_0) \neq 0$, so that $f'(z)$ cannot vanish identically.

Hence *if the first derivative of a regular analytic function $f(z)$ vanishes identically, the function $f(z)$ must be a constant.*

146. Now let $f(z)$ be a function that is regular and integrable in the region G; the second of these conditions is a consequence of the first if G is simply connected. We choose a point z_0 of G and we set

$$F_0(z) = \int_{\substack{\gamma \\ z_0}}^{z} f(\zeta)\, d\zeta, \quad (146.1)$$

where the path of integration γ is any rectifiable curve that lies in G and joins z_0 to z. Then the following relation holds:

$$F_0'(z) = f(z). \quad (146.2)$$

Let $F(z)$ stand for any analytic function that is regular in G and satisfies the differential equation

$$F'(z) = f(z) \quad (146.3)$$

in G. Then if we set

$$\varphi(z) = F(z) - F_0(z),$$

it follows that $\varphi'(z) \equiv 0$, so that by the preceding result, $\varphi(z)$ must be constant in G.

Conversely, every function of the form

$$F(z) = F_0(z) + C \qquad (C = \text{ a constant}) \qquad (146.4)$$

is a solution of equation (146.3). Hence just as in the real domain, we are able in the complex domain as well to write down *all* the solutions of the differential equation (146.3).

CHAPTER THREE

THE POISSON INTEGRAL AND HARMONIC FUNCTIONS

Determination of an Analytic Function by its Real Part (§ 147)

147. The theorem on preservation of neighborhoods for the mappings $w = f(z)$ (*cf.* § 144 above) will enable us to develop for the real part $\Re f(z)$ of an analytic function a theory quite analogous to that we obtained in §§ 136 *ff.* for the modulus $|f(z)|$.

Let $f(z)$ be an analytic function which is regular and not constant in some region G. Since the mapping $w = f(z)$ preserves neighborhoods, there must then exist, in every neighborhood of any given point z of G, at least one point z' and at least one point z'' such that

$$\Re f(z') < \Re f(z) < \Re f(z'')$$

holds. Hence if m and M denote the greatest lower bound and least upper bound, respectively, of $\Re f(z)$ in G, then we have

$$m < \Re f(z) < M. \tag{147.1}$$

Let us now assume that the function $f(z)$ is continuous not only at the interior points of G but also at the points of the frontier γ of G. Then the minimum and the maximum of $\Re f(z)$ must be assumed at certain points of γ; and this is true not only for non-constant functions $f(z)$ satisfying relations (147.1) at interior points of $(G + \gamma)$, but also for $f(z) = \text{const.}$ (which implies $m = M$).

In particular, we have the following theorem: *An analytic function $f(z)$ which is regular in the interior and at the points of a (closed) Jordan curve γ, and whose real part $\Re f(z)$ is constant along the curve γ, must itself be a constant.*[1]

All of the conditions in this theorem are necessary, as the following examples show. First, if the curve γ is not closed, then $f(z)$ need not be constant, as the example

$$f_1(z) = i\,z$$

---

[1] Note that for the modulus $|f(z)|$, an analogous theorem does not hold. This is because at a point where $f(z)$ is regular, $-f(z)$ must likewise be regular, whereas $1/f(z)$ need not be.

shows; the real part of this function vanishes identically on the entire real axis. Next, the real part of the function

$$f_2(z) = \frac{1-z}{1+z}$$

is zero everywhere on the circle $|z| = 1$ except at the point $z = -1$, at which $f_2(z)$ fails to be regular. Thus the conclusion of the theorem may be upset if the given function fails to be regular even at a single point of γ.

Finally, the function

$$f_3(z) = i\left(z + \frac{1}{z}\right)$$

is regular at all the points of the circle $|z| = 1$, and its real part vanishes on this circle. But $f_3(z)$ is not regular at $z = 0$, and the theorem is therefore not applicable.

The last theorem implies the following: *An analytic function regular in the interior and at the points of a (closed) Jordan curve is uniquely determined, to within a pure imaginary additive constant, by the values taken on by its real part along the curve.*

In the special case where the above Jordan curve is a circle, there is a simple way for calculating the function $f(z)$ from the values taken on by its real part on the circumference of the circle. We now turn our attention to this problem.

Transformations of Cauchy's Integral for the Circle (§§ 148-149)

148. Let the analytic function $f(z)$ be regular in a region which contains the closed circular disc $|z| \leqq 1$ in its interior. Let z be any fixed number for which $|z| < 1$; then the expression

$$\frac{f(\zeta)\,\bar{z}}{1 - \bar{z}\,\zeta}$$

represents a regular analytic function on the closed disc $|\zeta| \leqq 1$, where its denominator does not vanish. If $\varkappa$ denotes the boundary of this circle, then Cauchy's theorem of § 129 above yields the formula

$$0 = \frac{1}{2\pi i} \int_{\varkappa} \frac{f(\zeta)\,\bar{z}}{1 - \bar{z}\,\zeta}\, d\zeta \qquad\qquad (|z| < 1).$$

If we set, like in § 135 above,

$$\zeta = e^{it} = \cos t + i \sin t, \quad \frac{d\zeta}{dt} = i\,\zeta, \qquad\qquad (148.1)$$

then we obtain

$$0 = \frac{1}{2\pi} \int_{-\pi}^{\pi} f(\zeta) \frac{\bar{z}\,\zeta}{1-\bar{z}\,\zeta}\, dt. \tag{148.2}$$

On the other hand, (135.5) yields

$$f(0) = \frac{1}{2\pi} \int_{-\pi}^{\pi} f(\zeta)\, dt.$$

Adding the last two equations term by term, we obtain

$$f(0) = \frac{1}{2\pi} \int_{-\pi}^{\pi} \frac{f(\zeta)}{1-\bar{z}\,\zeta}\, dt. \tag{148.3}$$

Taking complex conjugates in this relation yields

$$\bar{f}(0) = \frac{1}{2\pi} \int_{-\pi}^{\pi} \bar{f}(\zeta) \frac{1}{1-z\,\bar{\zeta}}\, dt. \tag{148.4}$$

Now (148.1) implies that $\zeta\bar{\zeta} = 1$, so that

$$\frac{1}{1-z\,\bar{\zeta}} = \frac{\zeta}{(1-z\,\bar{\zeta})\,\zeta} = \frac{\zeta}{\zeta - z}.$$

Hence (148.4) may be re-written in the form

$$\bar{f}(0) = \frac{1}{2\pi} \int_{-\pi}^{\pi} \bar{f}(\zeta) \frac{\zeta}{\zeta - z}\, dt. \tag{148.5}$$

By (135.4), the Cauchy Integral Formula for $f(z)$ may here be written in the form

$$f(z) = \frac{1}{2\pi} \int_{-\pi}^{\pi} f(\zeta) \frac{\zeta}{\zeta - z}\, dt. \tag{148.6}$$

Let us use $\varphi(t)$ to denote the real part of $f(z)$, as a function of t, on the circle (148.1), i.e. let us set

$$\varphi(t) = \Re f(\zeta) = \frac{1}{2}\,[f(e^{it}) + \bar{f}(e^{it})]. \tag{148.7}$$

Addition of (148.5) and (148.6) then yields

$$f(z) + \bar{f}(0) = \frac{1}{2\pi} \int_{-\pi}^{\pi} \varphi(t) \frac{2\,\zeta}{\zeta - z}\, dt. \tag{148.8}$$

Let A be the imaginary part of $f(0)$, i.e. let

$$\frac{f(0) - \bar{f}(0)}{2} = i\,A.$$

(148.9)

Also note that setting $z = 0$ in (148.8) yields the relation

$$\frac{f(0) + \bar{f}(0)}{2} = \frac{1}{2\pi} \int_{-\pi}^{\pi} \varphi(t)\, dt.$$

(148.10)

If we now subtract equation (148.10) from (148.8), we obtain, as our final result,

$$f(z) = i\,A + \frac{1}{2\pi} \int_{-\pi}^{\pi} \varphi(t)\, \frac{\zeta + z}{\zeta - z}\, dt.$$

(148.11)

Since we can always transform any given circle into the unit circle by means of a very simple mapping, we may regard the last formula to be the solution of the problem posed at the end of the preceding section.

149. Equation (148.11) is extremely useful. Among other things, it enables us to calculate both the real part and the imaginary part of $f(z)$ in the interior of the disc $|z| < 1$, provided we know the number A and the real part of $f(z)$ on the boundary $|z| = 1$ of the disc. To this end, we introduce polar coordinates by writing

$$z = r\,(\cos\vartheta + i\sin\vartheta), \quad f(z) = U(r, \vartheta) + i\,V(r, \vartheta).$$

(149.1)

We further note that

$$\left.\begin{aligned}
\frac{\zeta + z}{\zeta - z} &= \frac{(\zeta + z)\,(\bar{\zeta} - \bar{z})}{(\zeta - z)\,(\bar{\zeta} - \bar{z})} \\[1mm]
&= \frac{(1 - z\bar{z}) + (z\bar{\zeta} - \bar{z}\zeta)}{(1 + z\bar{z}) - (z\bar{\zeta} + \bar{z}\zeta)} \\[1mm]
&= \frac{(1 - r^2) + 2\,i\,r\sin(\vartheta - t)}{(1 + r^2) - 2\,r\cos(\vartheta - t)}.
\end{aligned}\right\}$$

(149.2)

Substituting the last equation into (148.11), we obtain

$$U(r, \vartheta) = \frac{1}{2\pi} \int_{-\pi}^{\pi} \varphi(t)\, \frac{1 - r^2}{1 - 2\,r\cos(\vartheta - t) + r^2}\, dt,$$

(149.3)

$$V(r, \vartheta) = A + \frac{1}{2\pi} \int_{-\pi}^{\pi} \varphi(t)\, \frac{2\,r\sin(\vartheta - t)}{1 - 2\,r\cos(\vartheta - t) + r^2}\, dt.$$

(149.4)

Similarly, in rectangular coordinates we have

$$z = x + i\,y, \quad f(z) = u(x, y) + i\,v(x, y). \tag{149.5}$$

$$u(x, y) = \frac{1}{2\,\pi} \int_{-\pi}^{\pi} \varphi(t)\ \frac{1 - x^2 - y^2}{(x - \cos t)^2 + (y - \sin t)^2}\ dt, \tag{149.6}$$

$$v(x, y) = A + \frac{1}{2\,\pi} \int_{-\pi}^{\pi} \varphi(t)\ \frac{2\,y \cos t - 2\,x \sin t}{(x - \cos t)^2 + (y - \sin t)^2}\ dt. \tag{149.7}$$

Poisson's Integral (§§ 150-152)

150. The $\varphi(t)$ of the two preceding sections was the real part of a *given* analytic function that was *regular* on and within the unit circle $\zeta = e^{it}$. From now on, however, we shall assume that $\varphi(t)$ stands for an *arbitrary, sectionally continuous* function.[1] Using arguments quite similar to those of § 131 above, we can show that the function $f(z)$ defined by the resulting new right-hand side of (148.11) is regular at all points of the *interior* $|z| < 1$ of the unit circle.

The analytic functions obtainable in this way share a property that was discovered by H. A. Schwarz. We shall prove that *the real function that equals $\varphi(\vartheta)$ on the unit circle and coincides with the real part $U(r, \vartheta)$ of $f(z)$ in the interior of the unit circle, is continuous as a function of both variables r and ϑ at every point of continuity of $\varphi(\vartheta)$.*

This implies, for instance, that arbitrary continuous boundary values

$$\varphi(\vartheta) = \Re f(e^{i\,\vartheta})$$

can be prescribed for an analytic function $f(z)$ that is to be regular in the open disc $|z| < 1$ and the real part of which is to be extendable to a continuous function on the closed disc $|z| \leqq 1$. On the other hand, we can of course not assign the complex values of

$$\psi(\vartheta) = f(e^{i\,\vartheta})$$

arbitrarily, since the corresponding function $f(z)$—if it exists at all—is already determined to within an additive pure imaginary constant as soon as $\varphi(\vartheta) = \Re \psi(\vartheta)$ is assigned.

151. In view of these facts, a detailed study of the integral on the right-

---

[1] If it were not that we want to avoid explanations that lead too far afield, we could even assume $\varphi(t)$ in the sequel to be any *summable* function, representable as a limit of continuous functions (*cf.* Vol. 2, § 312).

hand side of (149.3) is called for. This integral was first investigated by S. D. Poisson (1781-1840), and it is for this reason called a *Poisson Integral*.

Many of the most important properties of the Poisson Integral (149.3) derive from the simple fact that the coefficient of $\varphi(t)$ in the integrand is positive whenever $r < 1$. More precisely, the following inequalities hold:

$$\frac{1+r}{1-r} = \frac{1-r^2}{(1-r)^2} \geqq \frac{1-r^2}{1-2\,r\cos(\vartheta-t)+r^2} \geqq \frac{1-r^2}{(1+r)^2} = \frac{1-r}{1+r}. \quad (151.1)$$

On the other hand, if $\varphi(t)$ equals a (real) constant c, the integral (149.3) can be evaluated explicitly. For if we choose $f(z) = c$, then by what was said earlier the real part $U(r, \vartheta)$ of $f(z)$, as given by equation (149.3), must also equal c. In particular, for $c = 1$ we have

$$\frac{1}{2\pi} \int_{-\pi}^{\pi} \frac{1-r^2}{1-2\,r\cos(\vartheta-t)+r^2}\, dt = 1 \quad (0 < r < 1). \quad (151.2)$$

We can now derive the analogue of the Maximum-Modulus Principle directly from the make-up of the Poisson Integral, without worrying about whether or not the value $U(r, \vartheta)$ of this integral can actually be interpreted to be the real part of a regular analytic function. To this end, let m and M be two constants, of any sign, for which

$$m \leqq \varphi(t) \leqq M \qquad (-\pi \leqq t < \pi), \quad (151.3)$$

so that $[M - \varphi(t)]$ is a non-negative function of t; then we have

$$M - U(r, \vartheta) = \frac{1}{2\pi} \int_{-\pi}^{\pi} [M - \varphi(t)]\, \frac{1-r^2}{1-2\,r\cos(\vartheta-t)+r^2}\, dt \geqq 0. \quad (151.4)$$

It follows similarly that $m \leqq U(r, \vartheta)$. If $\varphi(t)$ is not a constant, then we must have $m < U(r, \vartheta) < M$; the simplest way to see this is shown in § 156 below. This implies, in particular, the following theorem:

For $r < 1$, $|\varphi(t)| \leqq \varepsilon$ implies $|U(r, \vartheta)| \leqq \varepsilon$. $\quad (151.5)$

152. Now it is easy to set down Schwarz's proof for the continuity of $U(r, \vartheta)$ at a point $r = 1$, $\vartheta = \vartheta_0$ under the assumption that $\varphi(t)$ is continuous at $t = \vartheta_0$. We first extend the domain of definition of the function $\varphi(t)$, which so far is just the half-open interval $-\pi \leqq t < \pi$, by agreeing to make $\varphi(t)$ a periodic function of period 2π defined for all finite values of t. Then for all real values of α, we have the relation

$$U(r, \vartheta + \alpha) = \frac{1}{2\pi} \int\limits_{-\pi+\alpha}^{\pi+\alpha} \varphi(t + \alpha) \frac{1 - r^2}{1 - 2r\cos(\vartheta - t) + r^2} \, dt$$

$$= \frac{1}{2\pi} \int\limits_{-\pi}^{\pi} \varphi(t + \alpha) \frac{1 - r^2}{1 - 2r\cos(\vartheta - t) + r^2} \, dt,$$

in which we made use of the fact that the integrand is of period 2π. It is therefore sufficient to prove Schwarz's Theorem of § 150 under the additional assumption that $\vartheta_0 = 0$, which makes the calculations a little more convenient.

We assign a positive number ε and then determine a δ between 0 and $\pi/2$ such that

$$|\varphi(t) - \varphi(0)| < \varepsilon \quad \text{for} \quad |t| < 2\delta. \tag{152.1}$$

For short, we shall denote the interval $|t| < 2\delta$ by Δ_1, and the sum of the two intervals $-\pi \leq t < -2\delta$ and $2\delta < t < \pi$ by Δ_2. Then if we set

$$W_i(r, \vartheta) = \frac{1}{2\pi} \int\limits_{\Delta_i} [\varphi(t) - \varphi(0)] \frac{1 - r^2}{1 - 2r\cos(\vartheta - t) + r^2} \, dt \quad (i = 1, 2), \tag{152.2}$$

it follows from (149.3) and (151.2) that

$$U(r, \vartheta) - \varphi(0) = W_1(r, \vartheta) + W_2(r, \vartheta). \tag{152.3}$$

Now note that the function $W_1(r, \vartheta)$ may be regarded as a Poisson Integral, with the factor $\varphi(t)$ of (149.3) replaced by $[\varphi(t) - \varphi(0)]$ in the interval Δ_1 and by zero in the interval Δ_2. By (151.5) and (152.1), we therefore have

$$|W_1(r, \vartheta)| \leq \varepsilon \quad (0 \leq r < 1, \, -\pi \leq \vartheta \leq \pi). \tag{152.4}$$

As to $W_2(r, \vartheta)$, we shall investigate this function for values of ϑ that satisfy the condition $|\vartheta| < \delta$; then if t ranges over the interval Δ_2, we always have

$$\delta < |\vartheta - t| < \frac{3\pi}{2}, \quad \cos(\vartheta - t) < \cos\delta,$$

and this implies that

$$1 - 2r\cos(\vartheta - t) + r^2 > 1 - 2r\cos\delta + r^2.$$

The right-hand side, considered as a function of r, attains its minimum for $r = \cos\delta$, and the value of this minimum is $\sin^2\delta$. Now let M be an upper bound for $|\varphi(t)|$; then $|\varphi(t) - \varphi(0)| < 2M$, and the Mean-Value Theorem of § 123 applied to (152.2) yields

$$|W_2(r, \vartheta)| < \frac{2M}{\sin^2\delta} (1 - r^2) < \frac{4M}{\sin^2\delta} (1 - r). \tag{152.5}$$

In the region

$$|\vartheta| < \delta, \quad 1 - r < \frac{\varepsilon \sin^2 \delta}{4\,M} \tag{152.6}$$

we therefore have $|W_2(r, \vartheta)| < \varepsilon$, and hence by (152.4) and (152.3),

$$|U(r, \vartheta) - \varphi(0)| < 2\,\varepsilon. \tag{152.7}$$

We have thus proved the result of Schwarz stated earlier.

No analogous result can be expected to hold for the integral (149.4), if only because the denominator $2r \sin(\vartheta - t)$ changes its sign within the interval of integration. It may very well happen that $|U(r, \vartheta)|$ is bounded in the entire disc while the corresponding $|V(r, \vartheta)|$ assumes arbitrarily large values; this is the case, for instance, for the function discussed in § 158 below.

The Cauchy-Riemann Equations and Harmonic Functions (§§ 153-156)

153. From the definition of differentiability of a complex function given in § 124 above, it follows easily that the real part $u(x, y)$ and the imaginary part $v(x, y)$ of an analytic function $f(z)$ have continuous first partial derivatives with respect to x and y. We can therefore use the chain rule to take partial derivatives with respect to x and y of both sides of the relation

$$f(x + i\,y) = u(x, y) + i\,v(x, y), \tag{153.1}$$

and we obtain

$$f'(z) = \frac{\partial u}{\partial x} + i\,\frac{\partial v}{\partial x}, \quad i\,f'(z) = \frac{\partial u}{\partial y} + i\,\frac{\partial v}{\partial y}. \tag{153.2}$$

Comparison of these two identities yields

$$\frac{\partial u}{\partial x} = \frac{\partial v}{\partial y}, \quad \frac{\partial u}{\partial y} = -\frac{\partial v}{\partial x}. \tag{153.3}$$

The differential equations (153.3) are called the *Cauchy-Riemann equations*. Since the analytic function $f(z)$ is differentiable any number of times, the functions $u(x, y)$ and $v(x, y)$ have continuous partial derivatives of all orders.

Thus it follows from the Cauchy-Riemann equations, by differentiation, that

$$\frac{\partial^2 v}{\partial x\,\partial y} = \frac{\partial^2 u}{\partial x^2} = -\frac{\partial^2 u}{\partial y^2}. \tag{153.4}$$

Hence if for any function $F(x, y)$ we introduce the notation

$$\Delta F = \frac{\partial^2 F}{\partial x^2} + \frac{\partial^2 F}{\partial y^2}, \tag{153.5}$$

then (153.4) implies that

$$\Delta u = 0. \qquad (153.6)$$

The expression (153.5) is called the *Laplace operator*, or *Laplacian*, of F.

154. A function $u(x, y)$ defined in a region G of the (x, y)-plane is said to be a *harmonic function* (or a *potential function*) if it satisfies the following three conditions:

a) $u(x, y)$ is a continuous function of the two variables x, y at every (interior) point of G;

b) At every point of G, the derivatives

$$\frac{\partial u}{\partial x}, \quad \frac{\partial^2 u}{\partial x^2}, \quad \frac{\partial u}{\partial y}, \quad \frac{\partial^2 u}{\partial y^2}$$

exist, and $\partial u/\partial x$ is a continuous function of x while $\partial u/\partial y$ is a continuous function of y.

c) The equation $\Delta u = 0$ holds everywhere in G.

We note that this definition assumes neither the continuity in y of $\partial u/\partial x$ nor the continuity in x of $\partial u/\partial y$, and that as far as second partial derivatives are concerned, only the existence of those listed in b) is assumed. It turns out, however, that the condition $\Delta u = 0$ implies the existence and continuity of all the partial derivatives of u, of all orders; in fact, the following theorem holds true:

Let $u(x, y)$ be a function that is harmonic in a region G, and let κ be any circular disc that is contained within G. Then $u(x, y)$ is the real part of an analytic function that is regular in κ.

If the region G contains the circular disc

$$(x - x_0)^2 + (y - y_0)^2 \leq R^2,$$

then the function

$$u^*(\xi, \eta) = u(x_0 + R\,\xi,\ y_0 + R\,\eta)$$

is harmonic in the disc $\xi^2 + \eta^2 \leq 1$, and it clearly suffices to prove the theorem under the assumption that G is the interior $x^2 + y^2 < 1$ of the unit circle and that $u(x, y)$ is defined and continuous on the closed disc $x^2 + y^2 \leq 1$.

155. Let $\bar{u}(x, y)$ stand for the value of the Poisson Integral on the right-hand side of (149.6) with

$$\varphi(t) = u\,(\cos t, \sin t).$$

The function

$$\Phi(x, y) = [u(x, y) - \bar{u}(x, y)] - \frac{\varepsilon}{4}\,(x^2 + y^2 - 1), \qquad (155.1)$$

where ε denotes any positive number, is continuous on the closed disc $x^2 + y^2 \leq 1$ and vanishes identically on the boundary of this disc. Since the functions $\overline{u}(x, y)$ and $u(x, y)$ are harmonic and since $\varDelta(x^2 + y^2 - 1) = 4$, we must have

$$\varDelta \varPhi + \varepsilon = 0 \qquad (155.2)$$

at every interior point of the disc.

From these facts it now follows that $\varPhi \geq 0$. For if we had $\varPhi(x, y) < 0$ at any point, then the continuous function $\varPhi(x, y)$ would have to assume its minimum at an *interior* point (x_0, y_0) of the closed disc $x^2 + y^2 \leq 1$. On the straight line $y = y_0$, the function $\varPhi(x, y_0)$ of x would then have a minimum at $x = x_0$, so that at the point (x_0, y_0), we would have[1]

$$\frac{\partial \varPhi}{\partial x} = 0, \qquad \frac{\partial^2 \varPhi}{\partial x^2} \geq 0. \qquad (155.3)$$

Similarly, we find that at (x_0, y_0), we have

$$\frac{\partial \varPhi}{\partial y} = 0, \qquad \frac{\partial^2 \varPhi}{\partial y^2} \geq 0. \qquad (155.4)$$

Now (155.3) and (155.4) imply that $\varDelta \varPhi \geq 0$, and this is a relation that contradicts equation (155.2). Hence the inequality $\varPhi(x, y) \geq 0$ must hold for all positive values of ε, and (155.1) therefore implies that $u(x, y) \geq \overline{u}(x, y)$. If we interchange u and $\overline{u}$ in the defining equation of $\varPhi$, the same argument as used above yields $\overline{u}(x, y) \geq u(x, y)$, so that we obtain

$$u(x, y) = \overline{u}(x, y).$$

Since the function $\overline{u}(x, y)$ is by its definition the real part of an analytic function, we have thus proved the theorem stated in § 154 above.

156. Let $u(x, y)$ be a function harmonic in a region G, and let κ be a circle that is contained, along with its interior, in the region G. If (x_0, y_0) is the center and ϱ the radius of this circle, it follows from § 135 above—considering the real parts of the two sides of relation (135.5)—that

$$u(x_0, y_0) = \frac{1}{2\pi} \int_{-\pi}^{\pi} u(x_0 + \varrho \cos \vartheta, \ y_0 + \varrho \sin \vartheta) \, d\vartheta \qquad (156.1)$$

---

[1] For if $\partial \varPhi / \partial x \neq 0$ holds at the point (x_0, y_0), then the value $\varPhi(x_0, y_0)$ can not be a minimum of the function $\varPhi(x, y)$. If we had $\partial \varPhi / \partial x = 0$ and $\partial^2 \varPhi / \partial x^2 < 0$ at this point, then for $(x - x_0)$ positive and sufficiently small, $\partial \varPhi(x, y_0) / \partial x$ would be negative, and at such points (x, y_0) the Mean-Value Theorem of the Differential Calculus would yield

$$\varPhi(x, y_0) - \varPhi(x_0, y_0) < 0.$$

must hold true.   The same result can be obtained from the formulas of § 149 above. Now while there are, of course, complex functions that are *not* analytic but for which the Mean-Value Theorem of § 135 holds nevertheless (the above $u(x, y)$ is an example of such a function), the analogue (156.1) of relation (135.5) can actually be used to *characterize* harmonic functions.   In other words, we shall prove the following theorem: *If a continuous function $u(x, y)$ defined in a region G satisfies equation* (156.1) *at every interior point $z_0 = x_0 + i y_0$ of G and for every number ϱ for which the disc $|z - z_0| \leqq \varrho$ is contained in G, then $u(x, y)$ is a harmonic function in G.*

To prove this theorem, let m and M be the g.l.b. and the l.u.b., respectively, of $u(x, y)$ in G.   By the method of § 136 above, we can show that the hypotheses of our theorem imply the inequalities

$$m < u(x_0, y_0) < M$$

(equality signs excluded) for every interior point (x_0, y_0) of G, provided only that $u(x, y)$ is not a constant in G.

From this it follows, just as in § 147 above, that if $u(x, y)$ is continuous on the closure $\overline{G}$ of G and constant on the frontier $(\overline{G} - G)$ of G, then $u(x, y)$ is constant throughout G.

Now let $|z - z_0| < \varrho_0$ be a disc κ_0 whose closure is contained in G, and let $u(x, y)$ be the harmonic function defined in κ_0 whose boundary values, on the circle $|z - z_0| = \varrho_0$, coincide with those of $u(x, y)$.   Then by what has just been said before, the function $w(x, y) = u(x, y) - \overline{u}(x, y)$ must vanish identically in κ_0, because equation (156.1) holds for $w(x, y)$ in every circle κ that is contained in κ_0, while on the boundary of κ_0 we have $w(x, y) = 0$.

Hence we have

$$u(x, y) = \overline{u}(x, y)$$

in κ_0, so that $u(x, y)$ is a harmonic function that satisfies the differential equation $\Delta u = 0$.

It is a truly remarkable fact that the existence of all the derivatives of $u(x, y)$ follows from the validity of the integral equation (156.1) for the circles that are contained in G.

Harnack's Theorem (§ 157)

157. If the function $\varphi(t)$ is non-negative everywhere, then we may deduce from relations (151.1) above the following inequalities for the Poisson Integral:

$$
\begin{aligned}
\frac{1}{2\pi} \cdot \frac{1-r}{1+r} \int_{-\pi}^{\pi} \varphi(t)\, dt &\leq \frac{1}{2\pi} \int_{-\pi}^{\pi} \varphi(t)\, \frac{1-r^2}{1-2r\cos(\vartheta-t)+r^2}\, dt \\
&\leq \frac{1}{2\pi} \cdot \frac{1+r}{1-r} \int_{-\pi}^{\pi} \varphi(t)\, dt\,.
\end{aligned}
\tag{157.1}
$$

Hence if we note that

$$
\frac{1}{2\pi} \int_{-\pi}^{\pi} \varphi(t)\, dt = u(0,0) = u_0
$$

holds, we see that the values of the Poisson Integral in the disc $|z| \leq r < 1$ must lie between the two numbers

$$
\frac{1-r}{1+r} u_0 \quad \text{and} \quad \frac{1+r}{1-r} u_0\,.
$$

In particular, for $r = 1/2$ we obtain

$$
\frac{1}{3} u_0 \leq u(x,y) \leq 3 u_0\,.
\tag{157.2}
$$

This result can be generalized as follows. Let $u(x,y)$ be defined and non-negative, not in a disc but in any arbitrary region G, and let B be any given closed subset of G; then we can obtain an inequality on $u(z)$ analogous to (157.2) and valid for every point z of B, of the form

$$
\frac{1}{k} u_0 \leq u(x,y) \leq k u_0\,,
\tag{157.3}
$$

where z_0 is a point of B and $u(z_0) = u_0$.

To prove this generalization, we may assume that B is a connected point set, since we could otherwise enlarge B suitably so as to make it connected. d denoting the distance between the closed set B and the frontier of G, we cover the plane with a net (grill) of squares of sides $d/4$ in such a way that the (fixed) point z_0 is a vertex of four squares. We then form the closed set B' consisting of all the squares that have at least one interior point or boundary point in common with B. The set B' covers B and has a distance $\geq d/2$ from the frontier of G.

We denote the finitely many vertices of squares that belong to B' by $z_0, \ldots, z_p$, and we draw the circles $\kappa_i : |z - z_i| = d/2$, having these $(p+1)$

points as their centers.   The $(p + 1)$ discs cover B' and are themselves contained in (the interior of) the region G.   If we consider the Poisson Integral for the circle κ_0 with center z_0, we obtain for the points closest to z_0 among $z_1, \ldots, z_p$ the following inequality, analogous to (157.2):

$$\frac{1}{3}\, u_0 \leqq u(z_i) \leqq 3\, u_0.$$

Continuing in this way step by step, we obtain for each of the vertices of B' a similar inequality on $u(z_i)$, so that we may finally write

$$\frac{1}{3^p}\, u(z_0) \leqq u(z_i) \leqq 3^p\, u(z_0) \quad (i = 1, 2, \ldots, p). \quad (157.4)$$

Now we note that the closed discs

$$|z - z_i| \leqq \frac{d}{4} \qquad\qquad (i = 1, 2, \ldots, p)$$

cover the point set B', and therefore cover B as well, and that every point z in the interior or on the boundary of any of these discs satisfies the inequalities

$$\frac{1}{3^{p+1}}\, u(z_0) \leqq u(z) \leqq 3^{p+1}\, u(z_0).$$

We have thus obtained the following theorem: *Let $u(z)$ be a non-negative harmonic function defined and not identically equal to zero in a region G. Then on any given closed subset B of G, the function $u(z)$ has a greatest lower bound and a least upper bound that depend only on u_0, on G, and on B, and are independent of the particular choice of the function $u(z)$.*

Harmonic Measure (§ 158)

158.   Consider a fixed point z in the interior $|z| < 1$ of the unit circle, and an arc $\varphi_1 \leqq \varphi \leqq \varphi_2$ on the circle $|z| = 1$ itself (see Fig. 22 below). Through z and through the end points of the arc $\varphi_1 \varphi_2$, we draw the chords $\omega_1 \varphi_1$ and $\omega_2 \varphi_2$, and we shall show that the arc $\omega_1 \leqq \omega \leqq \omega_2$, considered as a function of z, can be expressed in terms of a Poisson Integral.   To this end, we first observe that the triangle whose vertices are z, $e^{i\varphi}$, and $e^{i\varphi'}$ is similar to the triangle whose vertices are z, $e^{i\omega}$, and $e^{i\omega'}$.   Hence for φ' tending to φ, we obtain the relation

$$\frac{d\omega}{d\varphi} = \frac{q}{p}, \qquad\qquad (158.1)$$

where q is the distance from z to $e^{i\omega}$, while p is the distance from z to $e^{i\varphi}$. Moreover, setting $z = r\, e^{i\vartheta}$, we obtain from a well-known theorem of Plane Geometry the relation

$$p\, q = (1 - r)(1 + r) = 1 - r^2.$$

Hence we finally have

$$\frac{d\omega}{d\varphi} = \frac{p\,q}{p^2} = \frac{1-r^2}{|e^{i\varphi}-r\,e^{i\vartheta}|^2} = \frac{1-r^2}{1-2\,r\cos(\vartheta-\varphi)+r^2} \cdot \tag{158.2}$$

Now if we write

$$u(x,\,y) = \frac{\omega_2-\omega_1}{2\,\pi} = \frac{\omega'}{2\,\pi}, \tag{158.3}$$

we obtain the relation

$$u(x,\,y) = \frac{1}{2\,\pi} \int_{\varphi_1}^{\varphi_2} \frac{1-r^2}{1-2\,r\cos(\vartheta-\varphi)+r^2}\,d\varphi. \tag{158.4}$$

The right-hand side of (158.4) represents a function that is harmonic in the disc $|z|<1$ and that, by Schwarz's Theorem of § 150 above, equals unity

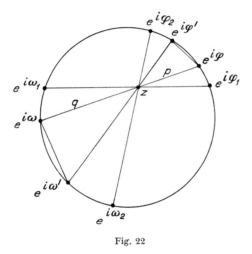

Fig. 22

at every interior point of the arc $\varphi_1 \leqq \varphi \leqq \varphi_2$ and equals zero at every interior point of the complementary arc of $|z|=1$.

The level lines of the harmonic function u can be determined as follows. We draw the circle that passes through the three points $e^{i\varphi_1}$, z, and $e^{i\varphi_2}$, and we denote by δ the angle at which this circle intersects the unit circle (see Fig. 23 below). From elementary Plane Geometry we find that $\omega'=2\delta$, so that, by (158.3),

$$u(x,\,y) = \frac{\delta}{\pi}. \tag{158.5}$$

Hence the level lines are arcs of circles through the end points of the arc $\varphi_1\,\varphi_2$.

For the arc $\varphi_1 < \varphi < \varphi_2$, that is, for $\delta = \pi$, we obtain $u = 1$; for the complementary arc, that is, for $\delta = 0$, we have $u = 0$.

The function $u(x, y)$, which is called the *harmonic measure* of the arc $\varphi_1 \varphi_2$ at the point z, may be given a second geometric interpretation that is just as simple as the first one.

To this end, we consider the disc $|z| < 1$ as a representation of a non-Euclidean plane, and we shall determine the non-Euclidean angle ω^* that is

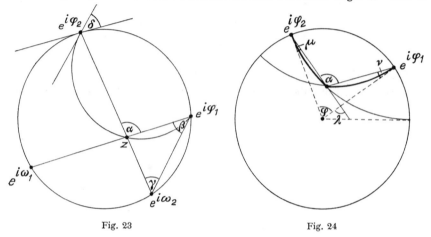

Fig. 23   Fig. 24

$$\varphi = 2\gamma, \quad \omega' = 2\beta, \quad \alpha = \beta + \gamma$$
$$\alpha = \delta + \varphi/2, \text{ hence } \quad \omega' = 2\alpha - \varphi = 2\delta$$

subtended at the point z by the portion $\varphi_1 \varphi_2$ of the horizon. From Fig. 24 above, we see that

$$\alpha = \lambda + \nu, \quad \lambda = \varphi + \mu,$$

hence

$$\omega^* = \alpha + \mu + \nu = 2\alpha - \varphi = \omega'.$$

The angle ω^* is therefore equal to the harmonic measure of the arc $\varphi_1 \varphi_2$ at the point z.

This interpretation shows that the harmonic measure is invariant under all non-Euclidean motions.

Remark. The concept of harmonic measure can be greatly generalized. If we translate the point z to the center of the disc $|z| \leqq 1$ by means of a non-Euclidean motion, then the harmonic measure of the arc $\varphi_1 \leqq \varphi \leqq \varphi_2$ becomes the *Euclidean* angle that is subtended by this arc at the center of the circle. Now if we replace the arc $\varphi_1 \leqq \varphi \leqq \varphi_2$ that figured in the above discussion by any Lebesgue-measurable subset of $|z| = 1$, then a construction similar to the above leads to harmonic functions that are called the harmonic measure of the given set with respect to the point z. In the sequel, however, we shall not make any use of this generalization, in spite of its fundamental importance.

An Inequality of Riemann (§ 159)

159. The Cauchy-Riemann equations (*cf.* § 153 above) enable us to prove a theorem due to Riemann that is often very useful. Let γ be a Jordan curve having a sectionally continuous derivative, let G be the interior region of γ, and let $P(x, y)$, $Q(x, y)$ be two functions that have continuous derivatives in the closed domain $(G + \gamma)$. As is well known, the following relation then holds true:

$$\int_\gamma [P(x, y)\, dx + Q(x, y)\, dy] = \int\int_G \left(\frac{\partial Q}{\partial x} - \frac{\partial P}{\partial y} \right) dx\, dy . \qquad (159.1)$$

Now let $f(z) = u(x, y) + iv(x, y)$ be an analytic function regular on the closed domain $(G + \gamma)$, and consider the integral

$$\int_\gamma u\, dv = \int_\gamma (u\, v_x\, dx + u\, v_y\, dy). \qquad (159.2)$$

Using the Cauchy-Riemann equations, we set

$$P(x, y) = u\, v_x = - u\, u_y, \quad Q(x, y) = u\, v_y = u\, u_x,$$
$$\left. \frac{\partial Q}{\partial x} - \frac{\partial P}{\partial y} = \left(\frac{\partial u}{\partial x} \right)^2 + \left(\frac{\partial u}{\partial y} \right)^2, \right\} \qquad (159.3)$$

and upon comparing (159.2) with (159.1) and (159.3), we obtain

$$\int_\gamma u\, dv = \int\int_G \left[\left(\frac{\partial u}{\partial x} \right)^2 + \left(\frac{\partial u}{\partial y} \right)^2 \right] dx\, dy. \qquad (159.4)$$

Now noting that

$$f'(z) = \frac{\partial u}{\partial x} + i\, \frac{\partial v}{\partial x} = \frac{\partial u}{\partial x} - i\, \frac{\partial u}{\partial y}, \qquad |f'(z)|^2 = \left(\frac{\partial u}{\partial x} \right)^2 + \left(\frac{\partial u}{\partial y} \right)^2$$

holds, we see that unless the analytic function $f(z)$ is a constant, we have

$$\int_\gamma u\, dv = \int\int_G |f'(z)|^2\, dx\, dy > 0, \qquad (159.5)$$

and the left-hand side of (159.5) can vanish only if $f(z)$ is a constant.

CHAPTER FOUR

MEROMORPHIC FUNCTIONS

Extension of the Definition of Analytic Functions (§§ 160-161)

160. We shall from this point on make it admissible for an analytic function to assume the value ∞ in the interior of its domain of definition. Furthermore, we shall allow the domain of definition to be any open connected point set G of the extended complex plane, which may also include the point $z = \infty$ as an interior point. To this end we must supplement the definition given in § 128 above, which we shall do as follows:

A function $f(z)$ is said to be analytic at a point $z_0 \neq \infty$ of its domain of definition if either $f(z)$ itself or $1/f(z)$ is a regular analytic function (in the sense of § 128) *in a certain neighborhood of z_0. If $z = \infty$ belongs to the domain G of definition of $f(z)$, then $f(z)$ is said to be analytic at $z = \infty$ if*

$$g(t) = f\left(\frac{1}{t}\right) \tag{160.1}$$

is analytic at $t = 0$.

According to this definition, a function that is analytic at all the points of G must be continuous in the chordal metric in G. Note that by our definition the constant ∞ is also an analytic function. Because of the exceptional role played by this particular function, some caution is required in the formulation of general theorems on analytic functions. To try to exclude the constant ∞ from the field of analytic functions would, however, lead to even greater complications in many cases, so that the definition we have adopted above will be the most useful on the whole.

161. If a non-constant analytic function $f(z)$ is regular at a point $z_0 \neq \infty$ (that is, if there is a neighborhood of z_0 in which $f(z)$ is regular), then we may write

$$f(z) = (z - z_0)^n \, g(z),$$
$$n \geq 0, \ g(z_0) \neq 0, \ g(z) \text{ not constant for } n = 0. \tag{161.1}$$

But if $f(z)$ is not regular at z_0, we must have

$$\frac{1}{f(z)} = (z - z_0)^m \, h(z) = \frac{(z - z_0)^m}{g(z)},$$
$$m > 0, \quad g(z_0) = \frac{1}{h(z_0)} \neq 0, \tag{161.2}$$

so that

$$f(z) = \frac{g(z)}{(z - z_0)^m} \quad \text{for} \quad z \neq z_0, \quad f(z_0) = \infty. \tag{161.3}$$

In this case, $f(z)$ is said to have a *pole of order* m at the point z_0. The two cases (161.1) and (161.3) can both be written in the form

$$\left. \begin{array}{c} f(z) = (z - z_0)^n \, g(z), \\[2mm] n \lessgtr 0, \quad g(z_0) \neq 0, \infty; \quad \text{if } n = 0, \text{ then } g(z) \text{ non-constant.} \end{array} \right\} \tag{161.4}$$

An analytic function for which poles are explicitly allowed is called a *meromorphic* function.

By a discussion just like the one above, we find that any non-constant function analytic at $z = \infty$ can be written in the form

$$f(z) = z^n \, g\left(\frac{1}{z}\right), \quad g(0) \neq 0; \tag{161.5}$$

here, n is an integer and $g(t)$ is an analytic function regular in a disc $|t| < r$. The function (161.5) is said to have a pole of order n at $z = \infty$ if $n > 0$, and a zero of order $(-n)$ at $z = \infty$ if $n < 0$.

Operations with Meromorphic Functions (§§ 162-163)

162. Consider two functions $f_1(z)$ and $f_2(z)$ meromorphic in a region G and neither one identically equal to ∞. Then to begin with, we can form the sum

$$s(z) = f_1(z) + f_2(z) \tag{162.1}$$

in accordance with the rules given in § 30 for all those points z_0 of G that are not poles of both $f_1(z)$ and $f_2(z)$ simultaneously. We can verify immediately that the sum is an analytic function at all these points z_0.

But if z_0 is a point at which both the given functions have the value ∞, then we may write

$$f_1(z) = \frac{g_1(z)}{(z - z_0)^{m_1}}, \quad f_2(z) = \frac{g_2(z)}{(z - z_0)^{m_2}}.$$

Assume first that $m_1 > m_2$; then we set

$$h(z) = g_1(z) + (z - z_0)^{m_1 - m_2} g_2(z),$$

and for $z \neq z_0$ we obtain

$$s(z) = \frac{h(z)}{(z - z_0)^{m_1}} \qquad (h(z_0) = g_1(z_0) \neq 0).$$

But we can define the function $s(z)$ also at the point z_0 itself, by requiring $s(z)$ to be continuous at z_0 in the chordal metric; the extended function $s(z)$ then has a pole of order m_1 at the point z_0. We proceed similarly if $m_1 < m_2$. Third and last, if $m_1 = m_2$ and if $g_1(z) + g_2(z)$ does not vanish identically, we may set

$$g_1(z) + g_2(z) = (z - z_0)^p h(z) \qquad (h(z_0) \neq 0).$$

Then for $z \neq z_0$ and in a certain neighborhood of z_0, we have

$$s(z) = (z - z_0)^{p - m_1} h(z).$$

Once more, the function $s(z)$ can be extended to a function analytic at z_0.

If $p \geq m_1$, then $s(z)$ is regular in some neighborhood of z_0. We see, in fact, that the sum $s(z)$ may even have a zero of any order at z_0. In the extreme case—excluded up to now—that $g_1(z) + g_2(z) \equiv 0$ holds, we must correspondingly set $s(z) \equiv 0$. But if $p < m_1$, then $s(z)$ has a pole of order $\leq m_1$ at z_0.

We use the same method for defining the product, the difference, and the quotient of two functions meromorphic in G. The product

$$p(z) = f_1(z) f_2(z) \qquad (162.2)$$

of the two given functions is first calculated in the region G^* that is obtained from G by removing the poles of both $f_1(z)$ and $f_2(z)$. The function $p(z)$ is a regular analytic function in G^* and we can easily see that it can be extended to a function that is analytic and chordally continuous in G. The meromorphic function extended in this way is *defined* to be the product of the two functions $f_1(z)$ and $f_2(z)$.

The difference $f_2(z) - f_1(z)$ may be considered as the sum of $f_2(z)$ and the product $(-1)f_1(z)$. The quotient

$$q(z) = \frac{f_2(z)}{f_1(z)} = f_2(z) \frac{1}{f_1(z)}$$

can be treated similarly, since $1/f_1(z)$ is analytic in G if $f_1(z)$ is analytic.

163. The derivative $f'(z)$ of a meromorphic function $f(z)$ is regular at all those points of the domain G of definition of $f(z)$ at which $f(z)$ itself is regular. At the poles of $f(z)$ and at $z = \infty$ (if the latter point is contained in G), $f'(z)$ can be extended to a function that is continuous in the chordal metric at these points.

To prove these statements, consider first a point $z_0 \neq \infty$; if in a certain neighborhood of z_0 we have

$$f(z) = \frac{g(z)}{(z - z_0)^p} \qquad (p \geq 1,\ g(z_0) \neq 0), \qquad (163.1)$$

then

$$f'(z) = \frac{-p\,g(z) + (z - z_0)\,g'(z)}{(z - z_0)^{p+1}} = \frac{h(z)}{(z - z_0)^{p+1}}\,,$$

$$h(z_0) = -p\,g(z_0) \neq 0.$$

(163.2)

In a certain neighborhood of the point $z = \infty$, we can in any case set

$$f(z) = z^n\,g\left(\frac{1}{z}\right) \qquad (g(0) \neq 0) \qquad (163.3)$$

if $f(z)$ is not constant, and from this we obtain for $z \neq \infty$ that

$$f'(z) = n\,z^{n-1}\,g\left(\frac{1}{z}\right) - z^{n-2}\,g'\left(\frac{1}{z}\right)$$

$$= z^{n-1}\left[n\,g\left(\frac{1}{z}\right) - \frac{1}{z}\,g'\left(\frac{1}{z}\right)\right].$$

(163.4)

From these equations we see that *the derivative of a meromorphic function is itself a meromorphic function.*

But it is not true that every meromorphic function is the derivative of a meromorphic function; by (163.2), the poles of $f'(z)$ at points $z_0 \neq \infty$ are at least of order 2, and by (163.4) the zeros of $f'(z)$ at $z = \infty$ are at least of order 2.

Partial Fraction Decomposition (§ 164)

164. If the function $f(z)$ has a pole of order m $(m \geq 1)$ at the point z_0, then

$$f(z) = \frac{g(z)}{(z - z_0)^m} \qquad (g(z_0) \neq 0)$$

$$= \frac{g(z_0)}{(z - z_0)^m} + \frac{g(z) - g(z_0)}{(z - z_0)^m}$$

$$= \frac{g(z_0)}{(z - z_0)^m} + \frac{g_1(z)}{(z - z_0)^{m_1}} \qquad (m_1 < m,\ g_1(z_0) \neq 0).$$

(164.1)

By repeating this process a suitable number of times, we obtain $f(z)$ in the form

$$f(z) = \frac{a_m}{(z - z_0)^m} + \frac{a_{m-1}}{(z - z_0)^{m-1}} + \cdots + \frac{a_1}{z - z_0} + h(z), \qquad (164.2)$$

where $h(z)$ is a meromorphic function regular at the point z_0. As to the coefficients $a_0, a_1, \ldots, a_m$, we have $a_m = g(z_0) \neq 0$; the remaining coefficients may assume the value zero.   The representation of the function $f(z)$ in the form (164.2) is called a *partial fraction decomposition of $f(z)$ at the point z_0*.

Similarly, for a function $f(z)$ that has a pole of order m at $z = \infty$, we can find in a certain neighborhood of $z = \infty$ a representation

$$f(z) = a_m z^m + a_{m-1} z^{m-1} + \cdots + a_1 z + h\left(\frac{1}{z}\right), \qquad (164.\,3)$$

where $h(t)$ is regular in a neighborhood of $t = 0$.

Isolated Essential Singularities (§§ 165-166)

165.   Let us consider a punctured disc

$$0 < |z - z_0| < r \qquad (165.\,1)$$

and a function $f(z)$ meromorphic in this region.

First, if $f(z)$ is bounded (165.1), then it must be regular in this region; by Riemann's Theorem of § 133 above, $f(z)$ can then be defined at z_0 in such a way that $f(z)$ is regular in the whole disc $|z - z_0| < r$.

Second, if there exists at least one positive number ε and at least one finite number a for which, at all the points of (165.1),

$$|f(z) - a| > \varepsilon, \qquad (165.\,2)$$

it follows that

$$\frac{1}{|f(z) - a|} < \frac{1}{\varepsilon}; \qquad (165.\,3)$$

in this case, the function $1/(f(z) - a)$ is meromorphic, and since it is also bounded, there is an analytic function $g(z)$ regular in the whole disc $|z - z_0| < r$ for which

$$\frac{1}{f(z) - a} = g(z) \qquad (165.\,4)$$

holds.   The equation

$$f(z) = \frac{1}{g(z)} + a \qquad (165.\,5)$$

then defines an analytic function $f(z)$ that is meromorphic in the whole disc $|z - z_0| < r$.   This case always obtains if the given $f(z)$ has at least two different boundary values at the point z_0.

Thus in each of the two cases we have discussed, we can suitably define $f(z_0)$ so as to extend the function $f(z)$ to a function continuous at z_0 in the chordal metric.   However, there do exist analytic functions (*cf.* § 219 below) that are meromorphic, or even regular, in the punctured disc $0 < |z - z_0| < r$

and which *cannot* be extended to a function continuous in the whole disc $|z - z_0| < r$.

In this last case, we say that $f(z)$ has an (isolated) *essential singularity* at the point z_0. The above discussion now shows that an analytic function cannot be bounded in *any* neighborhood of an essential singularity, nor can it satisfy an inequality of the form (165.2). To express these facts in a single statement, we may put them as follows: *The chordal distance cannot satisfy*

$$\chi(f(z), a) > \varepsilon$$

throughout any neighborhood of an essential singularity, where ε denotes a positive number and a denotes either a finite complex number or the number ∞.

This result is equivalent to the following theorem, called *Weierstrass' Theorem*:

The values of an analytic function $f(z)$ that has an essential singularity at z_0 will, in any given neighborhood of z_0, approximate every finite complex number a as closely as we wish. Using the concept of boundary values (*cf.* § 99 above), we may rephrase Weierstrass' Theorem as follows: *At an essential singularity z_0 of an analytic function $f(z)$, every point of the Riemann sphere is a boundary value of $f(z)$.*

166. We can make Weierstrass' Theorem more precise by making use of the property of preservation of neighborhoods (*cf.* § 144 above). Consider any circle $\varkappa_0$ of the w-plane having a given point a as its center. In the z-plane, we consider a sequence $k_1, k_2, \ldots$ of concentric circular discs

$$k_n: \quad |z - z_0| \leqq r_n ,$$
$$r_1 > r_2 > r_3 > \cdots, \quad \lim_{n = \infty} r_n = 0 . \qquad\qquad (166.1)$$

Now if the function

$$w = f(z) \qquad\qquad (166.2)$$

has an essential singularity at the point z_0 and if $f(z)$ is meromorphic at all the other interior points of k_1, then by Weierstrass' Theorem there is in the punctured disc

$$k_1^*: \quad 0 < |z - z_0| < r_1$$

at least one point z_1 whose image $w_1 = f(z_1)$ lies in the interior of the circle $\varkappa_0$. Furthermore, by the theorem on Preservation of Neighborhoods there is a closed circular disc $\bar{\varkappa}_1$ with center at w_1 and wholly contained in the interior of $\varkappa_0$, and which is such that *every* point of $\bar{\varkappa}_1$ is the image of at least one point of k_1^*. Similarly, by Weierstrass' Theorem there is in the punctured disc

$$k_2^*: \quad 0 < |z - z_0| < r_2$$

a point z_2 whose image $w_2 = f(z_2)$ lies in the interior of $\bar{\varkappa}_1$, and in $\bar{\varkappa}_1$ there is a closed disc $\bar{\varkappa}_2$ with center at w_2 and such that every point of $\bar{\varkappa}_2$ is the image of at least one point of k_2^*.   Continuing in this way, we obtain an infinite sequence of nested circular discs

$$\bar{\varkappa}_1 \geqq \bar{\varkappa}_2 \geqq \bar{\varkappa}_3 \geqq \cdots$$

in the w-plane having at least one common point ω (*cf.* § 94 above). By our construction, each of the infinitely many punctured discs k_n^* contains a point ζ_n for which

$$\omega = f(\zeta_n) \qquad\qquad (n = 1, 2, \ldots)$$

holds. These points ζ_n are all distinct from z_0 and by (166.1) converge to z_0; hence there must be infinitely many different ζ_n. Furthermore, the choice of the number a, and of the radius of the circle $\varkappa_0$ in which ω lies, was arbitrary. We can therefore restate our last result in the following form:

If z_0 is an essential singularity of the meromorphic (or regular) function $f(z)$, then in the w-plane there is an everywhere-dense set $\{\omega\}$ of points ω for each of which the equation

$$\omega = f(z)$$

has infinitely many solutions in every neighborhood of z_0.

In fact, as we shall see later, the point set $\{\omega\}$ always covers the entire Riemann sphere with the exception of at most two points (*cf.* Vol. 2, § 417).

Liouville's Theorem and its Application to Polynomials (§§ 167-169)

167. An analytic function that is regular everywhere in the finite complex plane (i.e. for all $z \neq \infty$) is called an *integral function* (or *entire function*). Let $f(z)$ be an integral function that is bounded, so that we have

$$|f(z)| < M. \qquad (167.1)$$

If r is positive and if we set

$$z = r\,u, \qquad \varphi(u) = \frac{f(r\,u) - f(0)}{2\,M}, \qquad (167.2)$$

then $\varphi(u)$ is a regular analytic function in the circle $|u| < 1$ and satisfies all the conditions of Schwarz's Lemma (*cf.* § 140 above).   Hence by this lemma, we have $|\varphi(u)| < |u|$, so that for $|z| < r$,

$$\left|\varphi\left(\frac{z}{r}\right)\right| < \frac{|z|}{r}, \qquad |f(z) - f(0)| < \frac{2\,M\,|z|}{r}. \qquad (167.3)$$

The second of these inequalities holds for every z and for every $r > |z|$. If we let r go to infinity, we find that $f(z) = f(0)$. This result, established by Liouville (1809-1882), may be stated as follows:

LIOUVILLE'S THEOREM: *Every bounded integral function is a constant.*

168. A simple generalization of Liouville's theorem leads to an important property of *polynomials.* By a polynomial of degree n is meant an integral function of the form

$$P(z) = a_0\,z^n + a_1\,z^{n-1} + \cdots + a_{n-1}\,z + a_n \qquad (a_0 \neq 0). \qquad (168.1)$$

We shall prove the following theorem:

Let $f(z)$ be an integral function that does not vanish identically. If there exist two positive numbers r and M and a natural number n such that the relation

$$|f(z)| < M\,|z^n| \qquad (168.2)$$

holds for all z satisfying $|z| > r$, then $f(z)$ is a polynomial of degree n at most.

For $n = 0$, this theorem is simply Liouville's theorem of the preceding section; for, a non-zero constant is a polynomial of degree zero, and every integral function bounded for $|z| > r$ must be bounded in the whole plane.

To prove the theorem by induction we assume it to be valid for $(n - 1)$ and consider an $f(z)$ satisfying the conditions of the theorem. We may assume without loss of generality that $r > 1$. If we set

$$Q(z) = \frac{f(z) - f(0)}{z}, \qquad (168.3)$$

then $Q(z)$ is an integral function (*cf.* § 134 above) which for $|z| > r$ satisfies

$$\left.\begin{aligned}
|Q(z)| &\leq \frac{|f(z)| + |f(0)|}{|z|} \\
&\leq \frac{M\,|z^n| + |f(0)|\,|z^n|}{|z|} = (M + |f(0)|)\,|z^{n-1}|.
\end{aligned}\right\} \qquad (168.4)$$

By the induction hypothesis, $Q(z)$ is therefore a polynomial of degree $(n - 1)$ at most, except if $Q(z)$ is identically zero. Hence

$$f(z) = z\, Q(z) + f(0) \qquad (168.5)$$

is a polynomial of degree n at most, and the theorem is thus proved for all values of n.

The converse of the theorem we have just proved is also true, since if $k \leqq n$, a k-th degree polynomial $P_k(z)$ satisfies for all $|z| > 1$ the relation

$$|P_k(z)| < (|a_0| + |a_1| + \cdots + |a_k|)\,|z^k|. \qquad (168.6)$$

Therefore there exist numbers $M > 0$ such that $|P_k(z)| < M\,|z|^n$ holds whenever $|z| > 1$. Thus *the polynomials of degree n at most are precisely those integral functions for which the hypotheses of the last theorem hold true.*

169. Let $P_n(z) = a_0\,z^n + \cdots + a_n$ be a polynomial of degree n. If we set

$$P_n(z) = a_0\,z^n + f(z), \qquad (169.1)$$

then the function $f(z)$ either vanishes identically or else is a polynomial of degree $(n-1)$ at most. In any case, there exist positive numbers M such that for $|z| > 1$,

$$|f(z)| < M\,|z^{n-1}| \qquad (169.2)$$

holds true. The last two relations imply that

$$|a_0|\,|z^n| \leqq |P_n(z)| + \frac{M}{|z|}\,|z^n| \qquad (|z| > 1). \quad (169.3)$$

For all z subject to the condition

$$|z| > \frac{2\,M}{|a_0|} + 1\,,$$

it then follows from (169.3) that

$$|P_n(z)| > \frac{|a_0|}{2}\,|z^n|\,, \qquad (169.4)$$

so that we have the following theorem:

If $P_n(z)$ is a polynomial of degree n, then there exist positive numbers m and r $(r > 1)$ such that

$$|P_n(z)| > m\,|z^n| \qquad (169.5)$$

holds for all z for which $|z| > r$.

The Fundamental Theorem of Algebra (§ 170)

170. If we now set $|z| = r_0$ and choose the positive number $r_0 > r$ large enough for

$$m\, r_0 > |P_n(0)| \tag{170.1}$$

to hold true, then by § 138 above, the analytic function $P_n(z)$ must have at least one zero in the disc $|z| < r_0$.

We therefore have the following theorem:

Every polynomial of degree $n \geq 1$ has at least one zero, i.e. there is at least one z for which

$$P_n(z) = 0$$

holds.

This is the Fundamental Theorem of Algebra, which was first proved by Gauss in 1799 (*cf.* § 9). On the basis of this, it is now easy to prove the following further theorem: *Every polynomial $P_n(z)$ of degree n can be written in the form*

$$P_n(z) = a_0\, (z - c_1)\, (z - c_2)\, \ldots\, (z - c_n) \tag{170.2}$$

and therefore has exactly n roots (zeros), which however need not all be distinct from each other.

The theorem is clearly true for $n = 1$, and we assume it true for polynomials of degree 2, 3, $\ldots$, $n - 1$, this being our induction hypothesis. Now if $P_n(z)$ is a polynomial of degree n and c_n a zero of $P_n(z)$ (the existence of at least one is guaranteed by the preceding result), then we set

$$Q(z) = \frac{P_n(z)}{z - c_n} = \frac{P_n(z) - P_n(c_n)}{z - c_n} \tag{170.3}$$

and we observe that $Q(z)$ is an integral function that, for $|z|$ sufficiently large, satisfies

$$|Q(z)| = \frac{|P_n(z)|}{|z - c_n|} \leq \frac{M\,|z^n|}{|z|\left|1 - \dfrac{c_n}{z}\right|} \leq \frac{M\,|z^n|}{|z|\left(1 - \left|\dfrac{c_n}{z}\right|\right)} < M_1\,|z^{n-1}|. \tag{170.4}$$

Hence $Q(z)$ is a polynomial of degree $k \leq n - 1$, so that $P_n(z)$ is a polynomial of degree $k + 1$. This implies that $k = n - 1$, and hence the induction hypothesis yields

$$Q(z) = a_0\, (z - c_1)\, (z - c_2) \cdots (z - c_{n-1}); \tag{170.5}$$

finally we obtain (170.2) by comparing (170.5) with (170.3).

Further Properties of Polynomials (§§ 171-173)

171. Let $f(z)$ be an integral function for which the relation

$$|f(z)| \geqq m \,|z^n| > m\, r^n \qquad (171.1)$$

holds everywhere in the exterior $|z| > r$ of the circle $|z| = r$; in this relation, m stands for some positive number and n stands for some natural number or zero. Then the zeros (if any) of $f(z)$ must all lie in the closed disc $|z| \leqq r$. Since each of the zeros is isolated, there can be no more than a finite number of them. Also, the multiplicity of each of them is finite. Therefore there exists a polynomial

$$P_k(z) = (z - c_1)\,(z - c_2) \ldots (z - c_k) \qquad (171.2)$$

which is such that the quotient

$$\frac{f(z)}{P_k(z)} \qquad (171.3)$$

represents an integral function that has no zeros. Then the expression $P_k(z)/f(z)$ likewise represents an integral function without zeros. Now considering (171.1) and (171.2), we see that for sufficiently large values of $|z|$, a relation of the following form must hold:

$$\left| \frac{P_k(z)}{f(z)} \right| < \frac{M\,|z^k|}{m\, r^n}. \qquad (171.4)$$

This implies that $P_k(z)/f(z)$ is a polynomial of degree k at most. But since this polynomial has no zeros, it must be a non-zero constant. Hence the same is true of the expression (171.3). Therefore

$$f(z) = a_0\,(z - c_1)\,(z - c_2) \ldots (z - c_k)$$

is a polynomial of degree k. Considering (171.1), we then have that for $|z|$ sufficiently large,

$$0 < m\,|z^n| \leqq |f(z)| \leqq M\,|a_0|\,|z^k| \qquad (|z| > r)$$

must hold, and this relation cannot be valid for arbitrarily large $|z|$ unless $k \geqq n$ holds true. We have thus proved the following theorem:

An integral function satisfying relation (171.1) for all $|z| > r$ must be a polynomial of degree n at least.

172. We can now determine the most general non-constant functions $f(z)$ that are analytic on the whole Riemann sphere. Since the poles of such a function $f(z)$ cannot have any points of accumulation, $f(z)$ cannot have more than a finite number of poles. If $Q_m(z)$ is a polynomial whose zeros are located at the same points as are the poles of $f(z)$ and have the same respective multiplicities as do the poles of $f(z)$—excepting the pole, if any, of $f(z)$ at $z = \infty$— then the function

$$g(z) = Q_m(z)\, f(z)$$

is an integral function that is continuous in the chordal metric (*cf.* § 86) at the point $z = \infty$, and that does not vanish identically; for otherwise, $f(z)$ itself would have to vanish identically. Hence by Liouville's theorem, we have $g(\infty) \neq 0$, and the theorem of the preceding section then implies that $g(z)$ is a polynomial or a constant (polynomial of degree zero). We see that in any case $f(z)$ can be written in the form

$$f(z) = \frac{P_n(z)}{Q_m(z)} \qquad (n \geq 0;\, m \geq 0), \quad (172.1)$$

and here the constant functions are also included. Thus we have proved the following theorem:

The only functions analytic everywhere on the Riemann sphere are the rational functions.

To study the behavior of $f(z)$ in the neighborhood of the point $z = \infty$, we write, in place of (172.1),

$$f(z) = z^{n-m}\, g\!\left(\frac{1}{z}\right) \qquad (g(0) \neq 0).$$

Hence if $n > m$, for example, then $f(z)$ has m poles in the finite plane and a pole of order $(n-m)$ at infinity, that is, n poles altogether; thus the function has as many poles as it has zeros. If $n \leq m$, the number of poles will also equal the number of zeros. A similar investigation of the number of zeros of the function $(f(z) - a)$ leads to the following result:

The number of points—each counted with the proper multiplicity—at which the rational function (172.1) *assumes any given value a, is independent of a; here, a may also be* ∞.

The simplest case is that in which every value is assumed just *once* by the function. In this case,

$$f(z) = \frac{\alpha z + \beta}{\gamma z + \delta} \qquad (\alpha\delta - \beta\gamma \neq 0)$$

must hold, so that we are led once again to the fractional linear functions that we studied earlier in connection with the theory of Moebius transformations.

173. It follows from the preceding section that the domain of definition of a single-valued analytic function other than a rational function cannot cover the entire Riemann sphere.   Hence for a function of this kind, there must be on the Riemann sphere—or, which is the same, in the extended complex plane—a non-empty closed point set A on which the function is not defined. Any isolated points which this point set A may have must be essential singularities of the function, i.e. singularities of the type discussed in § 165 above.

In particular, the point $z = \infty$ is an essential singularity of any integral function other than a polynomial.   For this reason, integral functions other than polynomials are called *transcendental integral functions*.

By using certain properties of polynomials, we can establish very simple characterizations of transcendental integral functions, such as the following:

A non-constant integral function is a transcendental function if and only if there is at least one sequence $z_1, z_2, \ldots$ of complex numbers converging to $z = \infty$ for which the sequence of numbers $|f(z_n)|$ $(n = 1, 2, \ldots)$ has a finite upper bound.

Another theorem along these lines is the following:

If a non-constant integral function has no zeros, it must be a transcendental integral function.

If $f(z)$ is a transcendental integral function, then there exist values a for which the equation $f(z) - a = 0$ has infinitely many solutions.   If $f(z)$ is a polynomial of degree 2 or more, then there are certain values of a for which the equation $f(z) - a = 0$ has several distinct solutions.   This implies that *the only integral functions $f(z)$ that always assume distinct values $f(z)$ for distinct values of z are the integral linear functions*

$$f(z) = \alpha z + \beta.$$

PART FOUR

ANALYTIC FUNCTIONS DEFINED BY LIMITING PROCESSES

CHAPTER ONE

CONTINUOUS CONVERGENCE

Continuous Convergence (§§ 174-175)

174. The simplest and most convenient method of studying specific analytic functions in detail consists in representing them as limits of convergent sequences of polynomials or rational functions. Usually, however, a representation of this sort holds good only in some part of the domain on which the given function exists, as even the simplest examples will show. For example, if we set

$$w = f_n(z) = z^n \qquad (n = 1, 2, \ldots), \quad (174.1)$$

then the sequence of numbers $f_1(z), f_2(z), \ldots$ converges to zero for $|z| < 1$, to infinity for $|z| > 1$, and to unity for $z = 1$. If z is unimodular and not equal to 1, the sequence diverges.

Inside the unit circle, the limit function

$$f(z) = \lim_{n = \infty} f_n(z) \qquad (174.2)$$

therefore represents the constant zero. The sequence of functions (174.1) fails, however, to represent this constant on the boundary or in the exterior of the unit circle.

Now if z_0 is a point of the *interior* of the unit circle and if $z_1, z_2, \ldots$ is *any* sequence of points that converges to z_0, then it is very easy to show that the sequence of numbers

$$w_n = f_n(z_n) = (z_n)^n \qquad (n = 1, 2, \ldots) \quad (174.3)$$

converges to zero. Similarly, if z_0 is a point of the exterior of the unit circle, then the numbers w_n converge to ∞. In either case, we say that the sequence of functions (174.1) *converges continuously* at the point z_0.

On the other hand, we can find sequences of numbers z_n that converge to $z = 1$ and for which the sequence of numbers (174.3) diverges, and we can also find sequences of z_n converging to $z = 1$ for which the sequence (174.3) converges to *any* pre-assigned limit a, including zero and ∞. We say that the sequence of functions (174.1) is convergent, but not continuously convergent, at the point $z = 1$.

The concept of continuous convergence plays a fundamental role in Function Theory. We shall therefore study this concept in greater detail.

175. Let A be any set of the extended complex plane that is dense in itself, and let $f_1(z), f_2(z), \ldots$ be a sequence of complex functions, not necessarily analytic nor even continuous, that are defined on A. Let z_0 be any point of accumulation of A, not necessarily belonging to A, and consider sequences $z_1, z_2, \ldots$ of points of A that converge to z_0. We form the sequence

$$w_n = f_n(z_n) \qquad\qquad (n = 1, 2, \ldots). \quad (175.1)$$

Now if the sequence (175.1) converges for *every* choice of a sequence of points $z_1, z_2, \ldots$ as described above, then we shall say that the sequence of functions $f_n(z)$ is *continuously convergent* at the point z_0.

By way of motivating the use of the term "continuous" in this connection, we shall prove that in the case of continuous convergence, the limit of the sequence (175.1) is independent of the choice of the sequence $z_1, z_2, \cdots$. In fact, if we have $\lim z_n' = \lim z_n'' = z_0$ along with

$$\lim_{n=\infty} f_n(z_n') = \alpha, \quad \lim_{n=\infty} f_n(z_n'') = \beta, \quad \chi(\alpha, \beta) > 0,$$

then for the sequence $z_1, z_2, \ldots$ defined by

$$z_{2k-1} = z_{2k-1}', \quad z_{2k} = z_{2k}'' \qquad\qquad (k = 1, 2, \ldots)$$

we would have the relation $\lim z_n = z_0$, while $\lim f_n(z_n)$ would not exist, contradicting the assumption of continuous convergence.

It is also very easy to show that if the sequence $f_1(z), f_2(z), \ldots$ converges continuously at the point z_0, then any subsequence $f_{n_1}(z), f_{n_2}(z), \ldots$ (where $n_1 < n_2 < n_3 < \ldots$) does likewise.

Finally, we note that the following important theorem is an immediate consequence of the definition of continuous convergence:

Let the sequence of functions $w = f_n(z)$ be continuously convergent at the point z_0 and let its limit at z_0 be w_0. Let B be a point set of the extended w-plane that contains all the points $w = f_n(z)$ for every n, with z ranging over the common domain A of definition of the functions $f_n(z)$, and assume that w_0 is a point of accumulation of B. Let the sequence of functions $\varphi_n(w)$ be defined on B and be continuously convergent at w_0. Then it follows that the sequence of functions

$$F_n(z) = \varphi_n\big(f_n(z)\big) \qquad\qquad (n = 1, 2, \ldots)$$

is continuously convergent at z_0.

The Limiting Oscillation (§§ 176-178)

176. With each point z_0 of accumulation of the common domain A of definition of the functions $f_n(z)$ of a given sequence, we can associate a non-negative number $\sigma(z_0)$ that will play a fundamental role in our theory. Let C_k be the circular discs defined by the relation

$$\chi(z, z_0) < \frac{1}{k} \qquad (k = 2, 3, \ldots) \quad (176.1)$$

and let S_{nk} be the chordal oscillation of the function $f_n(z)$ on the point set $A C_k$, i.e. let

$$S_{nk} = \sup \chi\left(f_n(z'), f_n(z'')\right) \quad \text{for} \quad z', z'' \in A\, C_k. \qquad (176.2)$$

We then form the numbers

$$\sigma_k = \overline{\lim_{n=\infty}} S_{nk} \qquad (k = 1, 2, \ldots). \quad (176.3)$$

Since we have $C_{k+1} \leq C_k$, it follows that for every n,

$$S_{n(k+1)} \leq S_{nk}, \qquad (176.4)$$

so that

$$\sigma_2 \geq \sigma_3 \geq \sigma_4 \geq \cdots \qquad (176.5)$$

holds.

Hence the limit

$$\sigma(z_0) = \lim_{k=\infty} \sigma_k \qquad (176.6)$$

exists; we shall call it the *limiting oscillation* of the sequence of functions $f_n(z)$ at the point z_0.

177. The main theorem of this chapter is the following:

a) *If we have $\sigma(z_0) > 0$ for the limiting oscillation at the point z_0, then the sequence $\{f_n(z)\}$ cannot converge continuously at z_0.*

b) *If, however, $\sigma(z_0) = 0$, then the sequence $\{f_n(z)\}$ converges continuously at z_0 provided only that it has in every neighborhood of z_0 a point of convergence (which may be z_0 itself).*

In proof, let us assume first that $\sigma(z_0) > 0$. Then for every k there are infinitely many functions of the given sequence that have on the point set $A C_k$ an oscillation greater than $\sigma_k/2$, and hence also greater than $\sigma(z_0)/2$. We can therefore find two sequences of points $z_1', z_2', \ldots$ and $z_1'', z_2'', \ldots$ and an increasing sequence of integers $n_1 < n_2 < n_3 < \cdots$ for which

$$z'_k \in A\,C_k, \quad z''_k \in A\,C_k, \quad \chi\big(f_{n_k}(z'_k), f_{n_k}(z''_k)\big) > \frac{\sigma(z_0)}{2} \tag{177.1}$$

holds. Now we have

$$\lim_{k=\infty} z'_k = \lim_{k=\infty} z''_k = z_0, \tag{177.2}$$

and the two sequences

$$w'_k = f_{n_k}(z'_k), \quad w''_k = f_{n_k}(z''_k) \tag{177.3}$$

either do not both converge or do both converge but have different limits. In either case, it follows that the $f_n(z)$ cannot converge continuously at z_0. This proves part a) of the theorem.

To prove part b), we assume that $\sigma(z_0) = 0$ and we assign a positive number ε as well as an arbitrary sequence of points z_n of A that converges to z_0. Then by (176.6), there is a value of k for which

$$\sigma_k < \frac{\varepsilon}{6} \tag{177.4}$$

holds. By the second condition under b), there exists in the point set $A\,C_k$ at least one point ζ at which the $f_n(z)$ converge. Hence we can find a natural number N_1 such that the relation

$$\chi\big(f_n(\zeta), f_m(\zeta)\big) < \frac{\varepsilon}{3} \tag{177.5}$$

holds whenever $n > N_1$ and $m > N_1$.

Furthermore, by (176.3) and (177.4) there exists a natural number N_2 such that for $n > N_2$, the oscillation S_{nk} satisfies $S_{nk} < \varepsilon/3$; there is also a natural number N_3 such that z_n is contained in $A\,C_k$ whenever $n > N_3$. Then if N denotes the largest of the three numbers N_1, N_2, N_3, the following relations will hold true whenever n and m are both $> N$:

$$\chi\big(f_n(z_n), f_n(\zeta)\big) < \frac{\varepsilon}{3}, \quad \chi\big(f_m(z_m), f_m(\zeta)\big) < \frac{\varepsilon}{3}. \tag{177.6}$$

If we now set

$$w_n = f_n(z_n), \tag{177.7}$$

then by comparing relations (177.5) and (177.6), we obtain

$$\chi(w_n, w_m) < \varepsilon \qquad (n > N,\ m > N). \tag{177.8}$$

By Cauchy's convergence criterion (cf. § 91 above), the sequence (177.7) must therefore be convergent, and hence we have proved that the given sequence of functions converges continuously at the point z_0.

In the case that the functions $f_n(z)$ are also defined at the point z_0, the above theorem implies the following result:

For the sequence $\{f_n(z)\}$ to converge continuously at a point z_0 belonging to the common domain of definition of the functions $f_n(z)$, it is necessary and sufficient that the limiting oscillation $\sigma(z_0)$ vanish and that the limit $\lim f_n(z_0)$ exist.

178. The results of the preceding section can be rounded out as follows. Let $f(z)$ be the limit function of a sequence of functions $f_n(z)$ and let B' be the domain of definition of $f(z)$, so that B' is that subset of the common domain A of definition of all the $f_n(z)$ on which

$$\lim_{n=\infty} f_n(z) = f(z)$$

exists. Also, let B'' be the set of those of the points z_0 of accumulation of B' at which the limiting oscillation satisfies $\sigma(z_0) = 0$. By the preceding section, the sequence $\{f_n(z)\}$ converges continuously at all the points of the set B''. We may therefore extend the domain of definition of $f(z)$ so as to include in it all the points of B''; the extended domain is then the union

$$B = B' \dotplus B''$$

of the sets B' and B''.

We shall now show that $f(z)$ *is continuous at every point of* B''.

To prove this, consider first a sequence $z_1, z_2, \ldots$ of points of B' that converges to z_0. Since $\sigma(z_0) = 0$ by assumption, we can assign to each point z_k a natural number n_k such that

$$\chi\big(f_{n_k}(z_k), f(z_k)\big) < \frac{1}{k} \tag{178.1}$$

holds, and we may at the same time arrange the choice of the n_k in such a way as to have $n_k > n_{k-1}$. On the other hand, the continuous convergence at the point z_0 of the sequence of the $f_{n_k}(z)$ implies that

$$\lim_{k=\infty} \chi\big(f_{n_k}(z_k), f(z_0)\big) = 0, \tag{178.2}$$

and upon comparison of (178.1) and (178.2) we find that

$$\lim_{k=\infty} \chi\big(f(z_k), f(z_0)\big) = 0. \tag{178.3}$$

Next, let z_0 be a point of accumulation of B'' and let $\zeta_1, \zeta_2, \ldots$ be a sequence of points of B'' that converges to z_0. The sequence of the $f_n(z)$ converges continuously at each of the ζ_k, and we can therefore determine a sequence $z_1, z_2, \ldots$ of points of A and a sequence of natural numbers $n_1 < n_2 < \ldots$ in such a way that

$$\chi(z_k, \zeta_k) < \frac{1}{k}, \quad \chi(f_{n_k}(z_k), f(\zeta_k)) < \frac{1}{k} \qquad (178.4)$$

both hold at the same time. Relation (178.2) holds true in this case too, since the sequence of the z_k also converges to z_0. Relations (178.2) and (178.4) then imply that

$$\lim_{k=\infty} \chi(f(\zeta_k), f(z_0)) = 0, \qquad (178.5)$$

and relations (178.3) and (178.5) now prove the statement in italics above.

Note, however, that the limit function $f(z)$ may be continuous at points where the convergence of the sequence is not continuous. For example, the sequence

$$f_n(z) = \frac{1}{n(nz+1)} \qquad (n = 1, 2, \ldots) \quad (178.6)$$

converges to the constant zero for all $z \neq \infty$; the limit function $f(z) \equiv 0$ is continuous throughout; but the convergence of the sequence is not continuous at $z = 0$.

The Normal Kernel of a Sequence of Functions (§ 179)

179. Let A be the common domain of definition of the functions of the sequence $\{f_n(z)\}$. We say that the sequence is *normal* at a point z_0 of the closure of A if $\sigma(z_0) = 0$. The set S of all the points z_0 at which $\{f_n(z)\}$ is normal will be called the *normal kernel* of the sequence of functions.

Now consider a denumerable sequence $\zeta_1, \zeta_2, \zeta_3, \ldots$ of points of A that are *dense in A*. By *Cantor's diagonal process* (cf. § 92 above), we can find in the sequence $\{f_n(z)\}$ a subsequence $f_{n_1}(z), f_{n_2}(z), \ldots$ which is such that for every j the limit

$$\lim_{k=\infty} f_{n_k}(\zeta_j) = f(\zeta_j)$$

exists. By the theorem of § 177 above, this subsequence $\{f_{n_k}(z)\}$ is continuously convergent at every point z_0 of the normal kernel S. By § 178 above, the limit function $f(z)$ is continuous at every point of S.

Comparison of Continuous Convergence with Uniform Convergence (§ 180)

180. Let S be the normal kernel of the sequence $\{f_n(z)\}$, and let S_1 be a closed subset of S on which the sequence converges continuously to the limit

$$\lim_{n=\infty} f_n(z) = f(z). \tag{180.1}$$

We shall prove that the convergence of $\{f_n(z)\}$ on S_1 is *uniform*.

If this were false, there would exist at least one positive number ε_0 with the property that to each natural number k there could be assigned a point z_k of S_1 and a natural number n_k such that the relations

$$\chi\big(f_{n_k}(z_k), f(z_k)\big) > \varepsilon_0, \quad n_{k+1} > n_k \tag{180.2}$$

would hold true simultaneously. We may assume without loss of generality that the sequence of points z_k converges to a point z_0, which must itself be a point of S_1 (since S_1 is closed). Now since, on the one hand, we have continuous convergence at z_0, while on the other hand $f(z)$ is continuous at z_0, we must have the two relations

$$\lim_{k=\infty} \chi\big(f_{n_k}(z_k), f(z_0)\big) = 0, \quad \lim_{k=\infty} \chi\big(f(z_k), f(z_0)\big) = 0, \tag{180.3}$$

and these contradict (180.2) ; this proves our statement above.

Let us assume, conversely, that the sequence $\{f_n(z)\}$ converges uniformly on a closed set S_1 and that the limit function $f(z)$ is continuous on S_1. We shall show that S_1 must then be a subset of the normal kernel S of the given sequence.

To prove this, let ε be any positive number and let z_0 be any point of accumulation of S_1. Since $f(z)$ is continuous at z_0, there is a neighborhood U_ε of z_0 which is such that the chordal oscillation of $f(z)$ on $U_\varepsilon S_1$ does not exceed $\varepsilon/3$. Also, since the convergence is uniform, there exists a number N_ε such that for $n \geq N_\varepsilon$,

$$\chi\big(f_n(z), f(z)\big) < \frac{\varepsilon}{3}.$$

Then if $n \geq N_{\varepsilon'}$, the chordal oscillation of $f_n(z)$ on $U_\varepsilon S_1$ does not exceed ε, and the same therefore applies to the limiting oscillation of the sequence $\{f_n(z)\}$ at the point z_0. Hence the given sequence is normal at z_0.

We have thus proved the following result:

Continuous convergence on a closed set is equivalent to uniform convergence to a continuous limit function on the closed set.

Remark. If the approximating functions $f_n(z)$ are continuous, then it is not necessary to prove continuity of the limit function, since the following well-known theorem holds: *A uniformly convergent sequence of continuous functions always converges to a continuous function.*

CHAPTER TWO

NORMAL FAMILIES OF MEROMORPHIC FUNCTIONS

The Limiting Oscillation for Sequences of Meromorphic Functions (§ 181)

181. Consider a sequence $\{f_n(z)\}$ of functions all of which are meromorphic (and hence continuous in the chordal metric) in a region G. Let z_0 be a point of G at which the limiting oscillation $\sigma(z_0)$ of the sequence is less than unity. If α denotes any positive number between $\sigma(z_0)$ and 1, then by § 176 above, there exists a neighborhood C_k of z_0 in which the number σ_k defined by (176.3) is $< \alpha$. Then the oscillation S_{nk} of the functions of the sequence on the point set $C_k G$ must be $\leq \alpha$ for all but a finite number, at most, of the functions of the sequence. Now we can find on the Riemann sphere a circular disc C_α lying in the interior of $C_k G$ and with center at z_0, and which is such that in this disc the oscillation of each of the above (finitely many and continuous) exceptional functions does not exceed α. Then all of the functions $f_n(z)$ are meromorphic in C_α, and each of these functions satisfies at every point of C_α the relation

$$\chi(f_n(z), f_n(z_0)) \leq \alpha. \tag{181.1}$$

If $f_n(z_0) \neq \infty$, we set

$$g_n(z) = \frac{f_n(z) - f_n(z_0)}{1 + \bar{f}_n(z_0) f_n(z)}, \tag{181.2}$$

and if $f_n(z_0) = \infty$, we set

$$g_n(z) = \frac{1}{f_n(z)}. \tag{181.3}$$

These functions $g_n(z)$ are meromorphic in the disc C_α and satisfy the following relation, which is based on (181.1) and on the invariance of chordal distance under rotations of the Riemann sphere (*cf.* § 86 above):

$$\frac{|g_n(z)|}{\sqrt{1 + |g_n(z)|^2}} = \chi(g_n(z), 0) = \chi(f_n(z), f_n(z_0)) \leq \alpha.$$

This implies

$$|g_n(z)| \leq \frac{\alpha}{\sqrt{1 - \alpha^2}} = M \quad (n = 1, 2, \ldots). \tag{181.4}$$

Thus we see that *all of the functions $g_n(z)$ are regular and uniformly bounded in the disc C_α. Moreover, they all vanish at the point z_0.*

Now let p be any natural number. Applying Schwarz's Lemma to the functions $g_n(z)/M$, we see that there exists on the Riemann sphere a circular disc C_p whose center is at z_0 and in which

$$|g_n(z)| < \frac{1}{p}$$

holds for all n. At all the points of C_p and for all n, we then have the relation

$$\chi\big(f_n(z), f_n(z_0)\big) = \frac{|g_n(z)|}{\sqrt{1 + |g_n(z)|^2}} \leq |g_n(z)| < \frac{1}{p}, \qquad (181.5)$$

so that the oscillation in C_p of any of the functions $f_n(z)$ is less than $2/p$. Hence we have

$$\sigma(z_0) \leq \sigma_p \leq \frac{2}{p}, \qquad (181.6)$$

and since p was arbitrary, it follows that the sequence $\{f_n(z)\}$ is normal at the point z_0.

The result we have just proved may be put briefly as follows:

In the interior of their common domain G of definition, the limiting oscillation of any sequence of meromorphic functions can assume only the values zero and unity.

For example, for the sequence of functions (174.1) the limiting oscillation is zero for all points of the plane for which $|z| \neq 1$, and it equals unity on the unit circle $|z| = 1$.

Some of the points in the above proof are of sufficient importance in applications to warrant a more detailed statement of the theorem, as follows:

A sequence $\{f_n(z)\}$ of functions meromorphic in a region G is normal at an interior point z_0 of G if and only if there exists at least one neighborhood U of z_0 and at least one positive number $a < 1$ such that for all points z of U, and for all functions $f_n(z)$ of the sequence,

$$\chi\big(f_n(z), f_n(z_0)\big) < \alpha \qquad (181.7)$$

holds. In this case, we can assign to any $\varepsilon > 0$ a neighborhood U_ε of z_0 such that for all points z of U_ε, we have

$$\chi\big(f_n(z), f_n(z_0)\big) < \varepsilon \qquad (n = 1, 2, \ldots). \qquad (181.8)$$

The set of those points of G at which the sequence $\{f_n(z)\}$ is normal is then an open subset of G, unless it is empty.

The last statement of the theorem is obvious, for if the sequence is normal at z_0 it must be normal at every point of U_ε if $\varepsilon < 1/2$.

By the preceding chapter, the concept of limiting oscillation is defined also at the points of the frontier of G. But the theorems of the present section do not hold at these points. However, it is only in special investigations that the frontier of G need be considered. In what follows, we shall therefore confine our attention to the interior points of G (cf., however, § 215 below).

Normal Families of Meromorphic Functions (§§ 182-183)

182. We now turn to arbitrary sets $\{f(z)\}$, not necessarily denumerable, of meromorphic functions all defined in a given region G. We speak in this case not of a sequence but rather of a *family* of functions, and we adopt the following definitions:

A point z_0 of (the interior of) G is said to be a *normal point* of the family $\{f(z)\}$ if there is at least one positive number $\alpha < 1$ and at least one neighborhood U of z_0 such that at all points z of U and for all functions of the given family, the relation

$$\chi\big(f(z), f(z_0)\big) < \alpha \qquad\qquad (z \in U)$$

holds.

The set S of all the normal points of a family of functions will be called, as before in § 179, the *normal kernel* of the family. S is of course a subset of G.

If every point of G is normal, that is if $S = G$, then we shall say that *the family is normal in G.*

With these definitions, the results of the preceding section can be carried over, along with the same proofs as before, to the case of arbitrary families of meromorphic functions. In particular, the normal kernel S is always an open point set.

183. Every sequence $f_1(z), f_2(z), \ldots$ of functions all of which belong to one and the same given family $\{f(z)\}$ of meromorphic functions is obviously normal at every point z_0 at which the family itself is normal. By § 179 above, we can select from the sequence of functions $f_n(z)$ a subsequence $f_{n_1}(z), f_{n_2}(z), \ldots$ that converges continuously at all the points of the normal kernel S of the family $\{f(z)\}$.

On the other hand, if z_0 is not a normal point of the given family, then we can associate with each natural number n a function $f_n(z)$ of $\{f(z)\}$ whose chordal oscillation in the neighborhood

$$\chi(z, z_0) < \frac{1}{n}$$

of z_0 is not less than $[1 - (1/n)]$. Since any subsequence

$$f_{k_1}(z), f_{k_2}(z), \ldots, f_{k_n}(z), \ldots$$

of a sequence as just constructed will have the same property, it follows that none of the subsequences of $f_1(z), f_2(z), \ldots$ can converge continuously at the point z_0.

This yields the following theorem:

A family $\{f(z)\}$ of meromorphic functions is normal in a region G if and only if from every sequence $f_1(z), f_2(z), \ldots$ of functions of the family, at least one subsequence $f_{k_1}(z), f_{k_2}(z), \ldots$ can be selected that converges continuously at every point of G.

The property stated in this theorem was used by P. Montel, who invented and developed the concept of normal families, as the definition of these families.

Starting from Montel's definition, A. Ostrowski introduced the concept of limiting oscillation and established its connection with the properties of normal families.

Compact Normal Families (§ 184)

184. A family of functions is said to be *compact* (*cf.* also § 91 above) if it contains all of its limit functions, i.e., if it contains every function g that is representable as the limit of a sequence of functions of the family.

Any given normal family $\{f\}$ of functions meromorphic in a region G can be extended to a compact normal family by adding to $\{f\}$ all of its limit functions.

Let us denote the family with these additions made, by $\{g\}$. If we admit subsequences of the family $\{f\}$ that contain one and the same function f an infinite number of times, we may regard every function g of $\{g\}$ as the limit of a sequence of functions of $\{f\}$ that converges continuously in the region G. We shall show a little later on (*cf.* § 190 below) that all of these functions g are meromorphic in G. We must now prove that the family $\{g\}$ is normal and compact.

To this end, we consider a monotonically increasing sequence

$$H_1 \subseteq H_2 \subseteq H_3 \subseteq \cdots \tag{184.1}$$

of closed subsets of G whose union is G, and an arbitrary sequence $g_1, g_2, g_3, \ldots$ of functions of $\{g\}$. By the construction of $\{g\}$, every one of these functions g_ν is the limit of a sequence of functions $f_{\nu j}$ of $\{f\}$. By § 180 above, this sequence converges uniformly on the set H_ν, so that we can find a subscript j_ν for which

$$\chi(f_{\nu j_\nu}, g_\nu) < \frac{1}{\nu} \qquad\qquad (z \in H_\nu) \quad (184.2)$$

holds. Since the family $\{f\}$ is normal, there must exist a subsequence $f_{n_k j_{n_k}} (k = 1, 2, \ldots)$ of the sequence $f_{\nu j_\nu}$ that converges continuously to a function g_0 at every point of G. By (184.2), the subsequence $g_{n_k} (k = 1, \ldots)$ of the sequence of g_ν must also converge continuously to g_0. Hence by Montel's theorem (see § 183 above), the family $\{g\}$ is normal. But this family is also compact, since any given limit g_0 of functions of $\{g\}$ can also be represented as the limit of a sequence of functions of $\{f\}$. Thus we have proved the result stated above.

Families of Analytic Functions Uniformly Bounded in the Small (§§ 185-186)

185. We introduce the following definition:

Given a region G not containing the point $z = \infty$, and a family $\{f\}$ of analytic functions regular in G, we shall say that $\{f\}$ is uniformly bounded in the small if we can assign to every point z_0 of G two positive numbers $r(z_0)$ and $M(z_0)$ which are such that the closed disc $|z - z_0| \leqq r$ lies in G and that $|f(z)| \leqq M$ holds in this disc for all f in $\{f\}$.

A family of this sort must clearly be normal; for if we set

$$g(z) = f(z) - f(z_0),$$

then for $0 < \vartheta < 1$ Schwarz's Lemma implies the validity, within the circular disc

$$|z - z_0| < r(z_0)\,\vartheta \qquad\qquad (185.1)$$

of the relation

$$|g(z)| < 2\,\vartheta\, M. \qquad\qquad (185.2)$$

Then if z' and z'' are any two points of the disc (185.1), we have

$$\chi\big(f(z'), f(z'')\big) < |f(z') - f(z'')| = |g(z') - g(z'')| < 4\,\vartheta\, M.$$

Hence within the disc

$$|z - z_0| < \frac{r(z_0)}{8\,M}\ ,$$

the chordal oscillation of each function of the family is less than $1/2$, so that the family is normal.

186. We shall now prove the following theorem:

If $\{f\}$ is a family of analytic functions uniformly bounded in the small in a region G, then the family $\{f'\}$ of the first derivatives of the functions $f(z)$ shares the same property, and is therefore also normal in G.

For if z_1 is any point of the closed disc

$$|z - z_0| \leq \frac{r(z_0)}{2}, \qquad (186.1)$$

then the function $\varphi(z)$ defined by

$$\left. \begin{array}{l} \varphi(z) = \dfrac{f(z) - f(z_1)}{z - z_1} \quad \text{for} \quad z \neq z_1, \\[2mm] \varphi(z_1) = f'(z_1) \end{array} \right\} \qquad (186.2)$$

is regular in the closed disc

$$|z - z_1| \leq \frac{r(z_0)}{2}$$

(*cf.* § 134 above), and by (186.2), this function satisfies at every boundary point ζ of the latter disc the relation

$$|\varphi(\zeta)| \leq \frac{|f(\zeta)| + |f(z_1)|}{|\zeta - z_1|} \leq \frac{4M}{r(z_0)}.$$

Hence by the Maximum-Modulus Principle, we have

$$|f'(z_1)| \leq \sup |\varphi(\zeta)| \leq \frac{4M}{r(z_0)},$$

which proves the theorem (see also Vol. II, § 290).

The Limit Functions of Normal Families of Meromorphic Functions (§§ 187-190)

187. We first consider a convergent sequence of functions $f_n(z)$ uniformly bounded in the small in G, where G is a region not containing the point $z = \infty$. Since the sequence $\{f_n(z)\}$ is normal in G, the limit function

$$f(z) = \lim_{n = \infty} f_n(z) \qquad (187.1)$$

must be continuous in G (*cf.* § 178 above).

Let z_0 be a point of G. The equations

$$g_n(z) =: \frac{f_n(z) - f_n(z_0)}{z - z_0} \quad \text{for} \quad z \neq z_0,$$

$$g_n(z_0) = f'_n(z_0) \tag{187.2}$$

define a sequence of functions $g_n(z)$ that are analytic and regular in G (cf. § 134 above). By our assumption concerning the $f_n(z)$, there is a closed disc $|z - z_0| \leq r$ in G on which $|f_n(z)| \leq M$ holds for all n. On the boundary of this disc, we must then have

$$|g_n(z)| \leq \frac{2M}{r}, \tag{187.3}$$

and by the Maximum-Modulus Principle, these relations also hold in the interior of $|z - z_0| \leq r$, whence it follows that the sequence of the $g_n(z)$ is uniformly bounded in the small, and therefore normal, in the disc $|z - z_0| < r$.

By (187.1) and (187.2), the sequence of the $g_n(z)$ converges for every $z \neq z_0$ to a function

$$g(z) = \lim_{n=\infty} \frac{f_n(z) - f_n(z_0)}{z - z_0} =: \frac{f(z) - f(z_0)}{z - z_0}. \tag{187.4}$$

By § 177 above, the $g_n(z)$ must then converge at the point z_0 also, and we have

$$g(z_0) = \lim_{n=\infty} g_n(z_0) = \lim_{n=\infty} f'_n(z_0). \tag{187.5}$$

By § 178 above, the limit $g(z)$ of the normal sequence of the $g_n(z)$ must also be continuous at the point z_0. Hence by (187.4), the function $f(z)$ is differentiable at z_0 (cf. § 124 above). This implies the following theorem:

If a sequence of analytic functions converges in a region G and is uniformly bounded in the small in G, then the limit of the sequence is a regular analytic function in G.

The importance of this theorem lies in the converse fact, which we shall prove later on in this book, that any given analytic function can be represented as the limit of a continuously convergent sequence of functions of some well-known type (such as polynomials or rational functions).

188. Relation (187.4), combined with the fact that the function $g(z)$ is continuous at the point z_0, yields the equation

$$g(z_0) = f'(z_0), \tag{188.1}$$

and this in turn, together with (187.5), yields the following theorem:

Let

$$f(z) = \lim_{n=\infty} f_n(z) \tag{188.2}$$

be the limit of a sequence of analytic functions $f_n(z)$ that are uniformly bounded in the small in the region G. Then for the derivatives of these functions, we have

$$f'(z) = \lim_{n=\infty} f'_n(z). \tag{188.3}$$

Furthermore, § 186 above shows that the sequence of the derivatives $f_n'(z)$ is likewise uniformly bounded in the small. We can therefore apply the result of the last theorem to the sequences, one by one, of the successive derivatives $f'_n(z)$, $f''_n(z)$, $\ldots$, and thus verify that the relations

$$\frac{d^p f(z)}{dz^p} = \lim_{n=\infty} \frac{d^p f_n(z)}{dz^p} \qquad (p = 2, 3, \ldots) \tag{188.4}$$

hold.

189. We now turn to the study of the limit functions of arbitrary normal families of meromorphic functions, and we begin with the following simple observation. The chordal distance between the two circles

$$|w| = 1, \quad |w| = 2$$

equals $\chi(1, 2) = 1/\sqrt{10}$, as does also the chordal distance between the two circles $|w| = 1$ and $|w| = 1/2$. Therefore if w', w'' are two points that satisfy either the two relations $|w'| \leq 1$ and $|w''| \geq 2$ or the two relations $|w'| \geq 1$ and $|w''| \leq 1/2$, we must have $\chi(w', w'') \geq 1/\sqrt{10}$.

Now if $\{f(z)\}$ is a family of meromorphic functions that is normal in a region G, then by § 183 above we can assign to every point z_0 of G a neighborhood $U(z_0)$ which is such that for every point z of $U(z_0)$ and for every function $f(z)$ of the given family,

$$\chi(f(z), f(z_0)) < \frac{1}{\sqrt{10}} \tag{189.1}$$

holds. Hence if $|f(z_0)| \leq 1$, then at every point z of $U(z_0)$ we must have $|f(z)| < 2$, while if $|f(z_0)| > 1$, we must have $|f(z)| > 1/2$ in $U(z_0)$. We are thus led to the following result:

If a family of meromorphic functions is normal in a region G, then we can assign to every (interior) point z_0 of G a neighborhood $U(z_0)$ throughout which every function $f(z)$ of the given family satisfies at least one of the relations

$$|f(z)| < 2 \quad \text{or} \quad \frac{1}{|f(z)|} < 2. \tag{189.2}$$

The converse also holds:

If we can assign to every point z_0 of a region G a neighborhood $U(z_0)$ throughout which every function $f(z)$ of a family $\{f(z)\}$ of meromorphic functions satisfies at least one of the inequalities (189.2), *then the family $\{f(z)\}$ must be normal in G.*

For we may consider the family $\{f(z)\}$ as the union of two families $\{g(z)\}$ and $\{h(z)\}$ which are such that all of the $g(z)$ and all of the $1/h(z)$ are uniformly bounded in $U(z_0)$. The families $\{g(z)\}$ and $\{h(z)\}$ are normal at z_0, and by Montel's theorem (*cf.* § 183 above), their union $\{f(z)\}$ must therefore likewise be normal at z_0 and hence in G.

190. Let $f_0(z)$ be the limit of a convergent sequence of meromorphic functions all of which belong to one and the same normal family. We know from the preceding section that for any given point z_0 of the domain of definition of $f_0(z)$, there exist neighborhoods in which either $f_0(z)$ itself or $1/f_0(z)$ can be represented as the limit of a convergent sequence of uniformly bounded analytic functions. By means of the theorem of § 187 above, we infer from this that $f_0(z)$ must be meromorphic in G.

Hence *functions that are limits of functions of a normal family of meromorphic functions are themselves meromorphic functions.*

If a subsequence of a normal family of meromorphic functions converges in G and if $f_0(z) \not\equiv \infty$ for its limit $f_0(z)$, then the subsequence is uniformly bounded in the small in the subregion of G in which $f_0(z)$ is finite.

However, the result of § 188, to the effect that the derivatives $f'(z)$ of the functions of a uniformly bounded sequence themselves constitute a normal sequence, does not carry over to the present case.

For example, the functions

$$f_n(z) = \frac{n^2}{1 - n^2 z^2} = \frac{1}{\frac{1}{n^2} - z^2} \qquad (n = 1, 2, \ldots)$$

converge in the whole plane continuously to

$$f_0(z) = -\frac{1}{z^2} \quad \text{and} \quad f_0(0) = \infty.$$

The sequence of derivatives

$$f_n'(z) = \frac{2 n^4 z}{(1 - n^2 z^2)^2} = \frac{2 z}{\left(\dfrac{1}{n^2} - z^2\right)^2}$$

is not continuously convergent at $z = 0$, and is therefore not normal at $z = 0$.

Vitali's Theorem (§ 191)

191. Consider a normal sequence $\{f_n(z)\}$ that fails to converge at a point z_0. There must be at least two subsequences $\{f_{n_j}(z)\}$ and $\{f_{m_j}(z)\}$ of $\{f_n(z)\}$ that converge at z_0 and for which we have

$$\lim_{j=\infty} f_{n_j}(z_0) = \alpha, \quad \lim_{j=\infty} f_{m_j}(z_0) = \beta, \quad \beta \neq \alpha. \tag{191.1}$$

By § 179, we can find in these subsequences two subsequences $\{f_{n_j'}(z)\}$ and $\{f_{m_j'}(z)\}$, respectively, that converge in the entire domain G of definition of the functions $f_n(z)$, and we denote the limits of these last two subsequences by $f(z)$ and $g(z)$, respectively. Since $f(z_0) = \alpha$, $g(z_0) = \beta$, $\alpha \neq \beta$, the functions $f(z)$ and $g(z)$ are not identically equal in G, and we have thus derived the following general result:

For a normal sequence $\{f_n(z)\}$ to converge at every point of the common domain of definition G of the $f_n(z)$, it is necessary and sufficient that all those subsequences of $\{f_n(z)\}$ that converge everywhere in G should have the same limit in G.

If $f(z)$ and $g(z)$ are two distinct meromorphic functions neither of which is the constant ∞, then $h(z) = f(z) - g(z)$ is not identically zero. The only points z_0 at which $f(z_0) = g(z_0)$ can hold are the zeros of $h(z)$ and the common poles of $f(z)$ and $g(z)$ (some of which may be among the zeros of $h(z)$). Thus the set of points where $f(z) = g(z)$ is possible cannot have any interior point of G as a point of accumulation. The same conclusion may be drawn if, say $f(z) \equiv \infty$. From this follows a theorem that G. Vitali (1875-1932) discovered as early as 1903:

If a sequence of meromorphic functions normal in a region G converges at a denumerable set of points $z_1, z_2, \ldots$ having at least one point z_0 of accumulation in (the interior of) G, then the sequence converges everywhere in G.

Uniform Convergence (§ 192)

192. As we saw in § 180 above, uniform convergence on a closed set of points is equivalent to continuous convergence *provided that the limit function $f(z)$ is continuous*. If the approximating functions $f_n(z)$ are meromorphic, the condition in italics may be omitted. In fact, we shall show more generally that the sequence of $f_n(z)$ is normal provided only that the $f_n(z)$ are known to approximate an arbitrary function $f(z)$ with a certain specified degree of approximation. To this end, let us assume of the sequence of meromorphic functions $f_n(z)$ that at all the points of a region G, and for all $n \geq N$,

$$\chi\big(f_n(z), f_N(z)\big) \leqq a < \frac{1}{2} \tag{192.1}$$

holds true. Let z_0 be an interior point of G and let $U(z_0)$ be a neighborhood of z_0 in which the chordal oscillation of $f_N(z)$ does not exceed $1/2 - a$. Then the chordal oscillation in $U(z_0)$ of the various functions $f_n(z)$, for $n \geqq N$, does not exceed

$$2a + \left(\frac{1}{2} - a\right) = a + \frac{1}{2} < 1.$$

Hence by § 182 above, the limiting oscillation at z_0 of the given sequence equals zero, and the sequence is normal.

Now we note that relations (192.1) follow if for any arbitrary function $f(z)$,

$$\chi\big(f_n(z), f(z)\big) \leqq \frac{a}{2} \quad \text{for} \quad z \in G, \ n \geqq N \tag{192.2}$$

holds true; this proves our statement above.

In particular, relations (192.2) are always satisfied for a sequence of meromorphic functions that converges uniformly in G, so that we have the following theorem:

If a sequence of meromorphic functions $f_n(z)$ converges uniformly to the limit $f(z)$ in a region G, the sequence must be normal in G. The limit function $f(z)$ must therefore also be meromorphic in G.

It is sometimes useful to have this theorem available in the following form:

If a complex function $f(z)$ can be approximated uniformly to any desired degree of approximation by means of meromorphic functions, then $f(z)$ is itself meromorphic in G.

Osgood's Theorem (§§ 193-194)

193. From the mere assumption of convergence at *all* of the points of a region G, we can draw certain conclusions regarding a given sequence of functions $f_n(z)$ meromorphic in G. We set

$$\psi_k(z) = \sup \chi\big(f_{k+p}(z), f_k(z)\big) \quad \text{for} \quad p = 1, 2, \ldots \tag{193.1}$$

and observe that

$$\lim_{k=\infty} \psi_k(z) = 0 \tag{193.2}$$

holds by assumption. We denote by U_k the (possibly empty) subset of G in which $\psi_k(z) > 1/6$ holds. If z_0 is any point of U_k, there is at least one value of p for which $\chi\big(f_{k+p}(z_0), f_k(z_0)\big) > 1/6$. The inequality

$$\chi\left(f_{k+p}(z), f_k(z)\right) > 1/6$$

then remains valid in some neighborhood of z_0, which implies that the point set U_k is an open subset of G.

From equation (193.2), it follows moreover that the intersection

$$D = U_1 U_2 U_3 \dots$$

of all the sets U_k must be empty, so that, as we shall show presently, there must be in the sequence of the U_k a first set, say U_{k_0}, that is not everywhere dense in G. Then there exists at least one point ζ of G that is not a point of accumulation of U_{k_0}.

To prove the statements just made, suppose to the contrary that all of the U_k were dense in G. Let κ_0 be any closed circular disc in G. Since U_1 is supposed to be dense in G, there is at least one point of ζ_1 of U_1 that lies in the interior of κ_0, and since U_1 is open, there must also exist a closed disc κ_1 that is contained in both κ_0 and U_1. Similarly, within κ_1 there is contained a closed disc κ_2 that is interior to U_2. Continuing in this way, we obtain a nested infinite sequence of closed discs $\kappa_0, \kappa_1, \kappa_2, \dots$, each containing the next, whose intersection contains at least one point ω (*cf.* § 94 above). But this point ω would then lie also in the intersection D of all the sets U_k, and D could not be empty.

Now consider a neighborhood V of ζ that contains no point of U_{k_0}, and let V also be sufficiently small for the chordal oscillation of $f_n(z)$ in V, for $n = 1, 2, \dots, k_0$, to be less than $1/6$. Keeping in mind (193.1) and the fact that $\psi_{k_0}(z) \leq 1/6$ holds in V, we can then show, just as in the preceding section, that the oscillation in V of each of the functions $f_n(z)$ does not exceed $3 \cdot 1/6 = 1/2$. Hence the given sequence of $f_n(z)$ is normal in V.

Given any subregion G_1 of G, we can apply the result just obtained to G_1, finding that G_1 must itself contain a subregion V_1 in which the sequence of $f_n(z)$ is normal. Thus we have proved the following theorem:

If a sequence of meromorphic functions converges at all of the points of a region G, then there exists an open subset S of G which is dense in G and in which the convergence of the sequence is continuous.

As is well known, S (like any other open set) is the union of a finite or denumerable number of subregions $S_1, S_2, \dots$ of G. In each of these subregions S_i, the limit function $f(z)$ is meromorphic and hence continuous (*cf.* § 187 above). However, at the points of G that do not belong to S, $f(z)$ need not be continuous. On the other hand, it may also happen that the limit function $f(z)$ is analytic throughout the entire region G while the normal kernel S of G is not identical with G (*cf.* the example in § 190 above).

The theorem of this section was first proved by W. F. Osgood for sequences of regular analytic functions. In this case, the subregions S_i must be simply connected.

194. There are sequences of meromorphic functions $f_n(z)$ no subsequence of which is normal at any point of the common domain G of definition of the $f_n(z)$. For such sequences, it follows from Osgood's theorem that the set of points at which any given subsequence $f_{n_1}(z), f_{n_2}(z), \ldots$ converges cannot have any interior points belonging to G.

Examples of sequences of this kind can be constructed in terms of the functions $\sigma(z; g_2, g_3)$ and $\wp(z; g_2, g_3)$ that occur in the Weierstrass theory of elliptic functions. In fact, the sequences

$$f_n(z) = \sigma(n\,z; g_2, g_3), \quad g_n(z) = \wp(n\,z; g_2, g_3)$$

will serve as examples.

Normal Families of Moebius Transformations (§§ 195-197)

195. Consider the totality of all those Moebius transformations

$$w = \frac{\alpha\,z + \beta}{\gamma\,z + \delta} = \frac{\alpha + \beta\,\dfrac{1}{z}}{\gamma + \delta\,\dfrac{1}{z}} \tag{195.1}$$

whose coefficients $\alpha, \beta, \gamma, \delta$ satisfy the conditions

$$\alpha\,\delta - \beta\,\gamma = 1; \quad |\alpha|, |\beta|, |\gamma|, |\delta| < M. \tag{195.2}$$

Here, M stands for any positive number. We shall show that this totality constitutes a normal family in the whole extended plane.

By § 183 above, it suffices to show that the conditions

$$\lim_{n=\infty} \alpha_n = \alpha_0, \ \lim_{n=\infty} \beta_n = \beta_0, \ \lim_{n=\infty} \gamma_n = \gamma_0, \ \lim_{n=\infty} \delta_n = \delta_0, \ \lim_{n=\infty} z_n = z_0 \tag{195.3}$$

imply that

$$\lim_{n=\infty} \frac{\alpha_n\,z_n + \beta_n}{\gamma_n\,z_n + \delta_n} = \frac{\alpha_0\,z_0 + \beta_0}{\gamma_0\,z_0 + \delta_0} \tag{195.4}$$

holds. This last equation allows of immediate verification if $z_0 \neq \infty$ and $\gamma_0\,z_0 + \delta_0 \neq 0$. If $z_0 \neq \infty$ and $\gamma_0\,z_0 + \delta_0 = 0$, then $\alpha_0\,z_0 + \beta_0 \neq 0$ must hold, and (195.4) may be replaced by the equivalent equation

$$\lim_{n=\infty} \frac{\gamma_n z_n + \delta_n}{\alpha_n z_n + \beta_n} = \frac{\gamma_0 z_0 + \delta_0}{\alpha_0 z_0 + \beta_0} = 0. \tag{195.5}$$

If, finally, $z_0 = \infty$, then we can proceed in a similar way by using the second of the two representations of the Moebius transformations in (195.1).

196. The normal families of Moebius transformations just considered have a geometric property that can be used in turn to characterize these families. Given a Moebius transformation (195.1), let us denote by

$$w_0 = \frac{\beta}{\delta}, \quad w_1 = \frac{\alpha + \beta}{\gamma + \delta}, \quad w_\infty = \frac{\alpha}{\gamma} \tag{196.1}$$

the images of the points $z = 0, 1, \infty$, and let us calculate the product of the three chordal distances of the points (196.1) from each other. This yields

$$\begin{aligned} &\chi(w_0, w_1) \cdot \chi(w_1, w_\infty) \cdot \chi(w_\infty, w_0) \\ &= \frac{|\alpha \delta - \beta \gamma|^3}{(|\alpha|^2 + |\gamma|^2)(|\beta|^2 + |\delta|^2)(|\alpha + \beta|^2 + |\gamma + \delta|^2)}. \end{aligned} \right\} \tag{196.2}$$

Now if the coefficients $\alpha, \beta, \gamma, \delta$ satisfy conditions (195.2), then the left-hand side of (196.2) must be greater than some positive number $1/N^2$. Conversely, if this latter condition is satisfied, then we must first of all have $\alpha \delta - \beta \gamma \neq 0$, and we may write (see (196.2))

$$\alpha \delta - \beta \gamma = 1, \tag{196.3}$$

$$(|\alpha|^2 + |\gamma|^2)(|\beta|^2 + |\delta|^2)(|\alpha + \beta|^2 + |\gamma + \delta|^2) < N^2. \tag{196.4}$$

But (196.3) implies

$$\alpha = \alpha \delta (\alpha + \beta) - \alpha \beta (\gamma + \delta), \tag{196.5}$$

so that (196.4) yields

$$|\alpha| \cdot |\delta| \cdot |\alpha + \beta| < N, \quad |\alpha| \cdot |\beta| \cdot |\gamma + \delta| < N. \tag{196.6}$$

Comparison of (196.5) and (196.6) gives $|a| < 2N$, and we find similarly that $|\beta|, |\gamma|$ and $|\delta|$ also have the bound $2N$. From this it follows that the Moebius transformations that satisfy the condition

$$\chi(w_0, w_1) \cdot \chi(w_1, w_\infty) \cdot \chi(w_\infty, w_0) > \frac{1}{N^2} \tag{196.7}$$

likewise constitute a normal family.[1]

---

[1] To insure that this family is not empty, we have to stipulate that $N^2 \geq 8/\sqrt{27}$, that is, that $N > 1.2408$. To see this, one must use the fact that of all the triangles inscribed in a circle, the equilateral triangle is the one for which the product of the three sides is a maximum.

197. If we use the criterion of § 183 above, we can derive from the results of the last two sections the following important theorem:

Let there be assigned to each function $f(z)$ of a family $\{f\}$ of functions meromorphic in G, four numbers $\alpha, \beta, \gamma, \delta$ that satisfy conditions (195.2) (with a fixed value of M). Consider the family $\{g\}$ of the functions

$$g(z) = \frac{\alpha f(z) + \beta}{\gamma f(z) + \delta}.$$ (197. 1)

Then each one of the two families $\{f\}$ and $\{g\}$ is normal if and only if the other family is also normal.

The Theorem of A. Hurwitz (§ 198)

198. We now turn to the derivation of some theorems that one obtains by specializing the functions of a normal sequence. The first of these theorems is due to A. Hurwitz (1859-1919), and can be stated as follows:

Let the functions of the sequence $f_1(z), f_2(z), \ldots$ be meromorphic in a region G, let the sequence be continuously convergent in G, and assume that every $f_n(z)$ is $\neq 0$ everywhere in G. Then the limit $f(z)$ of the sequence either is the constant zero or else has not a single zero in G.

An example of a case in which the limit $f(z) = \lim f_n(z)$ vanishes identically is furnished by $f_n(z) \equiv 1/n$ $(n = 1, 2, \ldots)$.

To prove the theorem, assume that for the meromorphic limit function $f(z)$ we have $f(z) \not\equiv 0$, and let z_0 be any (interior) point of G. Let $U(z_0)$ be the neighborhood of z_0 the existence of which was proved in § 189 above. If the given sequence contains infinitely many functions $f_{n_j}(z)$ for which the inequalities $|f_{n_j}(z)| > 1/2$ hold uniformly in $U(z_0)$, then we must also have $|f(z_0)| \geqq 1/2$ and hence $f(z_0) \neq 0$. But if there are only a finite number of such functions, then by § 189 above, after suppressing at most a finite number of functions we know that all of the remaining $f_n(z)$ are uniformly bounded and are therefore regular analytic functions. Furthermore, since $f(z)$ does not vanish identically, there is in $U(z_0)$ a circle

$$\chi(z, z_0) = r$$ (198. 1)

on which $f(z)$ is different from zero, and therefore there is a positive number ε such that at every point ζ of the circle (198.1),

$$|f(\zeta)| \geqq 2\varepsilon$$ (198. 2)

holds. Now since the functions $f_n(z)$ converge uniformly on the circle (198.1), we must have for sufficiently large values of n that

$$|f_n(\zeta)| \geqq \varepsilon.$$ (198. 3)

The functions $f_n(z)$, being regular and $\neq 0$ in the interior of the disc $\chi(z, z_0) < r$, satisfy $|f_n(z_0)| \geqq \varepsilon$ for the same values of n for which (198.3) holds (*cf.* § 138). This implies that $|f(z_0)| \geqq \varepsilon$ and hence that $f(z_0) \neq 0$, which proves the theorem.

Now let a be any finite complex number. By applying Hurwitz' theorem to the sequence of functions

$$g_n(z) = f_n(z) - a,$$

we obtain the following theorem:

Let $\{f(z)\}$ be a family of meromorphic functions that is normal in a region G and none of the functions of which assumes in G the value a, where a is a given finite complex number. Then none of the limits of convergent sequences of functions of the family can assume in G the value a, unless it is a constant (viz., a) in G.

If $f(z)$ is a regular analytic function in G, then $1/f(z)$ is a meromorphic function that omits the value 0 in G. Hence Hurwitz' theorem yields the following result:

The limit of any convergent subsequence of a normal family of regular analytic functions is either a regular analytic function or the constant ∞.

A Criterion for Normal Families Bounded in the Small (§ 199)

199. We shall prove the following further result: *If the functions $f(z)$ of a normal family of functions regular in a region G are bounded at a point z_0 of G, then they are uniformly bounded on any closed subset H of G.*

To prove this theorem, let M_H be the least upper bound of the moduli $|f(z)|$ of the functions of the family on H, and let

$$p_1 < p_2 < p_3 < \cdots$$

be a monotonic sequence of numbers that converges to M_H. For each p_n we can find a function $f_n(z)$ of the family that satisfies $|f_n(z_n)| > p_n$ for at least one point z_n of H. From the sequence of the $f_n(z)$ we select a subsequence $\{f_{n_j}(z)\}$ that converges continuously in G, and we denote the limit of this subsequence by $g(z)$. Since all of the numbers $|f_n(z_0)|$ are, by assumption, less than a fixed bound, it follows from the preceding section that $g(z)$ is regular in G, so that on the closed set H, $|g(z)|$ has a finite least upper bound M. On the other hand, the functions $f_{n_j}(z)$ converge uniformly to $g(z)$ on H (*cf.* § 180 above), which implies that for all sufficiently large values of j and at every point z of H we have

$$|f_{n_j}(z)| < M + 1.$$

Hence $p_{nj} < M + 1$ and therefore also $M_H < M + 1$. Thus M_H is finite, which proves the theorem.

Remark. The theorem just proved is closely related to *Harnack's theorem*, proved in § 157 above. For by relation (148.11) above, in any given circular disc we can find analytic functions

$$f(z) = u(x, y) + i\, v(x, y)$$

whose real part $u(x, y)$ is a pre-assigned harmonic function. If $u(x, y) > 0$ holds everywhere in the disc, then the function

$$g(z) = \frac{f(z) - 1}{f(z) + 1}$$

satisfies $|g(z)| < 1$. From this it follows that the family of functions $f(z)$ whose real part is positive in a region G is normal in G. But then the same must be true of the family of harmonic functions $u(x, y)$, since the limiting oscillation of a sequence $\{u_\nu(x, y)\}$ cannot exceed that of the corresponding sequence $\{f_\nu(z)\}$. Moreover, by the theorem of § 156 above, all of the limit functions of the family $\{u(x, y)\}$ are themselves harmonic. Hence the proof given earlier in this section carries over practically word for word, and a similar proof also works for the minimum of the functions of $\{u(x, y)\}$.

Simple[1] Functions (§ 200)

200. A meromorphic function is said to be *simple*[1] in a region if for any two distinct points z' and z'' of the region we always have $f(z') \neq f(z'')$. Consider a normal family $\{f\}$ of meromorphic functions that are simple in a region G, and let z_0 be any point of G.

To each function $f(z)$ of $\{f\}$ we assign a function $g(z)$ defined as follows:

$$
\left.
\begin{aligned}
g(z) &= f(z) - f(z_0), && \text{if} \quad |f(z_0)| \le 1, \\[2mm]
g(z) &= \frac{\dfrac{1}{f(z_0)}\, f(z) - 1}{\left(1 - \dfrac{1}{f(z_0)}\right) f(z) + 1}, && \text{if} \quad 1 < |f(z_0)| < \infty, \\[2mm]
g(z) &= -\frac{1}{f(z)}, && \text{if} \quad f(z_0) = \infty.
\end{aligned}
\right\} \quad (200.1)
$$

_____

[1] Or *schlicht.*

By § 197 above, the family $\{g(z)\}$ of these "transforms" of the $f(z)$ is itself normal in G. Also, each of the functions $g(z)$ is simple in G, and all of the $g(z)$ satisfy $g(z_0) = 0$. Hence in the punctured region G_0 obtained from G by removing the point z_0, all of the $g(z)$ satisfy $g(z) \neq 0$.

Now consider a sequence of functions $f_1(z), f_2(z), \ldots$ of functions of $\{f\}$ that converges in G to a function $f_0(z)$, and let

$$g_n(z) = \frac{\alpha_n f_n(z) + \beta_n}{\gamma_n f_n(z) + \delta_n} \qquad (n = 1, 2, \ldots) \qquad (200.2)$$

be the transforms of the $f_n(z)$ as defined in (200.1). Select from the sequence of $f_n(z)$ a subsequence $\{f_{n_j}(z)\}$ which is such that the four limits

$$\lim_{j=\infty} \alpha_{n_j} = \alpha_0, \quad \ldots, \quad \lim_{j=\infty} \delta_{n_j} = \delta_0$$

exist. Then the corresponding transforms $g_{n_j}(z)$ converge continuously in G to a function

$$g_0(z) = \frac{\alpha_0 f_0(z) + \beta_0}{\gamma_0 f_0(z) + \delta_0}.$$

By Hurwitz' theorem, we must have $g_0(z) \neq 0$ everywhere in G_0, unless $g_0(z) \equiv 0$. Hence unless $f_0(z)$ is constant in G, we must have $f_0(z) \neq f_0(z_0)$ for all z in G_0, and we have thus proved the following theorem:

The limit of a convergent sequence of simple meromorphic functions belonging to a given normal family must itself be a simple function, unless it is a constant.

CHAPTER THREE

POWER SERIES

Absolutely Convergent Series (§§ 201-204)

201. An infinite series

$$g = g_1 + g_2 + g_3 + \cdots \tag{201.1}$$

of complex numbers is said to be *absolutely convergent* if the moduli $|g_\nu|$ of its individual terms are dominated (majorized) by positive numbers ϱ_ν whose sum is finite; that is, the following two conditions must both be satisfied:

$$\left.\begin{array}{l} |g_\nu| \leqq \varrho_\nu \quad (\nu = 1, 2, \ldots), \\[2mm] \varrho_1 + \varrho_2 + \varrho_3 + \cdots = \varepsilon_0 < +\infty. \end{array}\right\} \tag{201.2}$$

If we set

$$\sum_{\nu=n+1}^{\infty} \varrho_\nu = \varepsilon_n \qquad (n = 0, 1, \ldots), \tag{201.3}$$

we must have

$$\varepsilon_0 \geqq \varepsilon_1 \geqq \varepsilon_2 \geqq \cdots, \quad \lim_{n=\infty} \varepsilon_n = 0. \tag{201.4}$$

Setting

$$s_n = g_1 + g_2 + \cdots + g_n, \quad \lim_{n=\infty} s_n = g,$$

we have

$$|s_n| \leqq \varepsilon_0, \ |s_{n+p} - s_n| \leqq |g_{n+1}| + \cdots + |g_{n+p}| \leqq \varepsilon_n, \ |g - s_n| \leqq \varepsilon_n. \tag{201.5}$$

202. We shall prove that any absolutely convergent series is also *unconditionally convergent*, meaning that the value of its sum remains unchanged if the terms of the series are written down in any other order; or in other words, a rearrangement of the series does not change its sum. This holds true even if the terms of a given absolutely convergent series are distributed so as to form a finite or infinite number of new series each of which is summed separately and whose sums are then added.

198

To show this, let us assume that the array

$$g_{11},\ g_{12},\ g_{13},\ \cdots$$
$$g_{21},\ g_{22},\ g_{23},\ \cdots \qquad\qquad (202.1)$$
$$\cdots\cdots\cdots\cdots\cdots$$

is formed from the totality of the original terms g_ν in such a way that each of these terms occurs *exactly once* in (202.1). Here, each line (row) of the array may contain either a finite or an infinite number of terms, and the number of rows may itself be either finite or infinite.

Clearly each of the series

$$h_k = g_{k1} + g_{k2} + g_{k3} + \cdots \qquad (k = 1, 2, \ldots) \quad (202.2)$$

is itself absolutely convergent; the statement we wish to prove is that

$$g = h_1 + h_2 + \cdots, \qquad\qquad (202.3)$$

where g has the same meaning as in (201.1). Expressed differently, the statement says that if we set

$$t_m = h_1 + h_2 + \cdots + h_m, \qquad\qquad (202.4)$$

then it follows that

$$\lim_{m = \infty} t_m = g. \qquad\qquad (202.5)$$

To prove this, we assign to every positive integer n a positive integer m_n' which is such that for $m \geq m_n'$, the first n terms $g_1, g_2, \ldots, g_n$ of the series (201.1) occur in those of the series (202.2) whose sum equals t_m.

Then the difference $(t_m - s_n)$ is a sum of finitely or infinitely many terms g_k for all of which $k > n$ holds. Hence (201.3) and (201.5) yield

$$|t_m - s_n| \leq \varepsilon_n \qquad\qquad (m \geq m_n'),$$
$$|t_m - g| \leq |t_m - s_n| + |g - s_n| \leq 2\,\varepsilon_n \quad (m \geq m_n'), \qquad (202.6)$$

and this in turn implies relation (202.5), which we wanted to prove.

203. We can operate with absolutely convergent series in the same way as with convergent series of positive numbers. For instance, if the two series

$$g = \sum_{\nu=1}^{\infty} g_\nu, \qquad h = \sum_{\mu=1}^{\infty} h_\mu \qquad\qquad (203.1)$$

are absolutely convergent—which implies that the series

$$p = \sum_{\mu,\,\nu} g_\nu\, h_\mu \tag{203.2}$$

is likewise absolutely convergent—then we see, by proceeding similiarly as in the preceding section and setting $s_n = g_1 + g_2 + \cdots + g_n$, $t_n = h_1 + h_2 + \cdots + h_n$, that

$$\lim_{n=\infty} (p - s_n\, t_n) = 0 \tag{203.3}$$

must hold. Hence $p = gh$.

On the other hand, if we set

$$u_n = g_1 h_n + g_2 h_{n-1} + \cdots + g_n h_1, \quad \sigma_n = u_1 + u_2 + \cdots + u_n, \tag{203.4}$$

then by the same method we are led to the relation

$$\lim_{n=\infty} (p - \sigma_n) = 0, \tag{203.5}$$

which yields

$$g\, h = u_1 + u_2 + u_3 + \cdots. \tag{203.6}$$

204. We consider next an infinite sequence of analytic functions $g_n(z)$ $(n = 1, 2, \ldots)$ all of which are regular in a region G and satisfy relations (201.2) in this region, where the sum of the ϱ_ν is again assumed to be finite. Then the partial sums

$$s_n(z) = g_1(z) + g_2(z) + \cdots + g_n(z) \quad (n = 1, 2, \ldots) \tag{204.1}$$

are uniformly bounded in G. Hence the sequence of functions $s_n(z)$ is normal in G (*cf.* § 185 above), and since it converges, its limit

$$g(z) = g_1(z) + g_2(z) + \cdots + g_n(z) + \cdots \tag{204.2}$$

is a regular analytic function in G, which moreover is bounded in G.

By § 188 above, we obtain the successive derivatives

$$g'(z), g''(z), \ldots, g^{(p)}(z), \ldots$$

of $g(z)$ from the relations

$$g^{(p)}(z) = \lim_{n=\infty} s_n^{(p)}(z). \tag{204.3}$$

But from (204.1), it follows that

$$s_n^{(p)}(z) = g_1^{(p)}(z) + g_2^{(p)}(z) + \cdots + g_n^{(p)}(z), \tag{204.4}$$

so that (204.3) can also be written in the form

$$g^{(p)}(z) = \sum_{\nu=1}^{\infty} g_{\nu}^{(p)}(z). \tag{204.5}$$

Thus *an absolutely and continuously convergent series whose terms are regular analytic functions, can be differentiated term by term.*

Comparing these results with earlier ones, we obtain the following: The totality of functions

$$h(z) = g_{n_1}(z) + g_{n_2}(z) + \cdots \tag{204.6}$$

that can be represented as a sum of finitely or infinitely many of the functions $g_{\nu}(z)$ constitutes a normal family of uniformly bounded functions in G, and every series (204.6) is not only absolutely convergent but also continuously convergent at every (interior) point of G. The family of derivatives

$$h'(z) = g'_{n_1}(z) + g'_{n_2}(z) + \cdots$$

is, to be sure, normal in G, but it need not be bounded in G. It can be proved, however, that the functions $|h'(z)|$ have a common upper bound in every subregion H of G whose closure $\overline{H}$ lies in G.

Finally, we note that the rules of operation of § 203 above carry over immediately to absolutely convergent series of analytic functions.

Power Series (§ 205)

205. By a *power series* is meant an expression of the form

$$a_0 + a_1 z + a_2 z^2 + \cdots = \sum_{\nu=0}^{\infty} a_{\nu} z^{\nu}. \tag{205.1}$$

We again set

$$s_n(z) = a_0 + a_1 z + \cdots + a_n z^n. \tag{205.2}$$

For the series (205.1) to converge at a point $z_0 \neq 0$ to a finite value $s(z_0)$, it is necessary that

$$\lim_{n=\infty} |s_n(z_0) - s_{n-1}(z_0)| = \lim_{n=\infty} |a_n z_0^n| = 0$$

should hold true, and the infinitely many numbers $|a_n z_0^n|$ for $n = 1, 2, \ldots$ must have a finite upper bound M. If we assume, conversely, the existence of a number M_0 for which

$$|a_n z_0^n| \leq M_0 \qquad (n = 1, 2, \ldots) \tag{205.3}$$

holds, and if we consider an arbitrary point z lying in the closed circular disc

$$|z| \leq \vartheta |z_0| \qquad (0 < \vartheta < 1), \quad (205.4)$$

then we find that for such a z,

$$|a_n z^n| \leq \vartheta^n |a_n z_0^n| \leq M_0 \vartheta^n \qquad (205.5)$$

holds, so that, using the notation of § 201 above,

$$\varrho_n = M_0 \vartheta^n, \quad \varepsilon_n = M_0 \frac{\vartheta^{n+1}}{1-\vartheta}. \qquad (205.6)$$

At every point of the closed disc (205.4), and hence at every point of the (open) disc

$$|z| < |z_0|, \qquad (205.7)$$

the series

$$f(z) = a_0 + a_1 z + a_2 z^2 + \cdots \qquad (205.8)$$

must converge continuously. It represents a regular analytic function in the disc (205.7) (*cf.* § 187 above).

The Radius of Convergence (§§ 206-207)

206. As one of the results implied by the developments of the preceding section, we obtain the following: If

$$\overline{\lim_{n = \infty}} |a_n z_0^n| < +\infty, \qquad (206.1)$$

then for every z in the open disc (205.7), we have

$$\lim_{n = \infty} |a_n z^n| = 0. \qquad (206.2)$$

This immediately yields that if

$$\overline{\lim_{n = \infty}} |a_n z_0^n| > 0, \qquad (206.3)$$

then every z for which $|z| > |z_0|$ satisfies

$$\overline{\lim_{n = \infty}} |a_n z^n| = \infty. \qquad (206.4)$$

We now consider the sequence of positive numbers

$$\alpha_1 = |a_1|, \quad \alpha_2 = |a_2|^{\frac{1}{2}}, \quad \alpha_3 = |a_3|^{\frac{1}{3}}, \quad \ldots \tag{206.5}$$

and form its upper limit

$$\lambda = \overline{\lim_{n=\infty}} \, \alpha_n. \tag{206.6}$$

Let us assume first that λ is finite and not equal to zero. Then there are numbers $z_0 \neq 0$ for which

$$|z_0| \, \lambda < 1 \tag{206.7}$$

holds. For all sufficiently small positive numbers η, we then also have $|z_0| \, (\lambda + \eta) < 1$. Now by (206.6), there are at most finitely many $\alpha_n \geq \lambda + \eta$. Hence for n sufficiently large, we always have $\alpha_n |z_0| < 1$, and therefore also

$$|a_n| \, |z_0^n| = (\alpha_n \, |z_0|)^n < 1, \tag{206.8}$$

so that the numbers $|a_n z_0^n|$ have a finite upper bound. In every disc $|z| < |z_0|$, and hence also in the disc $|z| < 1/\lambda$, the given series represents a regular analytic function.

If z is a complex number for which $\lambda \, |z| > 1$, then there are positive numbers η for which $(\lambda - \eta) \, |z| > 1$ holds, so that we can find infinitely many n for which $\alpha_n |z| > 1$ and therefore $|a_n z^n| > 1$. Thus the series cannot converge for such values of z.

We summarize the results of the foregoing discussion as follows:

If $0 < \lambda < +\infty$, and if we set

$$R = \frac{1}{\lambda} = \frac{1}{\overline{\lim_{n=\infty}} |a_n|^{\frac{1}{n}}}, \tag{206.9}$$

then the power series (205.8) *converges at every point z that lies in the (interior of the) disc*

$$|z| < R \tag{206.10}$$

to a regular analytic function $f(z)$. At every point z that lies in the exterior $|z| > R$ of the same disc, either the power series diverges, or it converges to ∞.

The circle $|z| = R$ is called the *circle of convergence*, and the number R of (206.9) is called the *radius of convergence*, of the given power series.

For the points z lying *on* the circle $|z| = R$ of convergence, it is not possible to decide without further discussion whether the given power series converges or diverges, nor whether in the case of convergence its limit is finite or infinite. This difficulty lies in the very nature of the situation; after all, simple examples can be given of each of the possibilities just mentioned. For instance, each of the two power series

$$\left.\begin{aligned}
\mathfrak{P}_1(z) &= z - z^2 + z^3 - z^4 + - \cdots, \\
\mathfrak{P}_2(z) &= z - \frac{z^2}{2} + \frac{z^3}{3} - \frac{z^4}{4} + - \cdots
\end{aligned}\right\}
\qquad (206.11)$$

converges to ∞ at $z = -1$; at $z = 1$, however, $\mathfrak{P}_1(z)$ is divergent while $\mathfrak{P}_2(z)$ converges to a finite value.

Having discussed the case $0 < \lambda < \infty$, we encounter no new difficulties in the two remaining cases $\lambda = 0$ and $\lambda = \infty$. We immediately see that if $\lambda = 0$, then the given power series converges at every point of the complex plane and hence represents an *integral function* (*cf.* § 167 above). But if $\lambda = \infty$, then the power series is nowhere convergent (except at $z = 0$), and is therefore useless.

207. The calculation of the radius R of convergence of a power series by means of formula (206.9) is usually quite cumbersome. In many cases, an estimate of R, or even the actual value of R, can be obtained by simpler means. If all of the coefficients a_n of a given power series are different from zero, we set

$$\beta_n = \left| \frac{a_n}{a_{n+1}} \right| \qquad (n = 1, 2, \ldots),$$

$$R' = \varliminf_{n = \infty} \beta_n, \qquad R'' = \varlimsup_{n = \infty} \beta_n.$$

Then if, first, $|z| < R'$, we have for sufficiently large values of n that

$$|z| < \beta_n, \quad |a_{n+1} z^{n+1}| < |a_n z^n|,$$

which implies that the set of all the $|a_n z^n|$ has a finite least upper bound and that the radius R of convergence of the series is at least equal to R'.

Second, if $|z| > R''$ then we find in the same way that for all sufficiently large n,

$$|a_{n+1} z^{n+1}| > |a_n z^n|$$

must hold. This implies that infinitely many of the numbers $|a_n z^n|$ must exceed a fixed positive number, and we must therefore have $R \leqq R''$.

Thus the radius R of convergence of the given power series must lie between R' and R'', and its actual value can be determined if

$$\lim_{n = \infty} \left| \frac{a_n}{a_{n+1}} \right|$$

exists (and can be found).

We can use a similar method in case all the coefficients with even (or with odd) subscripts vanish, and in other similar cases.

In this way we find, for example, that the power series

$$\sum_{n=1}^{\infty} z^n, \ \sum_{n=1}^{\infty} n\,z^n, \ \sum_{n=1}^{\infty} \frac{z^n}{n}, \ \sum_{n=1}^{\infty} \frac{z^n}{n^2}$$

all have $R = 1$ as their radius of convergence.

The Taylor Series (§§ 208-209)

208. The most important property of power series is the fact that every regular analytic function can be calculated, in a neighborhood of any given point of its domain of definition, by means of power series.

Let us assume first that the analytic function $f(z)$ is regular in a region that contains the closed unit disc $|z| \leq 1$. In the interior of this disc, $f(z)$ can then be represented by means of Cauchy's Integral Formula, as follows:

$$f(z) = \frac{1}{2\pi i} \int_{\varkappa} \frac{f(\zeta)}{\zeta - z}\, d\zeta \qquad (|\zeta| = 1, \ |z| < 1) \quad (208.1)$$

(*cf.* § 130 above).

Using the identity

$$\frac{1}{\zeta - z} = \frac{1}{\zeta} + \frac{z}{\zeta^2} + \frac{z^2}{\zeta^3} + \cdots + \frac{z^n}{\zeta^{n+1}} + \frac{z^{n+1}}{\zeta^{n+1}(\zeta - z)} \qquad (208.2)$$

and the abbreviations

$$a_\nu = \frac{1}{2\pi i} \int_{\varkappa} \frac{f(\zeta)}{\zeta^{\nu+1}}\, d\zeta, \ \ g_n(z) = \frac{1}{2\pi i} \int_{\varkappa} \frac{f(\zeta)}{\zeta^{n+1}(\zeta - z)}\, d\zeta, \\ s_n(z) = a_0 + a_1 z + \cdots + a_n z^n, \quad \Bigg\} \quad (208.3)$$

we obtain the relation

$$f(z) = s_n(z) + z^{n+1} g_n(z) \qquad (|z| < 1). \quad (208.4)$$

Now let $|f(z)| \leq M$ inside and on the unit circle $|z| = 1$; then (208.3) yields

$$|a_\nu| \leq M, \ \ |g_n(z)| \leq \frac{M}{1 - |z|}. \quad (208.5)$$

For z ranging over the closed disc $|z| \leqq \vartheta < 1$, we obtain the inequalities

$$|f(z) - s_n(z)| \leqq \frac{\vartheta^{n+1} M}{1 - \vartheta}, \quad |s_n(z)| < \frac{M}{1 - \vartheta}. \qquad (208.6)$$

Thus the sequence of $s_n(z)$ is normal in the open disc $|z| < 1$ and converges continuously in this disc to $f(z)$, so that we finally have

$$f(z) = a_0 + a_1 z + a_2 z^2 + \cdots \qquad (|z| < 1). \quad (208.7)$$

Since power series may be differentiated term by term, the following relations ensue:

$$f'(z) = a_1 + 2 a_2 z + 3 a_3 z^2 + \cdots,$$

$$f''(z) = 2 a_2 + 6 a_3 z + 12 a_4 z^2 + \cdots,$$

and more generally,

$$f^{(p)}(z) = \sum_{n=p}^{\infty} n(n-1) \cdots (n-p+1) a_n z^{n-p}. \qquad (208.8)$$

Hence the coefficients a_n can be calculated in terms of the successive derivatives of $f(z)$ at the point $z = 0$, as follows:

$$a_n = \frac{1}{n!} f^{(n)}(0). \qquad (208.9)$$

This shows the *uniqueness* of the power-series expansion (208.7) of $f(z)$.

209. If a function $f(z)$ is regular in a region G that contains the closed circular disc $|z - z_0| \leqq r$ in its interior, then the function

$$g(u) = f(z_0 + r u) \qquad (209.1)$$

is regular in the closed unit disc $|u| \leqq 1$, so that the results of the preceding section may be applied to $g(u)$. Hence in a neighborhood of z_0 we may write

$$\left. \begin{array}{c} f(z) = b_0 + b_1 (z - z_0) + b_2 (z - z_0)^2 + \cdots, \\[2mm] b_n = \dfrac{1}{n!} f^{(n)}(z_0), \end{array} \right\} \qquad (209.2)$$

and the radius of convergence of the power series (209.2) is at least equal to r.

If the function $f(z)$ is regular inside and on the boundary of the closed disc $|z - z_0| \leqq r$, then $f(z)$ must be regular inside a larger concentric circle as well. Hence the radius R of convergence of the power series (209.2) must be *greater* than r. From this it follows that *on the circle $|z| = R$ of converg-*

ence of a power series, there must be at least one point at which the function
$f(z)$ represented by the power series is not regular.

Let us denote the maximum of the modulus $|f(z)|$ on the circle $|z - z_0| = r$ $(r < R)$ by $M(r)$. Then, referring to (209.1) and (209.2) for the definition of the b_n and their relation to the a_n of § 208, we may rewrite the first of the two inequalities in (208.5) in the form

$$|b_n| \leqq \frac{M(r)}{r^n}. \qquad (209.3)$$

Hence if

$$|z - z_0| \leqq r \, \vartheta \qquad (0 < \vartheta < 1), \quad (209.4)$$

then

$$|b_n (z - z_0)^n| \leqq M(r) \, \vartheta^n. \qquad (209.5)$$

Normal Sequences of Power Series (§§ 210-212)

210. An infinite sequence of power series

$$f_\nu(z) = a_{\nu 0} + a_{\nu 1} z + a_{\nu 2} z^2 + \cdots \quad (\nu = 1, 2, \ldots), \quad (210.1)$$

whose radii of convergence are all greater than a positive number R_0, converges continuously at the point $z = 0$ to a finite number a_0 if and only if the following two conditions are satisfied: First, the limit

$$\lim_{\nu = \infty} a_{\nu 0} = a_0 \qquad (a_0 \neq \infty) \quad (210.2)$$

must exist, and second, the sequence of the $f_\nu(z)$ must be normal at the point $z = 0$ (*cf.* § 177 above). Because of (210.2), the sequence of $|a_{\nu 0}|$ must be bounded, so that the sequence of functions

$$g_\nu(z) = (f_\nu(z) - a_{\nu 0}) = a_{\nu 1} z + a_{\nu 2} z^2 + \cdots \qquad (210.3)$$

must likewise be normal at $z = 0$ (*cf.* § 197 above).

Hence by the theorem in § 189 above, there must be a circular disc $|z| \leqq r < R_0$ on which the functions $g_\nu(z)$ are uniformly bounded, and this must then hold for the $f_\nu(z)$ as well. We then have, say, $|f_\nu(z)| \leqq M$ for $|z| = r$, and this together with (209.3) implies the relations

$$|a_{\nu k}| \, r^k \leqq M, \quad (\nu = 1, 2, \ldots; \ k = 0, 1, \ldots), \quad (210.4)$$

for all ν and all k.

The condition that there exist at least two numbers r and M for which all the relations (210.4) hold may also be expressed as follows: *With the non-negative numbers A_k defined by*

$$A_k = \sup (|a_{1k}|, |a_{2k}|, \ldots) \quad (k = 0, 1, 2, \ldots), \quad (210.5)$$

the power series

$$P(z) = A_0 + A_1 z + A_2 z^2 + \cdots \quad (210.6)$$

must have all its coefficients finite and must have a radius of convergence $R > 0$.

By § 206, this requires that

$$\varlimsup_{n = \infty} (A_n)^{\frac{1}{n}} = \frac{1}{R} < + \infty \quad (210.7)$$

should hold. For if relations (210.4) are satisfied, then (210.5) gives

$$A_k r^k \leq M \quad (k = 0, 1, 2, \ldots), \quad (210.8)$$

whence the radius R of convergence of the power series $P(z)$ must be $\geq r$ and hence must be > 0. Then (210.7) must also hold true.

The converse of this result is almost obvious. In fact, given any power series (210.1) for which (with the notation of (210.5)) the inequality (210.7) holds, we choose any positive number $r < R$. Then for any point z of the circle $|z| = r$ and for every natural number ν, we have

$$\begin{aligned}|f_\nu(z)| &\leq |a_{\nu 0}| + |a_{\nu 1} z| + |a_{\nu 2} z^2| + \cdots \\ &\leq A_0 + A_1 r + A_2 r^2 + \cdots = P(r) < + \infty.\end{aligned} \quad \Bigg\} \quad (210.9)$$

The functions $f_\nu(z)$ then are regular and uniformly bounded in the closed disc $|z| \leq r$, and the sequence of $f_\nu(z)$ is normal at $z = 0$, even in the whole disc $|z| \leq r$. We have thus proved the following theorem:

For an infinite sequence of power series

$$f_\nu(z) = a_{\nu 0} + a_{\nu 1} z + a_{\nu 2} z^2 + \cdots \quad (\nu = 1, 2, \ldots) \quad (210.10)$$

to represent, in a neighborhood $|z| < R_0$ of the point $z = 0$, a sequence of regular analytic functions converging continuously at $z = 0$, the following two conditions are necessary and sufficient: First, the limit $\lim a_{\nu 0} = a_0$ must exist and be finite, and second, if

$$A_k = \sup (|a_{1k}|, |a_{2k}|, \ldots) \quad (210.11)$$

then the power series

$$P(r) = A_0 + A_1 r + A_2 r^2 + \cdots \qquad (210.12)$$

must have all its coefficients finite and must have a non-zero radius R of convergence.

If these two conditions are satisfied, then $R_0 \geqq R$, and the sequence of functions (210.10) is normal in the disc $|z| < R$.

The normal kernel of the sequence of functions $f_\nu(z)$ may of course contain a region that contains not only the disc $|z| < R$ but other points as well; but it does not necessarily contain such additional points. For example, if our sequence of functions is given by $f_\nu(z) = z^\nu$, then by § 174 above, the normal kernel of this sequence consists of the two regions $|z| < 1$ and $|z| > 1$. In this case, we have $P(r) = 1 + r + r^2 + \ldots$, and hence $R = 1$.

211. By Vitali's theorem (*cf.* § 191 above), the sequence (210.10) converges continuously in the whole disc $|z| < R$ to a regular function

$$f(z) = a_0 + a_1 z + a_2 z^2 + \cdots, \qquad (211.1)$$

provided only that the set of points at which the sequence converges has at least one point of accumulation in the interior of the disc. If this is so, then we have not only that

$$f(z) = \lim_{\nu = \infty} f_\nu(z), \qquad (211.2)$$

but by § 188 above we can also calculate the successive derivatives of $f(z)$ by means of the relations

$$f^{(p)}(z) = \lim_{\nu = \infty} f_\nu^{(p)}(z) \qquad (p = 1, 2, \ldots). \quad (211.3)$$

Applying relations (211.3) at $z = 0$, we find that the coefficients a_n in the series expansion (211.1) are determined from the equations

$$a_n = \lim_{\nu = \infty} a_{\nu n} \qquad (n = 1, 2, \ldots). \quad (211.4)$$

Conversely, if equations (211.4) all are valid, then every subsequence $\{f_{\nu_j}(z)\}$ of (210.1) that converges continuously in $|z| < R$ has as its limit a function whose power series expansion must have the coefficients given by (211.4); hence this limit $f(z)$ must always be the *same*, that is to say, independent of the particular convergent subsequence at hand. Just as in § 191 above, we then conclude that the given sequence (210.1) must itself be convergent. We therefore have the following result:

For the convergence in a neighborhood of $z = 0$ of the sequence of power series (210.1) satisfying condition (210.7), it is necessary and sufficient that all of the limits

$$\lim_{\nu = \infty} a_{\nu n} = a_n \qquad (n = 0, 1, \ldots) \qquad (211.5)$$

exist. If they do, then the convergence is continuous in the open disc $|z| < R$ and uniform in every smaller concentric closed disc $|z| \leqq r$ $(r < R)$. Also, the coefficients in the power series expansion of the limit function $f(z)$ are the numbers a_n defined by (211.5).

This result could of course also have been obtained by means of elementary estimates on the power series.

212. The last result immediately yields the following theorem:

Consider a sequence $\{f_\nu(z)\}$ of meromorphic functions that is normal in a region G. This sequence converges in G to a meromorphic function $f(z)$ whose value at the point z_0 of G is $\neq \infty$ if and only if all of the limits

$$\lim_{\nu = \infty} f_\nu(z_0), \quad \lim_{\nu = \infty} f_\nu'(z_0), \quad \ldots, \quad \lim_{\nu = \infty} f_\nu^{(p)}(z_0), \quad \ldots \qquad (212.1)$$

exist and if the first of these limits is finite.

By proceeding similarly as at the beginning of § 210 above, we can first show that the functions $f_\nu(z)$ are regular and uniformly bounded in some disc $|z - z_0| < r$. The assumption that all of the limits (212.1) exist then implies, by the result of the preceding section, that the limit $f(z) = \lim f_\nu(z)$ exists in the disc $|z - z_0| < r$. This in turn implies, by Vitali's theorem of § 191, that the given sequence also converges at all of the remaining points of G.

Another corollary of the result of § 211 above is the so-called *Weierstrass double-series theorem*, which states the following:

Consider an infinite sequence of power series $\mathfrak{P}_1(z)$, $\mathfrak{P}_2(z)$, ... each of which converges on the closed disc $|z| \leqq r$. Assume that the series

$$\mathfrak{P}_1(z) + \mathfrak{P}_2(z) + \cdots \qquad (212.2)$$

converges uniformly on the boundary $|z| = r$ of this disc. Then for every interior point z of the disc, we have

$$\mathfrak{P}_1(z) + \mathfrak{P}_2(z) + \cdots = \mathfrak{P}(z), \qquad (212.3)$$

where $\mathfrak{P}(z)$ stands for a power series whose terms are obtained by combining, on the left-hand side of (213.3), all the terms containing the same powers of z.

To prove this theorem, we need merely observe that the functions

$$f_\nu(z) = \mathfrak{P}_1(z) + \mathfrak{P}_2(z) + \cdots + \mathfrak{P}_\nu(z) \qquad (\nu = 1, 2, \ldots)$$

are regular and uniformly bounded on the disc $|z| \leqq r$, so that the result of the preceding section can be applied to them.

Operations with Power Series (§§ 213-214)

213. What makes power series especially convenient to use is the fact that we can calculate with them in just about the same way as we can with polynomials. Let us consider the two power series

$$\left. \begin{array}{l} f(z) = a_0 + a_1 z + a_2 z^2 + \cdots, \\[2mm] g(z) = b_0 + b_1 z + b_2 z^2 + \cdots, \end{array} \right\} \quad (213.1)$$

whose radii of convergence we denote by R_f and R_g, respectively, and let r be a positive number that is less than the smaller of the two numbers R_f and R_g. We set

$$\left. \begin{array}{l} s_\nu(z) = a_0 + a_1 z + \cdots + a_\nu z^\nu, \\[2mm] t_\nu(z) = b_0 + b_1 z + \cdots + b_\nu z^\nu. \end{array} \right\} \quad (213.2)$$

Then to begin with, it is obvious that on the disc $|z| \leqq r$, the sum $f(z) + g(z)$ can be calculated by means of the series

$$\left. \begin{array}{l} f(z) + g(z) = \lim_{\nu = \infty} \left[s_\nu(z) + t_\nu(z) \right] \\[2mm] = (a_0 + b_0) + (a_1 + b_1) z + (a_2 + b_2) z^2 + \cdots. \end{array} \right\} \quad (213.3)$$

To calculate the product $p(z) = f(z)g(z)$, we set $p_\nu(z) = s_\nu(z)\, t_\nu(z)$ and note that the functions $p_\nu(z)$ are uniformly bounded on the disc $|z| \leqq r$, and that $p(z) = \lim p_\nu(z)$. By the theorem of § 211 above, we then have

$$\left. \begin{array}{l} p(z) = c_0 + c_1 z + c_2 z^2 + \cdots, \\[2mm] c_0 = a_0 b_0, \quad c_1 = a_0 b_1 + a_1 b_0, \quad \ldots, \quad c_\nu = a_0 b_\nu + a_1 b_{\nu-1} + \cdots + a_\nu b_0. \end{array} \right\} \quad (213.4)$$

Next we turn to the quotient. If $a_0 \neq 0$, then there is a neighborhood of the point $z = 0$ in which the function

$$q(z) = \frac{g(z)}{f(z)} \qquad (213.5)$$

is regular; it can therefore be developed in a power series

$$q(z) = d_0 + d_1 z + d_2 z^2 + \cdots. \qquad (213.6)$$

To determine the coefficients d_ν, we apply formula (213.4) to the equation

$$g(z) = f(z)\, q(z) \qquad (213.7)$$

and obtain

$$b_0 = a_0 \, d_0$$
$$b_1 = a_0 \, d_1 + a_1 \, d_0$$
$$b_2 = a_0 \, d_2 + a_1 \, d_1 + a_2 \, d_0$$
$$\qquad (213.8)$$

$$\dots\dots\dots\dots\dots\dots\dots\dots\dots$$

Solving these equations one by one, we find that

$$a_0 \, d_0 = b_0, \quad a_0^2 \, d_1 = a_0 \, b_1 - a_1 \, b_0,$$
$$a_0^3 \, d_2 = a_0^2 \, b_2 - a_0 \, a_1 \, b_1 - (a_0 \, a_2 - a_1^2) \, b_0, \ \dots$$
$$\qquad (213.9)$$

The radii of convergence of the two power series (213.3) and (213.4) are at least equal to, and may actually be larger than, the smaller of the two numbers R_f and R_g.

As to $q(z)$, its radius of convergence depends not only on R_f and R_g but also on the location of the zero of $f(z)$ closest to the point $z = 0$, unless this zero happens to coincide with a zero of $g(z)$. Thus for an estimate of the radius of convergence of $q(z)$, more detailed information about $f(z)$ and $g(z)$ is required than merely their radii of convergence.

214. The theorem of § 211 above makes it possible to reduce the problem of finding power series expansions of composite functions $g(f(z))$ to calculations with polynomials. For example, assume that in a neighborhood of $z = 0$ we have

$$w = f(z) = a_0 + a_1 \, z + a_2 \, z^2 + \cdots, \qquad (214.1)$$

and that in a neighborhood of $w = a_0$,

$$g(w) = b_0 + b_1 \, (w - a_0) + b_2 \, (w - a_0)^2 + \cdots. \qquad (214.2)$$

Choose a positive number ϱ such that for

$$|w - a_0| < \varrho, \qquad (214.3)$$

the polynomials

$$g_n(w) = b_0 + b_1 \, (w - a_0) + \cdots + b_n \, (w - a_0)^n \quad (n = 1, 2, \dots) \quad (214.4)$$

are uniformly bounded. Then the function

$$g(w) = \lim_{n = \infty} g_n(w) \qquad (214.5)$$

is also bounded for $|w - a_0| < \varrho$. Next we choose a positive number r such that for

$$|z| < r, \qquad (214.6)$$

the polynomials

$$u_n(z) = a_1 z + a_2 z^2 + \cdots + a_n z^n \quad (n = 1, 2, \ldots) \quad (214.7)$$

all satisfy the inequality

$$|u_n(z)| < \varrho. \quad (214.8)$$

This is possible, since the $u_n(z)$ constitute a normal family in some disc $|z| < r_0$ and since they all vanish at $z = 0$. We then have

$$w - a_0 = \lim_{n = \infty} a_n(z). \quad (214.9)$$

Since the approximating functions $g_n(w)$ converge continuously to $g(w)$ in the disc (214.3), it follows that

$$g(f(z)) = \lim_{n = \infty} g_n(a_0 + u_n(z)) \quad (214.10)$$

$$= c_0 + c_1 z + c_2 z^2 + \cdots.$$

Now the sequence of polynomials

$$g_n(a_0 + u_n(z)) = b_0 + b_1 u_n(z) + b_2(u_n(z))^2 + \cdots + b_n(u_n(z))^n \quad (214.11)$$

is of a very special character. For by (214.7), each of the expressions

$$u_{n+1}(z) - u_n(z), \quad (u_{n+1}(z))^k - (u_n(z))^k, \quad (u_{n+1}(z))^{n+1}$$

is divisible by z^{n+1}, so that the difference

$$g_{n+1}(a_0 + u_{n+1}(z)) - g_n(a_0 + u_n(z))$$

is likewise divisible by z^{n+1}. Hence if in the sequence of polynomials

$$g_{n+p}(a_0 + u_{n+p}(z)) \quad (p = 0, 1, 2, \ldots)$$

we omit all those terms whose degree exceeds n, we always obtain one and the same polynomial $h_n(z)$. If, on the other hand, we apply the theorem of § 211 above to the sequence of polynomials $g_n(a_0 + u_n(z))$, which by (214.10) converges to the power series $c_0 + c_1 z + c_2 z^2 + \cdots$, then by omitting from the polynomials $g_p(a_0 + u_p(z))$ all terms of degree higher than n and letting p go to infinity, we obtain the expression

$$c_0 + c_1 z + c_2 z^2 + \cdots + c_n z^n. \quad (214.12)$$

Thus it turns out that the expression (214.12) is the same as the above $h_n(z)$ and can therefore be obtained from $g_n(a_0 + u_n(z))$ *without the use of any limiting process whatsoever.*

Abel's Transformation (§ 215)

215.   Let us consider a power series

$$f(z) = a_0 + a_1 z + a_2 z^2 + \cdots \tag{215.1}$$

whose radius of convergence is unity, and let us also assume that the series

$$s = a_0 + a_1 + a_2 + \cdots \tag{215.2}$$

converges to a finite number s.   (The convergence in (215.2) need not be absolute.)   Then we shall show that the sequence of approximating polynomials (partial sums)

$$f_n(z) = a_0 + a_1 z + \cdots + a_n z^n \tag{215.3}$$

of $f(z)$ is normal on certain closed sets that contain the point $z = 1$.   To prove this, we shall use the celebrated transformation due to N. H. Abel (1802-1829).

We introduce the abbreviations

$$\left. \begin{aligned} s_n &= a_0 + a_1 + \cdots + a_n, \quad r_n = s - s_n, \\ \varepsilon_n &= \sup \left(|r_n|, |r_{n+1}|, \ldots \right) \quad (n = 0, 1, 2, \ldots), \end{aligned} \right\} \tag{215.4}$$

and note that

$$\lim_{n=\infty} r_n = 0, \quad \varepsilon_0 \geqq \varepsilon_1 \geqq \varepsilon_2 \geqq \cdots, \quad \lim_{n=\infty} \varepsilon_n = 0. \tag{215.5}$$

For $|z| < 1$, we have the identity

$$\frac{1}{1-z} = 1 + z + z^2 + z^3 + \cdots, \tag{215.6}$$

which we multiply, term by term, by (215.3), obtaining

$$\frac{1}{1-z} f_n(z) = (1 + z + z^2 + \cdots)(a_0 + a_1 z + a_2 z^2 + \cdots + a_n z^n)$$
$$= s_0 + s_1 z + \cdots + s_n z^n + s_n z^{n+1} + s_n z^{n+2} + \cdots.$$

Subtracting this from the identity

$$\frac{1}{1-z} s = s + s z + \cdots + s z^n + s z^{n+1} + s z^{n+2} + \cdots,$$

we find that

$$\frac{1}{1-z} [s - f_n(z)] = r_0 + r_1 z + \cdots + r_n z^n + r_n \frac{z^{n+1}}{1-z}. \tag{215.7}$$

Subtracting (215.7) from the analogous equation

$$\frac{1}{1-z}\,[s - f_{n+p}(z)] = r_0 + r_1 z + \cdots + r_{n+p}\, z^{n+p} + r_{n+p}\,\frac{z^{n+p+1}}{1-z},$$

we finally obtain

$$\left.\begin{aligned}&\frac{1}{1-z}\,[f_n(z) - f_{n+p}(z)]\\[2mm]&= r_{n+1}\, z^{n+1} + \cdots + r_{n+p}\, z^{n+p} + \frac{r_{n+p}\, z^{n+p+1} - r_n\, z^{n+1}}{1-z}.\end{aligned}\right\} \quad (215.8)$$

But, using (215.4), we have

$$\left|r_{n+1}\, z^{n+1} + \cdots + r_{n+p}\, z^{n+p}\right| \leq \left|r_{n+1}\, z^{n+1}\right| + \cdots + \left|r_{n+p}\, z^{n+p}\right|$$

$$\leq \varepsilon_n\,(1 + |z| + \cdots + |z|^{p-1}) < \frac{\varepsilon_n}{1 - |z|},$$

$$\left|r_{n+p}\, z^{n+p+1} - r_n\, z^{n+1}\right| < 2\,\varepsilon_n,$$

so that equation (215.8) now yields the inequality

$$\left|f_n(z) - f_{n+p}(z)\right| < \varepsilon_n\left(2 + \frac{|1-z|}{1-|z|}\right). \tag{215.9}$$

From this we see that the sequence of approximating polynomials is uniformly convergent on any point set on which the expression $|1-z|/(1-|z|)$ is bounded. The same then holds for the closure S of any such point set; thus the limit $f(z)$ must not only exist but must also be continuous on S. Also, *the sequence of $f_n(z)$ is normal at every point of S* (cf. § 181 above).

We now consider a point z inside the circle that has the line segment $\overline{01}$ as a diameter (see Fig. 25, p. 216). Let ϱ stand for the distance $|1-z|$ between the points z and 1, and φ for the angle formed by the two line segments $\overline{z1}$ and $\overline{01}$. Applying the Law of Cosines to the triangle $01z$, we obtain

$$|z|^2 = 1 + \varrho^2 - 2\,\varrho \cos \varphi.$$

Therefore

$$\frac{|1-z|}{1-|z|} = \frac{|1-z|\,(1+|z|)}{1-|z|^2} < \frac{2\,\varrho}{2\,\varrho \cos \varphi - \varrho^2} = \frac{2}{2\cos \varphi - \varrho}.$$

On the line segment $\overline{1A}$, we have $\varrho \leq \cos \varphi$, and hence

$$\frac{|1-z|}{1-|z|} < \frac{2}{\cos \varphi}. \tag{215.10}$$

This inequality holds true not only on the line segments $\overline{A1}$ and $\overline{B1}$, but at every interior point of the sector $1AOB$ as well. The set S which we have obtained in this way consists of the sector just mentioned, including its boundary points one of which is the point $z = 1$.

A first result that follows from the above discussion is the fact that the funtion $f(z)$ is continuous at $z = 1$ whenever z approaches $z = 1$ along a straight line (inside the unit circle), and that $f(z)$ assumes at $z = 1$ the value

$$f(1) = \lim_{n = \infty} f_n(1) = s$$

This fact could also have been established by a somewhat shorter method (as it actually was by Abel), without using the approximating functions $f_n(z)$.

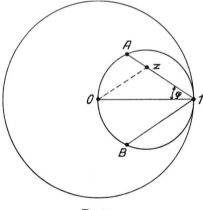

Fig. 25

However, the method we have used here permits us to recognize some important properties of these functions. For example, the limiting oscillation at $z = 1$ of the sequence $\{f_n(z)\}$ of functions equals zero *if we consider these functions only on the set S.*

But this limiting oscillation equals unity if we consider the $f_n(z)$ in a full neighborhood of $z = 1$ (*cf.* § 181 above). For if it were zero even then, the functions $f_n(z)$ would have to be uniformly bounded in some circle $|z - 1| < r_0$ (*cf.* § 189 above). The same would then be true of the $|f_n(z) - f_{n-1}(z)| = |a_n z^n|$, and the radius of convergence of the series (215.1) would have to be > 1, whereas it was assumed to be $= 1$.

CHAPTER FOUR

PARTIAL-FRACTION DECOMPOSITION AND
THE CALCULUS OF RESIDUES

The Laurent Expansion (§§ 216-218)

216. Let us consider an analytic function $f(z)$ that is single-valued and regular on the unit circle $|z| = 1$. The function must then have these same properties throughout a circular annulus

$$r_2 < |z| < r_1 \qquad\qquad (r_2 < 1 < r_1). \qquad (216.1)$$

Denoting the circle $|z| = r_j$ by $\varkappa_j$ $(j = 1, 2)$, we obtain from Cauchy's Integral Formula (*cf.* § 130 above) the following equation, valid for every point z of the annulus (216.1):

$$f(z) = \frac{1}{2\pi i} \int_{\varkappa_1} \frac{f(\zeta_1)}{\zeta_1 - z}\, d\zeta_1 - \frac{1}{2\pi i} \int_{\varkappa_2} \frac{f(\zeta_2)}{\zeta_2 - z}\, d\zeta_2; \qquad (216.2)$$

here, each of the two integrals is to be taken over its circle in the positive sense. By § 208 above, the first of these integrals may be expanded in a power series,

$$\frac{1}{2\pi i} \int_{\varkappa_1} \frac{f(\zeta_1)}{\zeta_1 - z}\, d\zeta_1 = c_0 + c_1 z + c_2 z^2 + \cdots, \qquad (216.3)$$

whose radius R_1 of convergence is at least r_1. To obtain a similar expansion for the second integral, we first write—noting that $|\zeta_2| < |z|$—

$$-\frac{1}{\zeta_2 - z} = \frac{1}{z} \cdot \frac{1}{1 - \dfrac{\zeta_2}{z}} = \frac{1}{z} + \frac{\zeta_2}{z^2} + \cdots + \frac{\zeta_2^k}{z^{k+1}} + \frac{\zeta_2^{k+1}}{z^{k+1}(z - \zeta_2)}. \qquad (216.4)$$

From this we obtain

$$-\frac{1}{2\pi i} \int_{\varkappa_2} \frac{f(\zeta_2)}{\zeta_2 - z}\, d\zeta_2 = \frac{c_{-1}}{z} + \frac{c_{-2}}{z^2} + \frac{c_{-3}}{z^3} + \cdots, \qquad (216.5)$$

where the power series

217

$$\mathfrak{P}_2(t) = c_{-1}\,t + c_{-2}\,t^2 + c_{-3}\,t^3 + \cdots \tag{216.6}$$

has a radius of convergence $1/R_2$ that is at least equal to $1/r_2$. The coefficients $c_0,\ c_1,\ c_2,\ \ldots$ occurring in (216.3), and the coefficients $c_{-1}, c_{-2}, \ldots$ occurring in (216.5), are given by

$$c_k = \frac{1}{2\,\pi\,i} \int_{\varkappa_1} \frac{f(\zeta_1)}{\zeta_1^{k+1}}\,d\zeta_1, \quad c_{-k} = \frac{1}{2\,\pi\,i} \int_{\varkappa_2} \zeta_2^{k-1}\, f(\zeta_2)\,d\zeta_2.$$

But by Cauchy's theorem of § 129, we can also represent them in terms of integrals taken along the unit circle $(\,|\,z\,| = 1)$, which yields for all of these coefficients the one uniform formula

$$c_k = \frac{1}{2\,\pi\,i} \int_{\varkappa} \frac{f(\zeta)}{\zeta^{k+1}}\,d\zeta \quad (k = 0, \pm 1, \pm 2, \ldots). \tag{216.7}$$

Thus we have obtained a theorem associated with the name of M. P. H. Laurent (1841-1908), the series development below being known as the *Laurent expansion* (or *Laurent series*) of $f(z)$:

Any analytic function $f(z)$ that is single-valued and regular on the unit circle $|\,z\,| = 1$ can be represented by a series

$$f(z) = \sum_{k=-\infty}^{\infty} c_k\, z^k \tag{216.8}$$

that converges absolutely and continuously in a circular annulus containing the circle $|\,z\,| = 1$.

217.   Conversely, given that in the annulus $r_2 < |z| < r_1$ $(1 < r_1, r_2 < 1)$ the Laurent series

$$f(z) = \sum_{k=-\infty}^{\infty} a_k\, z^k \tag{217.1}$$

is convergent, it follows that the sequence of numbers $|\,a_k\,|$ must have a finite upper bound, since otherwise the series (217.1) could not converge at $z = 1$.   Then each of the two power series

$$f_1(z) = \sum_{k=0}^{\infty} a_k\, z^k, \quad \varphi_2(t) = \sum_{k=1}^{\infty} a_{-k}\, t^k \tag{217.2}$$

has a radius of convergence greater than unity.   Therefore

$$f_2(z) = \varphi_2\!\left(\frac{1}{z}\right) = \sum_{k=1}^{\infty} a_{-k} \cdot \frac{1}{z^k}\ , \tag{217.3}$$

is defined for all $|z| > 1$, and the power series

$$f_1(z) = f(z) - f_2(z)$$

is convergent in the disc $|z| < r_1$, and hence *a fortiori* in the annulus $r_2 < |z| < r_1$. It follows similarly that $f_2(z)$ is convergent in the annulus. If $R_1 > 1$ is the radius of convergence of the power series $f_1(z)$ and $1/R_2 > 1$ that of the power series $\varphi_2(t)$, we see that in a certain neighborhood of the unit circle $|z| = 1$, the Laurent series (217.1) is the sum of an analytic function $f_1(z)$ regular in the disc $|z| < R_1$ and an analytic function $f_2(z)$ regular in the exterior $|z| > R_2$ of the circle $|z| = R_2$ and zero at $z = \infty$.

Therefore the Laurent series (217.1) is absolutely and continuously convergent on the unit circle, and is integrable term by term along this circle. The same is true of the series

$$\frac{f(z)}{z^{k+1}} = \frac{a_k}{z} + \sum_{n=1}^{\infty} a_{k+n} z^{n-1} + \sum_{n=1}^{\infty} a_{k-n} \cdot \frac{1}{z^{n+1}}$$

for all positive and negative integers k. Hence we have the formula

$$a_k = \frac{1}{2\pi i} \int_{\varkappa} \frac{f(\zeta)}{\zeta^{k+1}} \, d\zeta, \tag{217.4}$$

which implies that the Laurent series (217.1) cannot represent the constant zero unless each of the coefficients $a_0, a_1, a_{-1}, a_2, a_{-2}, \ldots$ vanishes separately. This proves the *uniqueness* of the representation (216.8) of the function $f(z)$, as given in the preceding section. It also proves that the decomposition $f(z) = f_1(z) + f_2(z)$ is uniquely determined by the properties of the functions $f_1(z)$ and $f_2(z)$ as stated above.

218. By means of a simple transformation, the results of the two preceding sections can be applied to any analytic function $f(z)$ that is single-valued and regular along any given circle

$$|z - a| = \varrho. \tag{218.1}$$

To this end, it suffices to note that the function $\varphi(u) = f(a + \varrho u)$ can be developed in a Laurent series based upon the circle $|u| = 1$. Hence there is *one and only one* decomposition

$$f(z) = f_1(z) + f_2(z) \tag{218.2}$$

which is such that $f_1(z)$ is regular in a disc $|z - a| < R_1$, where $R_1 > \varrho$, and $f_2(z)$ is regular in a region $|z - a| > R_2$, where $R_2 < \varrho$. Also, we can write

$$f(z) = \sum_{\nu = -\infty}^{\infty} c_\nu \, (z - a)^\nu, \tag{218.3}$$

where the coefficients c_ν are given by the formula

$$c_\nu = \frac{1}{2\pi i} \int_\varkappa \frac{f(\zeta)}{(\zeta - a)^{\nu+1}} \, d\zeta \quad (\nu = 0, \pm 1, \pm 2, \ldots). \tag{218.4}$$

Hence if we denote the maximum of $|f(z)|$ on the circle (218.1) by M, we have the inequality

$$|c_\nu| \, \varrho^\nu \leq M \quad (\nu = 0, \pm 1, \pm 2, \ldots). \tag{218.5}$$

Let us denote the radii of convergence of the two power series

$$\varphi_1(t) = \sum_{\nu=0}^{\infty} c_\nu t^\nu, \quad \varphi_2(t) = \sum_{\nu=1}^{\infty} c_{-\nu} t^\nu \tag{218.6}$$

by R_1 and $1/R_2$, respectively. If the first of these series represents an integral function, then $R_1 = \infty$; if the second does, then $R_2 = 0$.

In particular, the function $f(z)$ is regular in the whole disc $|z - a| < \varrho$ if and only if all of the c_ν with negative subscripts vanish. For this in turn to hold, it is necessary and sufficient that the equations

$$\int_\varkappa \zeta^n f(\zeta) \, d\zeta = 0 \quad (n = 0, 1, 2, \ldots) \tag{218.7}$$

should all be satisfied.

If $\varphi_2(t)$ is a polynomial of degree p, then the function $f(z)$ has a pole of order p at the point $z = a$. If $\varphi_2(t)$ is a transcendental integral function, then $f(z)$ has an essential singularity at $z = a$. In either of these two cases, $R_2 = 0$.

Analytic Functions with Finitely Many Isolated Singularities (§ 219)

219. We are now able to find specific representations for the most general analytic functions $f(z)$ that in the whole complex plane have only a finite number of isolated singularities, say at $a_1, a_2, \ldots, a_p$. Some of them may be essential singularities, some of them poles.

It is merely necessary to observe that in a certain neighborhood of each of these points a_j, an equation of the form

$$f(z) = h_j(z) + \varphi_j(z) \qquad (219.1)$$

holds, where $\varphi_j(z)$ is regular at a_j and where

$$h_j(z) = \mathfrak{P}_j\left(\frac{1}{z - a_j}\right), \qquad (219.2)$$

$\mathfrak{P}_j(t)$ being either a polynomial or a power series that converges in the whole t-plane and vanishes at $t = 0$. If we set

$$h(z) = h_1(z) + h_2(z) + \cdots + h_p(z), \qquad (219.3)$$

then the function

$$\varphi(z) = f(z) - h(z) \qquad (219.4)$$

is regular at every point of the complex plane, and hence is an *integral function*. To determine also the function $\varphi(z)$ by means of Laurent's theorem, we make use of the fact that $f(z)$ is regular for all z satisfying

$$|z| \geqq \varrho = |a_1| + |a_2| + \cdots + |a_p| + 1.$$

Hence we may write

$$\left. \begin{aligned} f(z) &= g(z) + k(z), \\ k(z) &= \mathfrak{P}\left(\frac{1}{z}\right), \quad \mathfrak{P}(0) = 0, \end{aligned} \right\} \qquad (219.5)$$

where $g(z)$ is an integral function and $\mathfrak{P}_j(t)$ is a power series whose radius of convergence is greater than $1/\varrho$.

From (219.4) and (219.5) it follows that

$$\varphi(z) - g(z) = k(z) - h(z). \qquad (219.6)$$

In the region $|z| > \varrho$, each of the two analytic functions $h(z)$ and $k(z)$ is regular and bounded; therefore by Liouville's theorem (*cf.* § 167 above), the integral function $\varphi(z) - g(z)$ must be a constant c. In order to determine c, we consider a sequence of points z_ν converging to $z = \infty$ and find that

$$c = \lim_{\nu = \infty} [k(z_\nu) - h(z_\nu)] = 0.$$

Thus we finally have the formula

$$f(z) = g(z) + h_1(z) + h_2(z) + \cdots + h_p(z), \qquad (219.7)$$

which serves to represent the given function $f(z)$ in terms of the integral function $g(z)$ and the everywhere-convergent power series $\mathfrak{P}_j(t)$.

Mittag-Leffler's Theorem   (§§220-222)

220. We shall now make use of the results of the preceding section to study functions that have an infinite number of isolated singularities. To be sure, those results cannot just be carried over without further ado to functions of this kind. Thus if the poles of a function $f(z)$ are located, say, at the points $z = 1, 2, 3, \ldots$, and if the term corresponding to a neighborhood of the pole $z = n$ in the decomposition (219.1) is given by

$$h_n(z) = \frac{1}{n - z}, \tag{220.1}$$

then we *cannot* write, by analogy with (219.3),

$$h(z) = \sum_{n=1}^{\infty} h_n(z), \tag{220.2}$$

because this series nowhere converges to a finite value. This difficulty was first overcome in many special cases, and finally, Mittag-Leffler (1846-1927) devised a general method that works for *all* cases.[1]

We begin by considering, in the extended complex plane, a denumerable set A of points $a_1, a_2, \ldots$ each of which is isolated, and we denote by T the closed set consisting of the points of accumulation of A. Then for the chordal distance from T of each of the points a_j, we have

$$\chi(a_j, T) = \delta_j > 0, \tag{220.3}$$

and there is on T at least one point α_j for which $\chi(a_j, \alpha_j) = \delta_j$.

We next assign to each of the points a_j an analytic function $h_j(z)$, defined by

$$\left. \begin{array}{ll} h_j(z) = \mathfrak{P}_j\left(\dfrac{1}{z - a_j}\right), & \text{if} \quad a_j \neq \infty, \\[2mm] h_j(z) = \mathfrak{P}(z), & \text{if} \quad a_j = \infty, \end{array} \right\} \tag{220.4}$$

which is regular on the entire Riemann sphere with the exception of the single

---

[1] In connection with Mittag-Leffler's theorem, mention should be made of the name of Weierstrass. For in developing his theory of elliptic functions, Weierstrass had been led to forming integral functions with arbitrarily prescribed zeros, i.e. with a set of zeros that coincided with an arbitrary given set of isolated points. He constructed such functions with prescribed zeros in the form of infinite products that converge continuously in the whole plane. Mittag-Leffler, who was a student of Weierstrass, noticed that the study of the logarithmic derivative of the Weierstrass products offers certain advantages, and he was able thus to extend the results to quite general distributions of singularities.

point a_j. We now set ourselves the problem of constructing a function $f(z)$ that is to be regular at every point z other than points of A and of T, and that is such that for all $j = 1, 2, \ldots$ the difference $[f(z) - h_j(z)]$ is regular at the point a_j (or more precisely, can be made regular at a_j by suitably defining its value at this point).

To this end, we assign a sequence $\varepsilon_1, \varepsilon_2, \varepsilon_3, \ldots$ of positive numbers whose sum is finite, and we then assign to each of the functions $h_j(z)$ a rational function $r_j(z)$ having the following properties: If $\delta_j \geq 1/2$, we take $r_j(z) \equiv 0$; if $\delta_j < 1/2$, then $r_j(z)$ is to have a single pole at the point $z = a_j$, and on the point set $\chi(z, \alpha_j) \geq 2 \delta_j$ it is to satisfy the relation

$$|h_j(z) + r_j(z)| < \varepsilon_j. \tag{220.5}$$

In order to find such a function $r_j(z)$, we shall make use of the transformation

$$u = \frac{\bar{\alpha}_j z + 1}{z - \alpha_j}, \quad z = \frac{\alpha_j u + 1}{u - \bar{\alpha}_j}, \tag{220.6}$$

which represents a rotation of the Riemann sphere by which the point $z = a_j$ is mapped onto the point $u = \infty$, while the region $\chi(z, \alpha_j) \geq 2 \delta_j$ is mapped onto the closed circular disc

$$|u| \leq \frac{\sqrt{1 - 4 \delta_j^2}}{2 \delta_j} \tag{220.7}$$

(*cf.* §§ 60 and 78). The transformed function

$$H_j(u) = h_j \left(\frac{\alpha_j u + 1}{u - \bar{\alpha}_j} \right) \tag{220.8}$$

of $h_j(z)$ then has its only singularity outside the disc (220.7), and its Taylor expansion

$$H_j(u) = c_0 + c_1 u + c_2 u^2 + \cdots$$

converges uniformly on the disc (220.7). We can therefore choose a natural number m_j large enough for the polynomial

$$R_j(u) = - c_0 - c_1 u - \cdots - c_{m_j} u^{m_j} \tag{220.9}$$

to satisfy, at all the points of the disc (220.7), the condition

$$|H_j(u) + R_j(u)| < \varepsilon_j.$$

Then the rational function

$$r_j(z) = R_j \left(\frac{\bar{\alpha}_j z + 1}{z - \alpha_j} \right) \tag{220.10}$$

clearly has all of the required properties.

221. Now it is practically obvious that the series

$$f(z) = \sum_{j=1}^{\infty} [h_j(z) + r_j(z)] \tag{221.1}$$

converges continuously at every point z_0 of the plane other than points of A and of T, and that at each point a_j, the series

$$\sum_{n=j+1}^{\infty} [h_n(z) + r_n(z)] \tag{221.2}$$

converges continuously, so that the function $f(z)$ given by (221.1) answers all of the requirements imposed on $f(z)$ as described in the preceding section. For if $3\varDelta$ denotes the chordal distance $\chi(z_0, T)$ between z_0 and the closed set T, and if $U_\varDelta$ is the open point set consisting of all the points z for which $\chi(z, T) > \varDelta$ holds, then $U_\varDelta$ contains *at most finitely many* of the points a_j. Hence there is a natural number m such that for $j \geqq m$, we have $\delta_j = \chi(a_j, T) \leqq \varDelta$. For $j \geqq m$, the two discs $\chi(z, \alpha_j) \leqq 2\,\delta_j$ and $\chi(z, z_0) \leqq \varDelta$ have no points in common; hence for all the points of a certain neighborhood of z_0, we have

$$\left| \sum_{j=m}^{\infty} [h_j(z) + r_j(z)] \right| \leqq \sum_{j=m}^{\infty} |h_j(z) + r_j(z)| \leqq \varepsilon_m + \varepsilon_{m+1} + \cdots. \tag{221.3}$$

Thus we may now derive the above-mentioned properties of the series (221.1) and (221.2) as immediate consequences of the results of § 204.

222. The complement of the set T is an open point set consisting of one or more regions $G, G', \cdots$. Let $F(z)$ be any analytic function that is regular at all of the points, other than those belonging to the denumerable set A, of one of these regions, say of G. Also, assume that for each of the points a_j that also lie in G, there is a neighborhood of a_j in which $F(z)$ can be written in the form

$$F(z) = h_j(z) + \psi_j(z),$$

where $\psi_j(z)$ denotes an analytic function regular at a_j. If $f(z)$ again denotes the function in (221.1) above, then the difference $F(z) - f(z)$ is a function $g(z)$ that is regular at every point of G. Hence any function $F(z)$ having the properties described above can be represented in the form

$$F(z) = f(z) + g(z),$$

where $g(z)$ is regular in G.

However, the various functions that one obtains in this way for *different* regions in the complement of T are not related to each other at all.

The great importance of Mittag-Leffler's theorem lies in the fact that the singular points a_j as well as the functions $h_j(z)$—which are called the *principal parts* of $F(z)$ at the point a_j—can be chosen at will. The theorem guarantees the existence of quite complicated single-valued analytic functions having certain prescribed properties. Needless to say, for many of the most important cases the location of the a_j and the choice of the $h_j(z)$ are quite simple.

Meromorphic Functions with Prescribed Simple[1] Poles (§ 223)

223. In this section we shall apply Mittag-Leffler's theorem to functions that are meromorphic in the whole plane and have simple poles at an infinite number of pre-assigned points $a_1, a_2, \ldots$ $(a_j \neq 0)$. Then we must have

$$\lim_{j=\infty} a_j = \infty, \qquad (223.1)$$

$$\left. \begin{aligned} h_j(z) &= \frac{c_j}{z - a_j} \\ &= -\frac{c_j}{a_j} \cdot \frac{1}{1 - \dfrac{z}{a_j}} \\ &= -c_j \left(\frac{1}{a_j} + \frac{z}{a_j^2} + \cdots + \frac{z^{n_j-1}}{a_j^{n_j}} + \frac{z^{n_j}}{a_j^{n_j}(a_j - z)} \right). \end{aligned} \right\} \qquad (223.2)$$

According to the general method of § 221 above, we may therefore take all of the a_j to be at the point ∞, and we may set

$$r_j(z) = \frac{c_j}{a_j} + \frac{c_j}{a_j^2} z + \cdots + \frac{c_j}{a_j^{n_j}} z^{n_j-1}, \quad h_j(z) + r_j(z) = \frac{c_j z^{n_j}}{a_j^{n_j}(z - a_j)}, \quad (223.3)$$

provided only that the natural numbers n_j are chosen in such a way that the series

$$f(z) = \sum_{j=1}^{\infty} [h_j(z) + r_j(z)] = \sum_{j=1}^{\infty} \frac{c_j z^{n_j}}{a_j^{n_j}(z - a_j)} \qquad (223.4)$$

converges continuously at every point of the complex plane. Conversely, for any such choice of the n_j, formula (223.4) furnishes a function of the required kind.

To find out how the n_j must be chosen, we first note that for any fixed value

---

[1] A *simple* pole is a pole of order unity.

of z, and for all sufficiently large integers j, we have $2|z| < |a_j|$, which implies that

$$\frac{2}{3|a_j|} < \frac{1}{|z - a_j|} < \frac{2}{|a_j|}$$

holds. From this it follows that the right-hand side of (223.4) and the power series

$$\sum_{j=1}^{\infty} \frac{|c_j|}{|a_j^{n_j+1}|} z^{n_j} \tag{223.5}$$

converge continuously at the same points of the complex plane. *We must therefore choose the natural numbers n_j in such a way that the power series (223.5) represents an integral function.*

This condition can of course be satisfied by any number of choices of the n_j. But it is desirable to keep the n_j as small as possible. If, for instance, the relation

$$\sum_{j=1}^{\infty} \frac{|c_j|}{|a_j|} < +\infty$$

holds true, then we may take all of the functions $r_j(z)$ to be $\equiv 0$. Or if for some natural number m we know that

$$\sum_{j=1}^{\infty} \frac{|c_j|}{|a_j^{m+1}|} < +\infty,$$

then we may take all of the n_j to have one and the same value, namely m.

Finally, if all of the $|c_j|$ have a common finite upper bound, or if, more generally,

$$\lim_{j=\infty} \frac{|c_j|^{\frac{1}{j+1}}}{|a_j|} = 0,$$

then we may choose $n_1 = 1, n_2 = 2, \cdots, n_j = j, \cdots$.

The Residue and its Applications (§§ 224-225)

224. Consider an analytic function $f(z)$ that has either a pole or an isolated essential singularity at the point $z = a$ $(a \neq \infty)$. If we apply formula (218.4) to $f(z)$, then we obtain, for $\nu = -1$,

$$c_{-1} = \frac{1}{2\pi i} \int_{\varkappa} f(\zeta) \, d\zeta. \tag{224.1}$$

Here $\varkappa$ denotes any sufficiently small circle with center at a. The number c_{-1} is called the *residue of* $f(z)$ *at the point* a, a term introduced by Cauchy.

More generally, consider a function $f(z)$ that is regular on a (closed) Jordan curve γ, as well as in the interior of this curve with the exception of a finite number of points $a^{(1)}, a^{(2)}, \ldots, a^{(p)}$. If $c_{-1}^{(v)}$ denotes the residue of $f(z)$ at the point $a^{(v)}$, then by § 127 above we have

$$\frac{1}{2\pi i} \int_\gamma f(\zeta)\, d\zeta = c_{-1}^{(1)} + c_{-1}^{(2)} + \cdots + c_{-1}^{(p)}. \tag{224.2}$$

Thus in order to evaluate the integral on the left-hand side of (224.2), it suffices to know the residues $c_{-1}^{(v)}$. In many cases it is quite easy to obtain these residues. Cauchy used this fact, and relation (224.2), for a great many applications.

If the function $f(z)$ is regular in the region exterior to a circle $\varkappa$, then the residue of $f(z)$ at the point $z = \infty$ is defined to be the value of the integral

$$- \frac{1}{2\pi i} \int_\varkappa f(\zeta)\, d\zeta.$$

Thus if we represent the function $f(z)$ by means of a Laurent series

$$\sum_{v = -\infty}^{\infty} c_v z^v$$

in a neighborhood of $z = \infty$, then the residue of $f(z)$ at $z = \infty$ is given by the number $- c_{-1}$. This definition has the advantage that for any function that is regular in the whole plane except for a finite number of poles or essential singularities, the sum of all its residues is clearly equal to zero.

225. In this section we derive the most important of the applications of the calculus of residues that we wish to consider in this book. Let $f(z)$ be a function that is meromorphic in the interior region G of a rectifiable Jordan curve γ, and that is regular and different from zero at every point of the curve γ itself. Let $g(z)$ be a function that is regular both on and within γ. We wish to evaluate the integral

$$J = \frac{1}{2\pi i} \int_\gamma g(\zeta)\, \frac{f'(\zeta)}{f(\zeta)}\, d\zeta. \tag{225.1}$$

At every point of G at which $f(z)$ is regular and has a non-zero value, the function $g(z)f'(z)/f(z)$ is regular. But at a point a at which $f(z)$ has a zero of order n, we may write

$$f(z) = (z - a)^n \, \varphi(z), \quad \varphi(a) \neq 0,$$

$$f'(z) = n \, (z - a)^{n-1} \, \varphi(z) + (z - a)^n \, \varphi'(z),$$

$$g(z) \, \frac{f'(z)}{f(z)} = \frac{n \, g(a)}{z - a} + n \cdot \frac{g(z) - g(a)}{z - a} + g(z) \, \frac{\varphi'(z)}{\varphi(z)} \, ; \qquad (225.2)$$

from this it follows that the residue of the function $g(z) f'(z)/f(z)$ at the zero a of order n is equal to $n g(a)$. In the same way, the residue of this function at a point $z = b$ at which $f(z)$ has a pole of order m is found to be $- m g(b)$.

If the zeros of $f(z)$ in the region G are denoted by $a^{(1)}, a^{(2)}, \ldots, a^{(p)}$ and the poles of $f(z)$ in G by $b^{(1)}, b^{(2)}, \ldots, b^{(q)}$, zeros or poles of orders higher than 1 being accounted for by listing the corresponding points $a^{(\nu)}, b^{(\mu)}$ an appropriate number of times, then it is clear from what we found above that the value J of the integral (225.1) is given by

$$J = \sum_{\nu=1}^{p} g(a^{(\nu)}) - \sum_{\nu=1}^{q} g(b^{(\nu)}). \qquad (225.3)$$

The Number of Zeros of a Function, and Rouché's Theorem (§ 226)

226. The result that we have proved in § 225 above is useful in many applications. Consider, for example, an analytic function $f(z)$ that is regular in the region G and $\neq 0$ on the boundary γ of G, and take the function $g(z)$ of § 225 to be $\equiv 1$. Then (225.3) shows that the integral

$$\frac{1}{2 \pi i} \int_{\gamma} \frac{f'(\zeta)}{f(\zeta)} \, d\zeta , \qquad (226.1)$$

the so-called *logarithmic residue of* f, equals the number of zeros of $f(z)$ in G, so that its value is a positive integer or zero. But if we allow $f(z)$ to have poles in G, then by (225.3), the integral (226.1) equals $(N - P)$, the difference between the number N of zeros and the number P of poles of $f(z)$ in G, each zero and each pole counted with the proper multiplicity.

Next, consider once more a function $f(z)$ that is regular in G, and a second function $\psi(z)$ that is likewise regular in G and for which at every point ζ of the boundary γ of G, we have the relation

$$|\psi(\zeta)| < |f(\zeta)|. \qquad (226.2)$$

If $m > 0$ denotes the minimum of the difference $|f(\zeta)| - |\psi(\zeta)|$ as ζ ranges over the curve γ, and if λ is any number from the interval $0 \leq \lambda \leq 1$, then

$$|f(\zeta) + \lambda\, \psi(\zeta)| \geq m > 0. \qquad (226.3)$$

This implies that the integral

$$J(\lambda) = \frac{1}{2\pi i} \int_{\gamma} \frac{f'(\zeta) + \lambda\, \psi'(\zeta)}{f(\zeta) + \lambda\, \psi(\zeta)}\, d\zeta$$

is a continuous function of λ as λ ranges over the interval $0 \leq \lambda \leq 1$. On the other hand, $J(\lambda)$ must be a non-negative *integer*; hence $J(\lambda)$ must be a constant, so that $J(0) = J(1)$, that is,

$$\frac{1}{2\pi i} \int_{\gamma} \frac{f'(\zeta) + \psi'(\zeta)}{f(\zeta) + \psi(\zeta)}\, d\zeta = \frac{1}{2\pi i} \int_{\gamma} \frac{f'(\zeta)}{f(\zeta)}\, d\zeta.$$

This relation implies the following theorem, due to E. Rouché (1832-1910) :

If the two functions $f(z)$ and $\psi(z)$ are regular in a region G and if $|\psi(\zeta)| < |f(\zeta)|$ holds at every point ζ of the boundary γ of G, then the two functions $f(z)$ and $f(z) + \psi(z)$ have the same number of zeros in G.

The Inverse of an Analytic Function (§§ 227-228)

227. Let $f(z)$ be a function whose value at $z = 0$ is zero but whose derivative at $z = 0$ is $\neq 0$:

$$f(0) = 0, \quad f'(0) \neq 0, \qquad (227.1)$$

or, which is the same,

$$f(z) = z h(z), \qquad h(0) \neq 0.$$

Then there are Jordan curves γ that contain the point $z = 0$ in their interior and which are such that $f(z)$ has no zeros other than $z = 0$ in the interior of γ nor on γ itself. Let m denote the minimum of $|f(\zeta)|$ as ζ ranges over such a curve γ.

Now if $|w| < m$, then by Rouché's theorem, the function $[f(z) - w]$ has *one and only one* zero inside γ. To locate this zero, we replace $f(z)$ on the right-hand side of (225.1) by the function $[f(z) - w]$, and we replace $g(z)$ by z, and thus by (225.3) find the zero to be at

$$z = \frac{1}{2\pi i} \int_{\gamma} \zeta \cdot \frac{f'(\zeta)}{f(\zeta) - w}\, d\zeta. \qquad (227.2)$$

We can verify by an easy calculation that the right-hand side of (227.2) is an analytic function $\varphi(w)$ of w that is regular in the disc $|w| < m$, or perhaps even in a larger disc.

In certain neighborhoods of the two corresponding points $z = 0$, $w = 0$, the two equations

$$w = f(z), \quad z = \varphi(w) \tag{227.3}$$

represent the *same* functional relation between z and w. For by the above developments, the second of the equations (227.3) assigns to every (interior) point of the disc $|w| < m$ a point z lying inside the curve γ, and we have the identity

$$w = f(\varphi(w)) \quad \text{for } |w| < m. \tag{227.4}$$

Hence to any two distinct points w_1, w_2 of the disc $|w| < m$, there correspond two distinct values $z_1 = \varphi(w_1)$, $z_2 = \varphi(w_2)$ of the function $\varphi(w)$. Thus the function $\varphi(w)$ is *simple* in the disc $|w| < m$. As w ranges over the disc $|w| < m$, then by the neighborhood-preserving character of the analytic function φ, the point z describes a region G^* that lies in the interior of the curve γ and contains the point $z = 0$. For all of the points of G^*, we then have the following analogue of (227.4) above:

$$z = \varphi(f(z)) \quad \text{for } z \in G^*. \tag{227.5}$$

Also, the function $f(z)$ is simple in the region G^*.

228. The results of the preceding section can be generalized immediately to a function $f(z)$ having a non-zero derivative at a point z_0 (which need not be the point 0), so that we know in particular that in a certain neighborhood of $f(z_0)$, the inverse function $\varphi(w)$ of $f(z)$ is a regular analytic function. If we set $f(z_0) = w_0$ and develop $f(z)$ in a power series for a neighborhood of z_0, we may write

$$w - w_0 = a_1 (z - z_0) + a_2 (z - z_0)^2 + \cdots \quad (a_1 \neq 0), \tag{228.1}$$

while for $\varphi(w)$, we have a power-series expansion of the form

$$z - z_0 = A_1 (w - w_0) + A_2 (w - w_0)^2 + \cdots, \tag{228.2}$$

the coefficients of which can be calculated one by one in terms of the a_n. To obtain them, we must substitute the power series (228.2) for $z - z_0$ in the power series (228.1), re-arrange the coefficients, and then equate the resulting coefficient of $(w - w_0)$ to 1, the coefficient of every higher power of $(w - w_0)$ to 0. We know that the series (228.2) has a non-zero radius of convergence, even if we cannot estimate its size by any general methods.

Using the procedure just described, we obtain the following expressions for the first few of the coefficients in (228.2):

$$A_1 = \frac{1}{a_1}, \quad A_2 = -\frac{a_2}{a_1^3}, \quad A_3 = \frac{2\,a_2^2 - a_1\,a_3}{a_1^5},$$

$$A_4 = \frac{-5\,a_2^3 + 5\,a_1\,a_2\,a_3 - a_1^2\,a_4}{a_1^7},$$

$$A_5 = \frac{14\,a_2^4 - 21\,a_1\,a_2^2\,a_3 + 3\,a_1^2\,(2\,a_2\,a_4 + a_3^2) - a_1^3\,a_5}{a_1^9}.$$

(228.3)

As the developments of § 229 below will imply (*cf.* especially equation (229.8) below), we may write generally

$$A_n = \frac{1}{n!}\left\{ \frac{d^{n-1}}{dz^{n-1}}\left(\frac{z - z_0}{f(z)}\right)^n \right\}_{z\,=\,z_0},$$

(228.4)

but this formula is not always convenient to use.

Lagrange's Series (§§ 229-230)

229. We continue here with the same notation and with the same assumptions as in § 227 above. If $g(z)$ is any analytic function that is regular on and inside the curve γ, then the results of § 225 above, applied to the function $[f(z) - w]$ in place of $f(z)$, yield

$$g(z) = \frac{1}{2\pi i}\int_\gamma g(\zeta)\,\frac{\cdot f'(\zeta)}{f(\zeta) - w}\,d\zeta,$$

(229.1)

and just as in § 227 above, we see that here too, the variables w and z are related by the equation

$$w = f(z).$$

(229.2)

The integrand on the right-hand side of (229.1) can be developed in a power series in w, and the resulting series of powers of w converges uniformly for $|w| < m$ and for all ζ on the curve γ. Hence this power series can be integrated term by term over the curve γ. In this way we obtain the relations

$$g(z) = g(0) + k_1\,w + k_2\,w^2 + k_3\,w^3 + \cdots,$$

(229.3)

$$k_n = \frac{1}{2\pi i}\int_\gamma g(\zeta)\,\frac{f'(\zeta)}{f(\zeta)^{n+1}}\,d\zeta \qquad (n = 1, 2, \ldots).$$

(229.4)

Now we shall make use of integration by parts, which applies to integrals of complex functions in the following form: If $u(z)$ and $v(z)$ are analytic functions that are regular and single-valued at every point of a curve γ, then we have

$$\frac{1}{2\pi i}\int_\gamma \frac{d}{d\zeta}(u\, v)\, d\zeta = 0,$$

which implies that

$$-\frac{1}{2\pi i}\int_\gamma u(\zeta)\, v'(\zeta)\, d\zeta = \frac{1}{2\pi i}\int_\gamma u'(\zeta)\, v(\zeta)\, d\zeta. \tag{229.5}$$

If we note that

$$\frac{f'(\zeta)}{f(\zeta)^{n+1}} = -\frac{1}{n}\cdot \frac{d}{d\zeta}\left(\frac{1}{f(\zeta)}\right)^n, \tag{229.6}$$

we see that (229.4) can now be re-written in the form

$$k_n = \frac{1}{2n\pi i}\int_\gamma \frac{g'(\zeta)}{f(\zeta)^n}\, d\zeta. \tag{229.7}$$

Hence the coefficient k_n of w^n in the power series (229.3) is equal to the n-th part of the residue of the function $g'(z)/f(z)^n$ at the point $z=0$, or, which is the same, to the n-th part of the coefficient of z^{n-1} in the power series expansion of the function $g'(z)\cdot z^n/f(z)^n$.

Since the latter function is regular at the point $z=0$ too, it now follows that

$$k_n = \frac{1}{n!}\left\{\frac{d^{n-1}}{dz^{n-1}}\left(\frac{g'(z)\, z^n}{f(z)^n}\right)\right\}_{z=0}. \tag{229.8}$$

230. In this section we shall obtain an important generalization of the formulas just derived, one that is useful in many applications.

Let $\varphi(z)$ be an analytic function that is regular and different from zero in a region G. Let γ be a Jordan curve lying in G, along with its interior, and let a be any point in the interior of γ. If in equation (229.1) above we take

$$f(z) = \frac{z-a}{\varphi(z)}, \tag{230.1}$$

then by applying the developments of the preceding section to the new function $f(z)$, we obtain

$$\left.\begin{aligned}
g(z) &= g(a) + k_1 w + k_2 w^2 + \cdots,\\[4pt]
k_n &= \frac{1}{n!}\left\{\frac{d^{n-1}}{dz^{n-1}}\left[g'(z)\,\varphi(z)^n\right]\right\}_{z=a}
\end{aligned}\right\} \tag{230.2}$$

This series is known as *Lagrange's series*. If $m(a, \gamma)$ denotes the minimum of the function

$$\frac{|\zeta - a|}{|\varphi(\zeta)|} \tag{230.3}$$

as ζ ranges over the curve γ, then the series (230.2) certainly converges in the disc $|w| < m(a, \gamma)$, and may converge in a larger disc. By (230.2), the coefficients k_n are regular functions of a.

By following a different method[1] of derivation, we shall be able to dispense with the condition—inherent above in (230.1) and the regularity requirements on $f(z)$—that $\varphi(z)$ be free of zeros inside the curve γ. To do this, we denote the points of γ by ζ and set

$$M = \max \left| \frac{\varphi(\zeta)}{\zeta - a} \right|, \tag{230.4}$$

so that

$$|w_0| < \frac{1}{M} \tag{230.5}$$

implies that, on γ,

$$|w_0 \, \varphi(\zeta)| < |\zeta - a|,$$

whence by Rouché's theorem, the function

$$F(z) = (z - a) - w_0 \, \varphi(z) \tag{230.6}$$

has one single zero z_0, of order unity, inside the curve γ. Therefore we also have $F'(z_0) \neq 0$.

Let $G(z)$ be an analytic function that is regular in a region containing the curve γ in its interior. Then the function $G(z)/F(z)$ has no singularities inside γ except possibly a pole of order unity at the point z_0, where the residue of $G(z)/F(z)$ has the value $G(z_0)/F'(z_0)$. This residue is given by the formula

$$\frac{G(z_0)}{F'(z_0)} = \frac{1}{2\pi i} \int_\gamma \frac{G(\zeta)}{F(\zeta)} \, d\zeta. \tag{230.7}$$

If we substitute the series expansion

$$\frac{1}{F(\zeta)} = \frac{1}{(\zeta - a) - w_0 \, \varphi(\zeta)} = \sum_{n=0}^{\infty} \frac{w_0^n \, \varphi(z)^n}{(\zeta - a)^{n+1}} \tag{230.8}$$

into (230.7), we obtain

$$\frac{G(z_0)}{F'(z_0)} = K_0 + K_1 w_0 + \cdots + K_n w_0^n + \cdots, \tag{230.9}$$

---

[1] *Cf.* E. Rouché, *Journal de l'École Polytechn.*, 39e cahier, p. 193 (1861).

where

$$K_n = \frac{1}{2\pi i} \int_\gamma \frac{G(\zeta)\,\varphi(\zeta)^n}{(\zeta - a)^{n+1}}\, d\zeta. \tag{230.10}$$

The power series (230.9) is convergent in the disc (230.5); for if we denote the maximum of $|G(\zeta)/(\zeta - a)|$ by $2\pi M_0$ and the length of γ by L_γ, then the Mean Value Theorem for integrals yields

$$|K_n\, w_0^n| < M_0\, L_\gamma. \tag{230.11}$$

We also see from (230.10) that

$$K_0 = G(a), \quad K_n = \frac{1}{n!} \cdot \frac{d^n}{da^n}\, [G(a)\,\varphi(a)^n], \tag{230.12}$$

so that we finally have

$$\frac{G(z_0)}{F'(z_0)} = G(a) + \sum_{n=1}^{\infty} \frac{1}{n!} \cdot \frac{d^n}{da^n}\, [G(a)\,\varphi(a)^n]\, w_0^n. \tag{230.13}$$

Now we set

$$G(z) = g(z)\, F'(z) = g(z)\,(1 - w_0\,\varphi'(z)) \tag{230.14}$$

and obtain

$$\frac{G(z_0)}{F'(z_0)} = g(z_0), \quad K_n = K_n' - w_0\, K_n'', \tag{230.15}$$

where

$$K_n' = \frac{1}{n!} \cdot \frac{d^n}{da^n}\, [g(a)\,\varphi(a)^n], \quad K_n'' = \frac{1}{n!} \cdot \frac{d^n}{da^n}\, [g(a)\,\varphi'(a)\,\varphi(a)^n].$$

We can also write

$$\left.\begin{aligned} K_{n-1}'' &= \frac{1}{n!} \cdot \frac{d^{n-1}}{da^{n-1}} \left(g(a)\,\frac{d}{da}\,\varphi(a)^n\right) \\ &= K_n' - \frac{1}{n!} \cdot \frac{d^{n-1}}{da^{n-1}}\, [g'(a)\,\varphi(a)^n]. \end{aligned}\right\} \tag{230.16}$$

Hence by (230.9) and (230.15), we have

$$\left.\begin{aligned} g(z_0) &= (K_0' - w_0\, K_0'') + (K_1' - w_0\, K_1')\, w_0 + \cdots \\ &= k_0 + k_1\, w_0 + k_2\, w_0^2 + \cdots, \end{aligned}\right\} \tag{230.17}$$

where, by (230.16),

$$k_0 = g(a), \quad k_n = K_n' - K_{n-1}'' = \frac{1}{n!} \cdot \frac{d^{n-1}}{da^{n-1}}\, [g'(a)\,\varphi(a)^n]$$

holds. Thus we have again obtained Lagrange's series (230.2).

Kepler's Equation (§ 231)

231. The application of the series of § 230 above to the equation

$$n t = u - e \sin u \qquad (231.1)$$

goes back to Lagrange himself. In this equation, t stands for time, nt for the so-called mean anomaly, u for the eccentric anomaly and e for the eccentricity of the elliptical path of the planet. The problem is to develop u and certain trigonometric functions of u in a power series according to powers of the (usually very small) eccentricity e, with coefficients that are trigonometric functions of nt. To find the connection between equation (230.6) of § 230 above and Kepler's equation (231.1), we must set $u = z$, $nt = a$, $e = w$, so that (231.1) is transformed into

$$z - a - w \sin z = 0 . \qquad (231.2)$$

It suffices to consider real values of a in (231.2). As our curve γ of § 230 above, we shall here take the circle

$$\zeta = a + R\, e^{i \varphi} = (a + R \cos \varphi) + i R \sin \varphi. \qquad (231.3)$$

Then by (241.4) below,

$$|\sin^2 \zeta| = \cosh^2 (R \sin \varphi) - \cos^2 (a + R \cos \varphi), \qquad (231.4)$$

so that, with the notation of (230.4) above,

$$|\sin \zeta| \leqq \cosh R = \frac{e^R + e^{-R}}{2}, \quad M \leqq \frac{e^R + e^{-R}}{2\,R}. \qquad (231.5)$$

Hence by the result of the preceding section, Lagrange's series converges at least for

$$|w| < \frac{2\,R}{e^R + e^{-R}} = \psi(R). \qquad (231.6)$$

We now wish to determine the value of R for which $\psi(R)$ assumes its maximum; for this R,

$$\lambda(R) = (e^R + e^{-R}) - R\,(e^R - e^{-R}) = 0 \qquad (231.7)$$

must hold. Since

$$\lambda'(R) = - R\,(e^R + e^{-R}) < 0,$$

it follows that $\lambda(R)$ has just one positive root R_0 for which the relations

$$e^{R_0} = \frac{R_0 + 1}{\sqrt{R_0^2 - 1}}, \quad e^{-R_0} = \frac{R_0 - 1}{\sqrt{R_0^2 - 1}}, \quad \psi(R_0) = \sqrt{R_0^2 - 1} \qquad (231.8)$$

must also hold. The number R_0 can be calculated by means of successive approximations from the transcendental equation (231.7). Its value to quite a few places was found by T. J. Stieltjes[1] (1856-1894), as follows:

$$R_0 = 1.19967\ 86402\ 57734\ \dots,$$

$$\psi(R_0) = \sqrt{R_0^2 - 1} = 0.66274\ 34193\ 492\ \dots. \qquad\qquad (231.9)$$

The equality sign will hold in relations (231.5) for $a = \varphi = \pi/2$, that is, for $\zeta = \pi/2 + iR$. For this value of ζ, we have

$$\sin\left(\frac{\pi}{2} + i\,R\right) = \cos i\,R = \frac{e^R + e^{-R}}{2}, \quad \cos\left(\frac{\pi}{2} + i\,R\right) = -\sin i\,R = \frac{e^{R} - e^{-R}}{2\,i},$$

$$w(\zeta) = i\,\psi(R), \quad \frac{dw}{dz}\bigg|_{z=\zeta} = \frac{2\,\lambda(R)}{(e^R + e^{-R})^2}.$$

Hence if $R = R_0$, then $w(\zeta)$ lies on the boundary of the disc $|w| \leq 0.662\dots$, and $w'(\zeta) = 0$. But inside the circle of convergence of Lagrange's series for $g(z) = z$, we must have $dz/dw \neq \infty$, hence $dw/dz \neq 0$. Therefore $|w| < \psi(R_0)$ is the largest disc in which Lagrange s series for Kepler's equation (231.1) converges for all values of the time t.

The Monodromy Theorem (§§ 232-233)

232. Let us consider two convex regions G_1 and G_2 in the complex plane that have at least one interior point in common, and let $f_1(z)$ and $f_2(z)$ be two analytic functions that are regular in G_1 and in G_2, respectively. We assume that at every point of the intersection of G_1 and G_2 the two functions coincide, i.e. have the same value. Then in the union $G_1 + G_2$ there is defined a regular analytic function $f(z)$ that coincides with $f_1(z)$ in G_1 and with $f_2(z)$ in G_2. We call $f_2(z)$ the *analytic continuation* of the function $f_1(z)$ into the region G_2.

We consider next a closed line segment AB and a chain of finitely many convex regions G_j whose union $\Sigma \dotplus G_j$ contains the segment AB, and we assign to each of these regions a regular analytic function $f_j(z)$ that is the analytic continuation of $f_{j-1}(z)$. We then say that the function $f_1(z)$ has been continued analytically along the line segment AB. In the union of the given regions G_j, there is thus defined a single-valued, regular analytic function $f(z)$. The same kind of construction can be applied to polygonal trains (broken straight-line paths).

---

[1] *Correspondance d'Hermite et de Stieltjes*, Vol. 1, p. 434 (Gauthier-Villars, Paris 1905).

Now consider a simply-connected region containing the point z_0, and an analytic function $f_0(z)$ that is defined and regular in a certain neighborhood of z_0. Assume that $f_0(z)$ can be continued analytically along any polygonal train that connects z_0 with any point z of G and is wholly contained within G. We shall prove that there is defined thereby a single-valued regular analytic function $f(z)$ in G that coincides with $f_0(z)$ in the initial neighborhood of z_0.

To this end, we consider first an arbitrary triangle ABC that is wholly contained, along with its interior, in the region G (see Fig. 26 below). By continuing $f_0(z)$ analytically along a polygonal train that connects z_0 with the

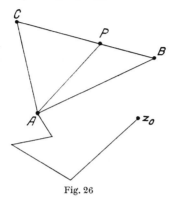

Fig. 26

vertex A, we are led to an analytic function $f^*(z)$ regular in a certain neighborhood of A, and by the above assumption, we can continue $f^*(z)$ analytically along any line segment AP, where P is any point on the closed line segment BC. By means of this continuation, we have defined a single-valued function regular in a certain neighborhood of the segment AP. Thus for any triangle $AP'P''$ lying in this neighborhood, analytic continuation of $f^*(z)$ along the closed path $AP'P''A$ will lead to a final function in a neighborhood of A that coincides with the initial function $f^*(z)$ in the neighborhood of A. Moreover, the above points P' and P'' may obviously be any two points of the segment BC that lie within a suitable interval which has P as an interior point and whose length is δ. But by the Borel Covering Theorem, the closed segment BC can be covered by a finite number of intervals of this kind, which implies that the analytic continuation of $f^*(z)$ along the closed path $ABCA$ also leads back to the initial function $f^*(z)$ at A.

Our next step will be to generalize this result from triangles to arbitrary closed polygons, which we shall do by mathematical induction. Let us assume we had proved the desired result for all polygons having n sides. Then its validity for polygons of $(n + 1)$ sides follows immediately from the fact that any such polygon can be decomposed into two polygons of at most n sides each by drawing a suitable diagonal through the interior of the given polygon (*cf.* § 126 above).

Finally, it is easy to generalize the concept of analytic continuation to paths that are Jordan arcs γ. For any arc of this kind, there will be, after continuation along the arc, a neighborhood in which a regular analytic function $f(z)$ is defined. The same analytic function $f(z)$ results from analytic continuation along polygonal trains that approximate γ sufficiently closely. This implies that if z is any point of G and if γ' and γ'' are two polygonal trains each of which connects z_0 with z, then analytic continuation along γ' and along γ'' will lead to the same final function at z.

We summarize the results obtained as follows:

Monodromy Theorem : *Let z_0 be a point of a simply-connected region G and let $f_0(z)$ be an analytic function defined and regular in a neighborhood of z_0. If $f_0(z)$ can be continued analytically along any polygonal train that emanates from z_0 and is wholly contained in G, then all of the possible continuations of this kind serve to define a single-valued analytic function regular in all of G.*

233.   We return briefly to the problem treated in § 227 above, and consider a single-valued analytic function $w = f(z)$ regular in a region G_z of the z-plane. Since the mapping given by $w = f(z)$ is neighborhood-preserving (*cf.* § 144 above), the totality of image points w of points z of G_z constitutes a region G_w in the w-plane. Let us mark the points z_ν in G_z at which $f'(z) = 0$, as well as the corresponding points $w_\nu = f(z_\nu)$ in G_w. If $G_w{}^*$ is any simply-connected subregion of G_w that does not contain any of the points w_ν in its interior, then we can start at any (interior) point $w_0 = f(z_0)$ of $G_w{}^*$ and continue analytically the inverse function $\varphi_0(w)$ of $f(z)$—whose existence in some neighborhood of w_0 we proved in § 227 above—along any polygonal train emanating from w_0 and lying wholly in $G_w{}^*$.

By the monodromy theorem, it follows that there is defined in the whole region $G_w{}^*$ a single-valued analytic function $z = \varphi(w)$ which must be simple in this region, being the inverse function of $w = f(z)$. The mapping given by the equation $z = \varphi(w)$ singles out a corresponding subregion $G_z{}^*$ of the region G_z, and the mapping of $G_w{}^*$ onto $G_z{}^*$ is one-to-one.

PART FIVE

SPECIAL FUNCTIONS

CHAPTER ONE

THE EXPONENTIAL AND TRIGONOMETRIC FUNCTIONS

The Exponential Function e^z (§ 234)

234. We wish to find the most general analytic function of the form

$$f(z) = a_0 + a_1 \frac{z}{1!} + a_2 \frac{z^2}{2!} + a_3 \frac{z^3}{3!} + \cdots \qquad (234.1)$$

that is regular at $z = 0$ and that satisfies the differential equation

$$\frac{dw}{dz} = w. \qquad (234.2)$$

Differentiating (234.1), we obtain

$$f'(z) = a_1 + a_2 \frac{z}{1!} + a_3 \frac{z^2}{2!} + a_4 \frac{z^3}{3!} + \cdots,$$

so that (234.2) yields

$$a_1 = a_0, \quad a_2 = a_1 = a_0, \quad \ldots, \quad a_n = a_{n-1} = \cdots = a_0, \quad \ldots,$$

whence, with the notation

$$e^z = 1 + \frac{z}{1!} + \frac{z^2}{2!} + \frac{z^3}{3!} + \cdots, \qquad (234.3)$$

we see that every solution of (234.2) must be of the form

$$w = a_0 e^z. \qquad (234.4)$$

From the criterion of § 207 above, we see that the series (234.3) converges for every value of z and hence represents an integral transcendental function (cf. § 173 above). This integral function is called the *exponential function*.

If a is any complex number, then for the derivative $d\varphi/dz$ of the function

$$\varphi(z) = e^z e^{a-z},$$

we find

$$\varphi'(z) = \left(\frac{d}{dz} e^z\right) e^{a-z} + e^z \left(\frac{d}{dz} e^{a-z}\right) = 0.$$

Hence $\varphi(z)$ is a constant, equal to $\varphi(0)$, and we therefore have the following functional equation:

$$e^z \, e^{a-z} = e^a. \tag{234.5}$$

If we set $a = 0$, (234.5) becomes

$$e^z \, e^{-z} = 1, \tag{234.6}$$

and this shows that *the exponential function has no zeros.* Thus there exist integral transcendental functions that have no zeros, notwithstanding the obvious fact that any such function can be approximated as closely as we

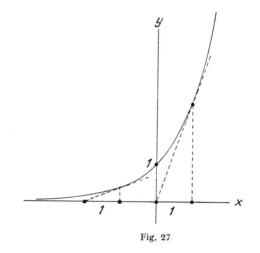

Fig. 27

please by polynomials having an arbitrarily large number of zeros. This fact becomes more plausible if we realize that to any disc $|z| < N$, no matter how large, we can assign an integer $n_0(N)$ such that for $n > n_0$, the equation

$$1 + \frac{z}{1!} + \frac{z^2}{2!} + \cdots + \frac{z^n}{n!} = 0 \tag{234.7}$$

has no solutions inside the given disc.

If in (234.5) above we replace the numbers z and a by z_1 and $z_1 + z_2$ respectively, we obtain the *addition theorem of the exponential function,* in the form

$$e^{z_1 + z_2} = e^{z_1} \, e^{z_2}. \tag{234.8}$$

The exponential function is also a *real analytic function,* that is, a function whose power series expansion has none but real coefficients. Hence for real values x of z,

$$y = e^x \qquad (234.9)$$

is likewise real, and its graph in the (x, y)-plane is shown in Fig. 27 above. For small values of $|x|$, the series (234.3) serves very conveniently to calculate e^x (for real x) with very good accuracy. Thus for $x = \pm 1$, for instance, we obtain

$$\left.\begin{array}{l} e = e^1 \approx 1 + \dfrac{1}{1!} + \dfrac{1}{2!} + \cdots + \dfrac{1}{14!} = 2.71828\ 18285 \ldots \\[3mm] \dfrac{1}{e} = e^{-1} \approx 1 - \dfrac{1}{1!} + \dfrac{1}{2!} - \cdots + \dfrac{1}{14!} = 0.36787\ 94411\ 7 \ldots \end{array}\right\} \qquad (234.10)$$

But even for $x = \pm 2$, the power series is no longer particularly advantageous, and for $x = \pm 5$ it is as good as useless, although we could obtain from it as accurate a value for $e^{\pm 5}$ as we please by using sufficiently many terms. A much better way of calculating e^x for larger values of x is to make use of the addition theorem (234.8).

The Trigonometric Functions (§§ 235-237)

235. For complex values $z = x + iy$ of the argument, we see from (234.8) above that

$$e^z = e^x e^{iy}. \qquad (235.1)$$

This suggests investigation of the function e^{iz}, which by (234.3) above is given by the formula

$$e^{iz} = 1 + i\,\frac{z}{1!} - \frac{z^2}{2!} - i\,\frac{z^3}{3!} + \frac{z^4}{4!} + i\,\frac{z^5}{5!} - \cdots; \qquad (235.2)$$

and (235.2) in turn suggests introducing the two integral transcendental functions

$$\cos z = 1 - \frac{z^2}{2!} + \frac{z^4}{4!} - \cdots, \qquad (235.3)$$

$$\sin z = z - \frac{z^3}{3!} + \frac{z^5}{5!} - \cdots, \qquad (235.4)$$

both of which are real analytic functions (in the sense of § 234 above). A look at the last three power series shows that

$$e^{iz} = \cos z + i \sin z. \qquad (235.5)$$

We also see that $\cos z$ is an even function and $\sin z$ an odd function, i.e. that the following relations hold:

$$\cos(-z) = \cos z, \quad \sin(-z) = -\sin z. \tag{235.6}$$

Furthermore, we have

$$\cos 0 = 1, \quad \sin 0 = 0. \tag{235.7}$$

Replacing z by $-z$ in (235.5), we obtain

$$e^{-iz} = \cos z - i \sin z \tag{235.8}$$

and the two equations (235.5) and (235.8) can be solved for $\cos z$ and $\sin z$. This yields *Euler's Formulas*

$$\cos z = \frac{e^{iz} + e^{-iz}}{2}, \quad \sin z = \frac{e^{iz} - e^{-iz}}{2i}, \tag{235.9}$$

differentiation of which gives

$$\frac{d \cos z}{dz} = -\sin z, \quad \frac{d \sin z}{dz} = \cos z. \tag{235.10}$$

Now by the addition theorem (234.8),

$$e^{i(z_1 + z_2)} = e^{iz_1} e^{iz_2}, \tag{235.11}$$

so that, by (235.5),

$$\cos(z_1 + z_2) + i \sin(z_1 + z_2) = (\cos z_1 + i \sin z_1)(\cos z_2 + i \sin z_2). \tag{235.12}$$

Replacing z_1 and z_2 in (235.12) by $-z_1$ and $-z_2$, respectively, we find, using (235.6), that

$$\cos(z_1 + z_2) - i \sin(z_1 + z_2) = (\cos z_1 - i \sin z_1)(\cos z_2 - i \sin z_2). \tag{235.13}$$

We now multiply out on the right-hand sides of (235.12) and (235.13) and then solve for $\cos(z_1 + z_2)$ and $\sin(z_1 + z_2)$, obtaining in this way the following *addition theorems for the trigonometric functions*:

$$\cos(z_1 + z_2) = \cos z_1 \cos z_2 - \sin z_1 \sin z_2, \tag{235.14}$$

$$\sin(z_1 + z_2) = \sin z_1 \cos z_2 + \sin z_1 \cos z_2. \tag{235.15}$$

Finally, if we set $z_1 = z$ and $z_2 = -z$ in (235.14) and once more use (235.6), we obtain

$$\cos^2 z + \sin^2 z = 1. \tag{235.16}$$

The foregoing shows that all of the well-known formulas of trigonometry (in the real domain) remain valid if the trigonometric functions are defined for all complex arguments by means of the power series (235.3) and (235.4), and it also shows that the simplest way of obtaining these formulas is to use the addition theorem for e^z.

236. We now introduce the function

$$u(z) = \frac{\sin z}{1 + \cos z} = \frac{z}{2} + \frac{z^3}{24} + \frac{z^5}{120} + \frac{17 \, z^7}{40320} + \cdots, \qquad (236.1)$$

which is regular in a neighborhood of $z = 0$ and which by (235.16) above can also be written in the form

$$u(z) = \frac{1 - \cos z}{\sin z}. \qquad (236.2)$$

It follows from the above that

$$\cos z + u \sin z = 1, \qquad (236.3)$$

$$- u \cos z + \sin z = u, \qquad (236.4)$$

$$\cos z = \frac{1 - u^2}{1 + u^2}, \quad \sin z = \frac{2 \, u}{1 + u^2}. \qquad (236.5)$$

Let $z(u)$ be the inverse of the function in (236.1) (we know from § 227 above that this inverse exists), and let us substitute $z(u)$ for z in (236.3) and (236.4), which makes these relations identities in u. Then by differentiation of (236.3) with respect to u, we obtain

$$(- \sin z + u \cos z) \frac{dz}{du} + \sin z = 0,$$

which by (236.4) and (236.5) yields

$$\frac{dz}{du} = \frac{\sin z}{u} = \frac{2}{1 + u^2} = 2 \, (1 - u^2 + u^4 - u^6 + \cdots). \qquad (236.6)$$

Integrating the last relation term by term, we find the following power series expansion for $z(u)$:

$$z = 2 \left(u - \frac{u^3}{3} + \frac{u^5}{5} - \frac{u^7}{7} + \cdots \right). \qquad (236.7)$$

237. The series (236.7) may be used to study the behavior of $\cos z$ and $\sin z$ for real values x of z and, in particular, to establish the periodicity properties of these functions. The radius of convergence of the series in (236.7) above equals unity, and the series is convergent also at $u = 1$, where it assumes a value that we denote by

$$\frac{\pi}{4} = 1 - \frac{1}{3} + \frac{1}{5} - \frac{1}{7} + \cdots. \tag{237.1}$$

From Abel's theorem (*cf.* § 215 above), combined with the fact that

$$\frac{dz}{du} = \frac{2}{1+u^2} > 0 \tag{237.2}$$

holds for real values of u, it follows that as u goes through the interval $0 \le u \le 1$, $z = x + iy$ traverses the interval $0 \le x \le \pi/2$. By (236.5) above, the two functions $\cos x$ and $\sin x$ are positive for values of u between 0 and 1, except that at each end of this interval one of the functions vanishes.

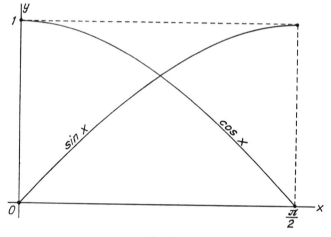

Fig. 28

By (235.10), $\cos x$ is monotonically decreasing and $\sin x$ monotonically increasing as x traverses the interval $0 < x < \pi/2$ (see Fig. 28 above). Finally, we see that if $u = 1$, i.e. $x = \pi/2$, we have

$$\cos \frac{\pi}{2} = 0, \quad \sin \frac{\pi}{2} = 1. \tag{237.3}$$

This, combined with the addition theorem for the trigonometric functions, shows that for any complex number z, we have

$$\cos \left(\frac{\pi}{2} + z \right) = - \sin z, \quad \sin \left(\frac{\pi}{2} + z \right) = \cos z. \tag{237.4}$$

For $z = \pi/2$, this yields

$$\cos \pi = - 1, \quad \sin \pi = 0, \tag{237.5}$$

so that we also have

$$\cos{(\pi + z)} = -\cos z, \quad \sin{(\pi + z)} = -\sin z, \quad \cos 2\pi = 1, \quad \sin 2\pi = 0, \quad (237.6)$$

$$\cos{(2\pi + z)} = \cos z, \quad \sin{(2\pi + z)} = \sin z. \quad (237.7)$$

Hence the trigonometric functions are periodic and of period 2π. We shall soon see that any other period of $\cos z$ and $\sin z$ must be an integral multiple of 2π.

To continue the graphs of $\cos x$ and $\sin x$ in Fig. 28 above as far as we please, we need merely apply relations (237.4) through (237.7) to real values x of z.

The Periods of the Exponential Functions (§§ 238-239)

238. For $z = x + iy$, we have by (235.1) and (235.5) above that

$$e^z = e^{x+iy} = e^x (\cos y + i \sin y), \quad (238.1)$$

which shows how to separate e^z into its real and imaginary parts. If we set $x = 0$ and $y = 2\pi$ in (238.1), we obtain

$$e^{2\pi i} = e^0 (\cos 2\pi + i \sin 2\pi) = 1. \quad (238.2)$$

More generally, assume that $\omega = x + iy$ is any root of the equation

$$e^\omega = e^x (\cos y + i \sin y) = 1. \quad (238.3)$$

Then we must have

$$e^x \cos y = 1, \quad e^x \sin y = 0, \quad (238.4)$$

and hence

$$e^{2x} = (e^x \cos y)^2 + (e^x \sin y)^2 = 1 \quad (238.5)$$

must also hold. This yields

$$x = 0 \quad \text{and} \quad \cos y = 1, \quad \sin y = 0;$$

furthermore, y must be a real number, so that by the preceding section we must have $y = 2k\pi$ $(k = 0, \pm 1, \pm 2, \ldots)$. Hence the solutions of equation (238.3) must all be of the form $\omega = 2k\pi i$, where k is any integer.

Now if ω is any one of the solutions of equation (238.3), then for any complex number z we must have

$$e^{z+\omega} = e^z e^\omega = e^z. \quad (238.6)$$

Conversely, if (238.6) holds even for one single value of z, it follows that

$e^\omega = 1$ and hence that $\omega = 2k\pi i$.

We have thus obtained the following result: *The exponential function e^z is a periodic function. Every period ω of e^z is a multiple of $\omega_0 = 2\pi i$, which is referred to as one of the "primitive periods" of e^z. The other primitive period is $\overline{\omega}_0 = -2\pi i$.*

239. The general equation

$$e^z = a + i\,b \tag{239.1}$$

can now be treated very easily, a and b being any two real numbers not both of which vanish. We have to solve the two equations

$$e^x \cos y = a, \quad e^x \sin y = b,$$

which are in turn equivalent to the following three:

$$e^x = +\sqrt{a^2 + b^2}, \quad \cos y = \frac{a}{\sqrt{a^2 + b^2}}, \quad \sin y = \frac{b}{\sqrt{a^2 + b^2}}. \tag{239.2}$$

These have *one and only one* solution in the strip

$$0 \leqq y < 2\pi, \tag{239.3}$$

(*cf.* Fig. 29 below), and all the other solutions are obtained by adding the various periods of e^z to the specific solution just indicated.

The Hyperbolic Functions (§ 240)

240. The study of the trigonometric functions $\cos z$ and $\sin z$ for complex values of z is simplified by the introduction of the functions

$$\cosh z = \cos i\,z, \quad \sinh z = \frac{1}{i} \sin i\,z, \tag{240.1}$$

which are real analytic functions (in the sense of § 234 above) and which are called the *hyperbolic cosine* and *hyperbolic sine* of z, respectively. Equations (240.1) may also be written in the form

$$\cosh z = \frac{e^z + e^{-z}}{2} = 1 + \frac{z^2}{2!} + \frac{z^4}{4!} + \cdots, \tag{240.2}$$

$$\sinh z = \frac{e^z - e^{-z}}{2} = z + \frac{z^3}{3!} + \frac{z^5}{5!} + \cdots. \tag{240.3}$$

Hence $\cosh z$ and $\sinh z$ are uniquely determined by the three conditions

$$\cosh(-z) = \cosh z, \ \sinh(-z) = -\sinh z, \ e^z = \cosh z + \sinh z, \tag{240.4}$$

which imply that

$$e^{-z} = \cosh z - \sinh z \qquad (240.5)$$

holds.

If we multiply $e^z = \cosh z + \sinh z$ by (240.5), we obtain

$$\cosh^2 z - \sinh^2 z = 1. \qquad (240.6)$$

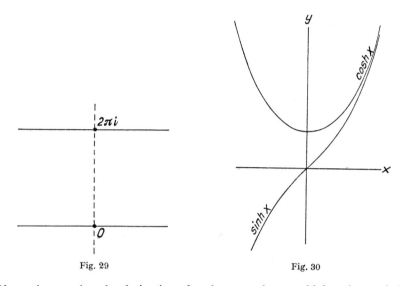

Fig. 29   Fig. 30

If we observe that the derivative of $\cosh z$ must be an odd function and that of $\sinh z$ an even function, and make use of the relation

$$e^z = \frac{d}{dz} \cosh z + \frac{d}{dz} \sinh z,$$

then we find that

$$\frac{d}{dz} \cosh z = \sinh z, \quad \frac{d}{dz} \sinh z = \cosh z. \qquad (240.7)$$

Finally we can prove, just as for the trigonometric functions in § 235 above, the following *addition theorems for the hyperbolic functions*:

$$\cosh (z_1 + z_2) = \cosh z_1 \cosh z_2 + \sinh z_1 \sinh z_2, \qquad (240.8)$$

$$\sinh (z_1 + z_2) = \sinh z_1 \cosh z_2 + \cosh z_1 \sinh z_2. \qquad (240.9)$$

The graphs of

$$y = \cosh x, \quad y = \sinh x \qquad (240.10)$$

for real values x of z are shown in Fig. 30 above. The first of these curves is called a *catenary* (or chain curve), since any thread or chain suspended at its two ends takes on the shape of an arc of this curve.

Periods and Fundamental Regions of the Trigonometric Functions (§§ 241-242)

241. If $z = x + iy$, we obtain from (235.14) that

$$\cos z = \cos x \cos i\,y - \sin x \sin i\,y,$$

or with the notation of the preceding section,

$$\cos z = \cos x \cosh y - i \sin x \sinh y \quad (z = x + i\,y). \quad (241.1)$$

Similarly we find that

$$\sin z = \sin x \cosh y + i \cos x \sinh y. \quad (241.2)$$

Using (241.1) and (240.6), we see that

$$\left.\begin{aligned}
|\cos z|^2 &= \cos^2 x \cosh^2 y + \sin^2 x \sinh^2 y \\
&= \cos^2 x\,(1 + \sinh^2 y) + \sin^2 x \sinh^2 y \\
&= \cos^2 x + \sinh^2 y = \cosh^2 y - \sin^2 x,
\end{aligned}\right\} \quad (241.3)$$

and in the same way we obtain

$$|\sin z|^2 = \sin^2 x + \sinh^2 y = \cosh^2 y - \cos^2 x. \quad (241.4)$$

Hence the functions $\sin z$ and $\cos z$ can vanish only for real values of z, and therefore *all* of the zeros of $\sin z$ are of the form $z = k\pi$, where k is any integer (*cf.* § 237 above).

Now if ω is any period of $\sin z$, then $\sin(z + \omega) = \sin z$, whence $z = 0$ gives $\sin \omega = 0$. From this it follows that *all of the periods of $\sin z$ are real, and the only primitive periods of this function are* $\pm 2\pi$.

The periods of $\cos z = \sin(\pi/2 - z)$ are the same as those of $\sin z$.

242. Let a and b be any two real numbers. We propose to find all of the roots of the equation

$$\cos z = a + b\,i, \quad (242.1)$$

or, which is the same, all of the roots of the two equations

$$\cos x \cosh y = a, \quad \sin x \sinh y = -b. \quad (242.2)$$

If we set

$$\sinh^2 y = u, \tag{242.3}$$

then elimination of x from (242.2) yields

$$\frac{a^2}{u+1} + \frac{b^2}{u} = 1. \tag{242.4}$$

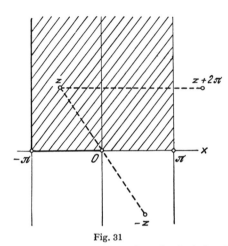

Fig. 31

The shaded fundamental region also includes the
ray $\Re z = -\pi$, $\Im z \geq 0$ and the line segment $-\pi \leq x \leq 0$.

Hence u is the positive root of the quadratic equation

$$u^2 + (1 - a^2 - b^2) u - b^2 = 0. \tag{242.5}$$

With the notation

$$R^2 = (1 - a^2 - b^2)^2 + 4 b^2 = (1 + a^2 + b^2)^2 - 4 a^2, \tag{242.6}$$

and choosing R to be ≥ 0, we finally obtain

$$\sinh^2 y = \frac{R - (1 - a^2 - b^2)}{2}, \quad \cosh^2 y = \frac{R + (1 + a^2 + b^2)}{2}. \tag{242.7}$$

We denote the non-negative root of the last two equations by y_0 and observe
that y_0 vanishes if and only if $b = 0$ and $a^2 \leq 1$. If $y_0 > 0$, then the equations

$$\cos x_0 = \frac{a}{\cosh y_0}, \quad \sin x_0 = -\frac{b}{\sinh y_0} \tag{242.8}$$

resulting from (242.2) determine one and only one number x_0 in the half-open interval $-\pi \leqq x < \pi$. But if $y_0 = 0$, then only the first of equations (242.8) has to be satisfied, and we may require x_0 to lie in the closed interval $0 \leqq x \leqq \pi$.

In either case, it is clear that if $z_0 = x_0 + iy_0$ is a solution of equation (242.1), then $-z_0$ is likewise a solution, so that we can finally state the following result (see also Fig. 31): *If $a + bi \neq \pm 1$, then there are in the half-open strip $-\pi \leqq x < \pi$ of the complex plane exactly two solutions of the equation (242.1). If $a + bi = +1$, then the above strip contains only one solution, viz. $z = 0$; if $a + bi = -1$, it contains only the solution $z = -\pi$. All the remaining solutions of equation (242.1) differ from the ones just indicated by one of the periods of $\cos z$, i.e. by a multiple of 2π.*

The Functions tg z and tgh z (§§ 243-244)

243.   We turn to the study of the functions

$$\operatorname{tg} z = \frac{\sin z}{\cos z}, \quad \operatorname{tgh} z = \frac{\sinh z}{\cosh z} = \frac{1}{i}\operatorname{tg} i z. \qquad (243.1)$$

Both of these are meromorphic functions; their poles are at the zeros of $\cos z$ and of $\cosh z$, respectively. Both are odd functions. The function $\operatorname{tg} z$ has the primitive period π, the function $\operatorname{tgh} z$ the primitive period $i\pi$. The function $\operatorname{tg} z$ can be written in the form

$$\operatorname{tg} z = \frac{1}{i}\frac{e^{iz} - e^{-iz}}{e^{iz} + e^{-iz}} = \frac{1}{i}\frac{e^{2iz} - 1}{e^{2iz} + 1}; \qquad (243.2)$$

thus it is a Moebius transform of e^{2iz} and obviously cannot take on the values $\pm i$, since at a point z where $\operatorname{tg} z = \pm i$ we would have to have e^{2iz} equal to zero or to infinity. Similarly, $\operatorname{tgh} z$ omits the values ± 1. However, $\operatorname{tg} z$ assumes every value $a + ib$, other than $\pm i$, once and only once within the strip

$$-\frac{\pi}{2} \leqq x < \frac{\pi}{2} \qquad (243.3)$$

(*cf.* § 239 above).

The *addition theorems* for $\operatorname{tg} z$ and $\operatorname{tgh} z$ are as follows:

$$\operatorname{tg}(z_1 + z_2) = \frac{\operatorname{tg} z_1 + \operatorname{tg} z_2}{1 - \operatorname{tg} z_1 \operatorname{tg} z_2}, \quad \operatorname{tgh}(z_1 + z_2) = \frac{\operatorname{tgh} z_1 + \operatorname{tgh} z_2}{1 + \operatorname{tgh} z_1 \operatorname{tgh} z_2}. \qquad (243.4)$$

Differentiation of (243.1) yields

$$\frac{d}{dz}\operatorname{tg} z = \frac{1}{\cos^2 z} = 1 + \operatorname{tg}^2 z, \qquad (243.5)$$

$$\frac{d}{dz}\operatorname{tgh} z = \frac{1}{\cosh^2 z} = 1 - \operatorname{tgh}^2 z. \qquad (243.6)$$

If we set

$$\operatorname{tg} z = u, \quad \operatorname{tgh} z = v \quad (u \neq \pm i, \; v \neq \pm 1), \quad (243.7)$$

and if we consider z as a function of u and of v, respectively, then by proceeding as in § 236 above we obtain

$$\frac{dz}{du} = \frac{1}{1+u^2}, \quad \frac{dz}{dv} = \frac{1}{1-v^2}. \quad (243.8)$$

From this we obtain power-series expansions of z valid in the discs $|u| < 1$ and $|v| < 1$ respectively, as follows:

$$z = \frac{u}{1} - \frac{u^3}{3} + \frac{u^5}{5} - \cdots, \quad z = \frac{v}{1} + \frac{v^3}{3} + \frac{v^5}{5} + \cdots. \quad (243.9)$$

For real values x of z, the function tg z is monotonic in x, increasing from $-\infty$ to $+\infty$ as x traverses the interval $-\pi/2 < x < \pi/2$.

Similarly, tgh x is a monotonic function of x that goes from -1 to $+1$ as x ranges from $-\infty$ to $+\infty$.

244. With $z = x + iy$, we have, by (241.1) and (241.2), that

$$\operatorname{tg} z = \frac{\sin x \cosh y + i \cos x \sinh y}{\cos x \cosh y - i \sin x \sinh y}. \quad (244.1)$$

Multiplying both the numerator and denominator by $(\cos x \cosh y + i \sin x \sinh y)$, we obtain

$$\operatorname{tg} z = \frac{\sin 2 x + i \sinh 2 y}{\cos 2 x + \cosh 2 y}. \quad (244.2)$$

Thus if $z = x + iy$ is to satisfy tg $z = a + bi$, the following two equations must hold:

$$a (\cos 2 x + \cosh 2 y) = \sin 2 x, \quad (244.3)$$

$$b (\cos 2 x + \cosh 2 y) = \sinh 2 y, \quad (244.4)$$

and these are equivalent with the equations

$$\left. \begin{array}{l} a \cosh 2 y = \sin 2 x - a \cos 2 x, \\[2mm] a \sinh 2 y = b \sin 2 x. \end{array} \right\} \quad (244.5)$$

Eliminating y from the last two equations, we obtain

$$a^2 = (\sin 2 x - a \cos 2 x)^2 - b^2 \sin^2 2 x$$

or

$$\sin 2 x \left[(1 - a^2 - b^2) \sin 2 x - 2 a \cos 2 x \right] = 0. \quad (244.6)$$

Since the point $z = x + iy$ for which we are looking is not a pole of tg z,

$$\cos 2\,x + \cosh 2\,y > 0$$

must hold true, and according to (244.3), $\sin 2x$ cannot vanish unless $a = 0$. Thus condition (244.6) implies that

$$\text{tg } 2\,x = \frac{2\,a}{1 - a^2 - b^2}, \tag{244.7}$$

whence from (244.5),

$$\text{tgh } 2\,y = \frac{b \text{ tg } 2\,x}{\text{tg } 2\,x - a} = \frac{2\,b}{1 + a^2 + b^2}. \tag{244.8}$$

Now y can be determined uniquely from (244.8). In order to also determine, from (244.7), a unique value of x in the interval (243.3), we must use the fact that $\sin 2x$ must have the same sign as a, and $\cos 2x$ the same sign as $(1 - a^2 - b^2)$.

Numerical Calculation of π (§ 245)

245. The two series in (243.9) are convenient to use only if a few of their terms suffice for the calculation of the desired number with the required accuracy. For this, the numbers $|u|$ or $|v|$ must be substantially less than unity. If it is required to solve equations (243.7) for z in the case of larger values of $|u|$ or $|v|$, use must be made, for the numerical calculations, not only of equations (243.9) but also of the addition theorems (243.4).

We shall in this way obtain the number π from the equation

$$\text{tg } \frac{\pi}{4} = 1, \tag{245.1}$$

and establish a formula that was discovered shortly after 1700 by the English astronomer J. Machin. To this end, we consider the positive number α that is defined by

$$\text{tg } \alpha = \frac{1}{5}. \tag{245.2}$$

By (243.4), we then have

$$\text{tg } 2\,\alpha = \frac{\dfrac{2}{5}}{1 - \dfrac{1}{25}} = \frac{5}{12}, \tag{245.3}$$

$$\text{tg } 4\,\alpha = \frac{\dfrac{10}{12}}{1 - \dfrac{25}{144}} = \frac{120}{119}. \tag{245.4}$$

Setting

$$\beta = 4\alpha - \frac{\pi}{4}, \tag{245.5}$$

we find that

$$\operatorname{tg} \beta = \frac{\operatorname{tg} 4\alpha - 1}{1 + \operatorname{tg} 4\alpha} = \frac{1}{239}. \tag{245.6}$$

Thus

$$\left.\begin{array}{c} \pi = 16\alpha - 4\beta, \quad \alpha = \dfrac{1}{5} - \dfrac{1}{3\cdot 5^3} + \dfrac{1}{5\cdot 5^5} - \cdots, \\[3mm] \beta = \dfrac{1}{239} - \dfrac{1}{3\cdot 239^2} + \cdots, \end{array}\right\} \tag{245.7}$$

and to determine π to 10 decimal places, we need only set

$$16\alpha \approx 16\left(\frac{1}{5} - \frac{1}{3\cdot 5^3} + \cdots - \frac{1}{15\cdot 5^{15}}\right) = 3.15832\ 89576\ 00\ \ldots$$

$$4\beta \approx 4\left(\frac{1}{239} - \frac{1}{3\cdot 239^2}\right) \qquad\qquad = 0.01673\ 63040\ 04\ \ldots$$

$$\overline{\hspace{4cm}\pi = 3.14159\ 26536\ \ldots}$$

If we used the series (237.1), instead of the above, we would need many hundreds of terms to calculate π to even as few as three decimal places.[1]

---

[1] We obtain a similar formula, even more convenient for the calculations, by setting $\operatorname{tg}\alpha = 1/2$, $\operatorname{tg}\beta = 1/5$, $\operatorname{tg}\gamma = 1/8$. Then $\operatorname{tg}(\alpha + \beta + \gamma) = 1$.

CHAPTER TWO

THE LOGARITHMIC FUNCTION AND THE
GENERAL POWER FUNCTION

The Natural Logarithm (§§ 246-250)

246. The inverse function of the exponential function is called the *natural logarithm* of z, and we shall denote it by

$$w = l\,z. \tag{246.1}$$

This function is therefore obtained by solving the equation

$$z = e^w \tag{246.2}$$

for w. Since the exponential function omits the value zero, the logarithmic function lz is defined only for $z \neq 0$. We shall see that $z = 0$ is a singularity of lz which is of an entirely different character than are the singularities that we have considered thus far.

If z_0 is any non-zero complex number, we have seen in § 239 above that there is a number w_0 for which

$$z_0 = e^{w_0} \tag{246.3}$$

holds. But since e^w is a periodic function, the numbers

$$w_0 + 2\,i\,\pi, \;\; w_0 - 2\,i\,\pi, \;\; w_0 + 4\,i\,\pi, \;\ldots,$$

as well as w_0 itself, are solutions of the equation $z_0 = e^w$, so that the function lz is many-valued; there are, in fact, infinitely many values of lz_0. Among these values, there is one and only one whose imaginary part satisfies the condition

$$-\pi < \Im l\,z_0 \leq \pi. \tag{246.4}$$

This particular value is called the *principal value* of lz_0.

247. If w_0 is a solution of the equation (246.3), then equation (246.2) may be rewritten in the form

$$z = e^{w_0}\,e^{w - w_0} = z_0 + z_0\,\frac{w - w_0}{1!} + z_0\,\frac{(w - w_0)^2}{2!} + \cdots, \tag{247.1}$$

256

and the inverse of this power series—which always exists, by § 228 above—represents one of the values of lz in a neighborhood of the point z_0. The calculation of the inverse function is done best by first differentiating (246.2) or (247.1) with respect to z, which yields

$$1 = e^w \frac{dw}{dz} = z \frac{dw}{dz}.$$

For then we have

$$\frac{dw}{dz} = \frac{1}{z}$$
$$= \frac{1}{z_0 + (z - z_0)}$$
$$= \frac{1}{z_0} - \frac{z - z_0}{z_0^2} + \frac{(z - z_0)^2}{z_0^3} - \cdots , \tag{247.2}$$

and term-by-term integration yields

$$w - w_0 = \frac{z - z_0}{z_0} - \frac{(z - z_0)^2}{2 z_0^2} + \frac{(z - z_0)^3}{3 z_0^3} - \cdots . \tag{247.3}$$

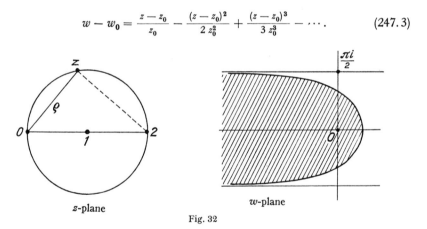

z-plane w-plane

Fig. 32

The power series (247.3) converges in the disc

$$|z - z_0| < |z_0|, \tag{247.4}$$

which has its center at z_0 and passes through the point $z = 0$. As mentioned earlier and as is apparent from (247.2), this last point (i.e. $z = 0$) is a singular point of the function $w(z)$.

Conversely, if we start from equation (247.3), where $z_0 \neq 0$ and w_0 are any complex numbers, we can differentiate this equation term by term within the disc (247.4), and if we compare the result with (247.2), we see that the function $w(z)$ defined by (247.3) is an integral of the differential equation

$dw/dz = 1/z$. But this integral cannot be regarded as a piece of the function lz unless the constant of integration w_0 satisfies the equation $e^{w_0} = z_0$.

In particular, if $w_0 = 0$ and $z_0 = 1$, then

$$l z = (z - 1) - \frac{(z-1)^2}{2} + \frac{(z-1)^3}{3} - \cdots \qquad (|z - 1| < 1). \quad (247.5)$$

248. It is now very easy to determine the portion of the w-plane that is the image of the disc $|z - 1| < 1$ under the mapping given by equation (247.5). To this end, we note that the boundary of this disc is given in polar coordinates as follows:

$$\varrho = 2 \cos \vartheta, \quad z = 2 \cos \vartheta \cdot e^{i\vartheta} = e^w. \quad (248.1)$$

Hence if we set $w = u + iv$, then the image of the curve (241.8) is given by the equation

$$e^u = 2 \cos v. \quad (248.2)$$

Therefore the disc $|z - 1| < 1$ is mapped one-to-one by the power series (247.5) onto the shaded region in Fig. 32. The more general equation (247.3) maps the disc (247.4) onto a region of the w-plane that results from the shaded region of Fig. 32 by the translation that moves the point $w = 0$ to the point $w = w_0$.

Thus if, for instance, z_0 takes on larger and larger real values, then the corresponding images of the curve (248.1) move farther and farther to the right in the strip $|v| < \pi/2$, filling up a greater and greater portion of this strip, so that the strip represents the one-to-one image of the half-plane $\Re z > 0$.

249. We can get a very good geometric idea of the mapping under consideration by introducing the *Riemann surface with a logarithmic branch point at $z = 0$*.

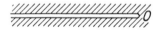

Fig. 33

By the equation $e^w = z$, the strip

$$|\Im w| < \pi$$

is mapped onto the z-plane slit along the negative real axis (see Fig. 33 above), and within this region the inverse function $w = lz$ represents the principal value of the logarithmic function. The upper "bank" of the cut is mapped by the logarithm onto the upper boundary $\mathfrak{J}w = \pi$ of the strip, the lower bank of the cut onto the lower boundary $\mathfrak{J}w = -\pi$.

The adjacent strip

$$\pi < \mathfrak{J}w < 3\pi$$

of the w-plane is mapped by the equation $e^w = z$ onto a similar z-plane, also slit along the negative real axis. Let us imagine one of the two slit z-planes to be laid on top of the other and the upper bank of the first z-plane to be glued to the lower bank of the z-plane above it.

If we continue in this way, adding more and more strips in the w-plane, also more and more specimens of z-planes, we are led to a construction of the mapping of the entire w-plane (excluding the point $w = \infty$) onto a surface of infinitely many sheets over the z-plane (or a surface of infinitely many z-planes) that winds around the point $z = 0$ of the z-plane like a winding staircase, an infinitely flat one to be sure, and extending indefinitely in both directions ("up" and "down"). This surface is called a *Riemann surface*; on it, the function lz is *single-valued*. The point $z = 0$, *which is not counted as belonging to the surface*, is said to be a *logarithmic branch point* of the surface. The point $z = \infty$ is a second logarithmic branch point of the same surface.

The introduction of Riemann surfaces—which were invented by Riemann and used in his dissertation (1851)—makes the treatment of many-valued functions just as geometrically intuitive as that of single-valued functions. Needless to say, many-valued functions could also be studied without this particular tool; its great usefulness consists in the fact that to think in terms of Riemann surfaces immediately suggests ideas that one might otherwise not be able to arrive at without the greatest effort.

250. The functional equation (234.8) satisfied by the exponential function yields a functional equation for the logarithm. In fact, the equations

$$z_1 = e^{w_1}, \quad z_2 = e^{w_2}, \quad z_1 z_2 = e^{w_1 + w_2},$$

may be written in the form

$$l\, z_1 = w_1, \quad l\, z_2 = w_2, \quad l\, z_1 z_2 = w_1 + w_2,$$

which implies that

$$l\, z_1 + l\, z_2 = l\, z_1 z_2. \tag{250.1}$$

But since the logarithm is a many-valued function, we must be careful in the interpreting of equation (250.1). This equation merely states that the sum of one of the (infinitely many) logarithms of z_1 and one of the (infinitely many) logarithms of z_2 can be found among the (infinitely many) logarithms of z_1, z_2, and that, conversely, every logarithm of $z_1 z_2$ can be represented as a sum of this kind (with a suitable choice of lz_1 and of lz_2).

But (250.1) does *not* state that the principal value of $lz_1 z_2$ equals the sum of the principal value of lz_1 and that of lz_2. This is the case only if the sum of the amplitudes of z_1 and z_2 is less than π in absolute value. In particular, (250.1) may always be applied to the three principal values in question if z_1 and z_2 are positive real numbers.

Series Expansions and Numerical Calculation of the Logarithm (§§ 251-253)

251. By a change of notation, we obtain from (247.5) above a power series expansion for the principal value of $l(1 + z)$, valid in the disc $|z| < 1$, as follows:

$$l(1+z) = z - \frac{z^2}{2} + \frac{z^3}{3} - \frac{z^4}{4} + \cdots, \tag{251.1}$$

and in the same disc we find for the principal value of $l(1 - z)$ the expansion

$$l(1-z) = -z - \frac{z^2}{2} - \frac{z^3}{3} - \frac{z^4}{4} - \cdots. \tag{251.2}$$

As z ranges over the disc $|z| < 1$, the point $x = (1 + z)/(1 - z)$ varies in the half-plane $\Re x > 0$ of the x-plane, and the principal value of lx is a regular analytic function in this half-plane. Thus we first obtain from (251.1) and (251.2) the formula

$$\frac{1}{2} l \frac{1+z}{1-z} = z + \frac{z^3}{3} + \frac{z^5}{5} + \frac{z^7}{7} + \cdots \tag{251.3}$$

for the principal value of $l[(1 + z)/(1 - z)]$, valid in the disc $|z| < 1$, and from this we deduce the relation

$$\frac{1}{2} l x = \frac{x-1}{x+1} + \frac{1}{3}\left(\frac{x-1}{x+1}\right)^3 + \frac{1}{5}\left(\frac{x-1}{x+1}\right)^5 + \cdots \tag{251.4}$$

for the principal value of lx, valid for all x in the half-plane $\Re x > 0$. Finally, it is useful for some purposes to make one more change of variable and to set

$$x = 1 + \frac{1}{y}, \quad \frac{x-1}{x+1} = \frac{1}{2y+1}$$

in (251.4), which yields

$$\frac{1}{2} l \left(1 + \frac{1}{y}\right) = \frac{1}{2y+1} + \frac{1}{3} \frac{1}{(2y+1)^3} + \frac{1}{5} \frac{1}{(2y+1)^5} + \cdots. \quad (251.5)$$

This series represents the principal value of $\frac{1}{2} l(1 + 1/y)$ for all y lying outside the circle of radius $1/2$ and with the point $-1/2$ as its center.

252. The series (251.4) is used for the calculation of logarithmic tables. We set $x = b/a$, where a and b are positive real numbers, and obtain

$$\frac{1}{2} l b - \frac{1}{2} l a = \frac{b-a}{b+a} + \frac{1}{3}\left(\frac{b-a}{b+a}\right)^3 + \frac{1}{5}\left(\frac{b-a}{b+a}\right)^5 + \cdots. \quad (252.1)$$

For $b = 2$, $a = 1$, this yields

$$l\,2 = \frac{2}{3} + \frac{2}{3}\left(\frac{1}{3}\right)^3 + \frac{2}{5}\left(\frac{1}{3}\right)^5 + \cdots. \quad (252.2)$$

By Abel's theorem (cf. § 215 above), we could also get $l\,2$ from the series (251.1) with $z = 1$, thus:

$$l\,2 = 1 - \frac{1}{2} + \frac{1}{3} - \frac{1}{4} + \frac{1}{5} - \frac{1}{6} + \cdots; \quad (252.3)$$

but the series in (252.3) converges much too slowly to be useful for the numerical evaluation of $l\,2$. The series (252.2), on the other hand, enables us to determine a number of decimal places of $l\,2$ with very little trouble; for example, we need but five terms of the series to obtain the first four digits in the decimal expansion of the number

$$l\,2 = 0.69314\ 71805 \ldots.$$

Now we set, in (252.1), $b = 128 = 2^7$, $a = 125 = 5^3$, whence

$$7\,l\,2 - 3\,l\,5 = \frac{2\cdot3}{253} + \frac{2}{3}\left(\frac{3}{253}\right)^3 + \frac{2}{5}\left(\frac{3}{253}\right)^5 + \cdots,$$

and from this relation we calculate $l\,5$. To determine $l\,3$ and $l\,7$, we set $b = 81 = 3^4$ and $b = 2401 = 7^4$, respectively, and we take $a = b - 1$ in both cases. This yields

$$4\,l\,3 - 4\,l\,2 - l\,5 = \frac{2}{161} + \frac{2}{3}\left(\frac{1}{161}\right)^3 + \cdots,$$

$$4\,l\,7 - 5\,l\,2 - l\,3 - 2\,l\,5 = \frac{2}{4801} + \frac{2}{3}\left(\frac{1}{4801}\right)^3 + \cdots.$$

Similar procedures are used for the other prime numbers, as far as they may be needed. In calculating logarithmic tables, all we need determine by these methods are, of course, the logarithms of the prime numbers, since the other logarithms are then obtained from these by simple addition. To convert from the above natural (or Napierian) logarithms to common (or Briggsian) logarithms, we must divide the former by $l10 = 1/M$, i.e. multiply them by $M = 0.43429 \cdots$.

253. It is very easy to obtain estimates for the remainders of the various series used in the two preceding sections. From (251.1), for instance, we see that

$$
\left.
\begin{aligned}
| l(1 + z) - z | &\leq \frac{|z^2|}{2} + \frac{|z^3|}{3} + \cdots \\[2mm]
&\leq \frac{|z^2|}{2} (1 + |z| + |z|^2 + \cdots) \\[2mm]
&\leq \frac{|z^2|}{2(1 - |z|)} .
\end{aligned}
\right\} \qquad (253.1)
$$

Again by (251.1), we have that for positive real values x of z,

$$
x - \frac{x^2}{2} < l(1 + x) < x \qquad (0 < x < 1). \quad (253.2)
$$

Setting $x = 1/y$, we obtain from this the relation

$$
\frac{1}{y} - \frac{1}{2 y^2} < l\left(1 + \frac{1}{y}\right) < \frac{1}{y} \qquad (y > 1). \quad (253.3)
$$

Making use of the identity

$$
\frac{1}{y} - \frac{1}{2 y^2} = \frac{1}{y + 1} + \frac{y - 1}{2 y^2 (y + 1)} ,
$$

we can also replace (253.3) by the simpler relation

$$
\frac{1}{y + 1} < l\left(1 + \frac{1}{y}\right) < \frac{1}{y} \qquad (y > 1). \quad (253.4)
$$

Equation (251.5) yields a similar but considerably more accurate estimate. For if $y > 0$, then

$$
\frac{1}{3} \frac{1}{(2 y + 1)^2} + \frac{1}{5} \frac{1}{(2 y + 1)^4} + \cdots < \frac{1}{3} \frac{1}{(2 y + 1)^2} \left(1 + \frac{1}{(2 y + 1)^2} + \frac{1}{(2 y + 1)^4} + \cdots\right),
$$

and the right-hand side can be evaluated in terms of a closed expression, being equal to

$$
\frac{1}{3 [(2 y + 1)^2 - 1]} = \frac{1}{12 y (y + 1)} = \frac{1}{12 y} - \frac{1}{12 (y + 1)} .
$$

Comparison of the last result with relation (251.5) gives the estimate

$$\frac{1}{y + \frac{1}{2}} < l\left(1 + \frac{1}{y}\right) < \frac{1}{y + \frac{1}{2}}\left(1 + \frac{1}{12\,y} - \frac{1}{12\,(y+1)}\right), \quad (253.5)$$

and this can be seen at once to have better (closer) bounds than (253.4).

The General Power Function (§§ 254-255)

254. The identities

$$z = e^{lz}, \quad z^2 = e^{2lz}, \quad z^{-1} = \frac{1}{z} = e^{-lz}, \quad z^{-2} = e^{-2lz}$$

suggest what must be done to define a regular analytic function that might be called the general power z^α of z, where α is any given complex number. Accordingly, we define

$$w = z^\alpha = e^{\alpha lz}. \quad (254.1)$$

Except for special cases (see § 255 below), these functions are infinitely-many-valued and must therefore be considered as being defined on a Riemann surface with a logarithmic branch point at $z = 0$. On this surface they are regular analytic functions. At $z = 0$, they are not defined, and they cannot be extended to functions continuous at $z = 0$ unless α is a real number. This is seen, for example, by considering the formulas

$$z = \varrho\, e^{i\varphi}, \quad z^i = e^{-\varphi + il\varrho}. \quad (254.2)$$

If we use the principal value of lz (cf. § 246 above) in (254.1), then we call the corresponding value of w the *principal value* of z^α. The same rules of calculation apply to the symbol z^α as to ordinary (integral) powers. To prove this, we note first that (254.1) may be written in the form

$$l\,w = \alpha\, l\, z. \quad (254.3)$$

This implies that

$$(z^\alpha)^\beta = e^{\beta l w} = e^{\beta (\alpha l z)} = z^{\alpha\beta}, \quad (254.4)$$

$$z^\alpha z^\beta = e^{\alpha l z}\, e^{\beta l z} = z^{\alpha + \beta}, \quad (254.5)$$

$$w = z^\alpha \quad \text{gives} \quad z = w^{\frac{1}{\alpha}}. \quad (254.6)$$

Differentiating (254.1) with respect to z, we obtain

$$\frac{dw}{dz} = \alpha \, e^{\alpha l z} \cdot \frac{1}{z} = \alpha \, e^{\alpha l z} \cdot e^{-l z} = \alpha \, z^{\alpha - 1}.$$

Using the last relation, we can derive the following expansion, the so-called *binomial series*

$$(1 + z)^\alpha = 1 + \frac{\alpha}{1} z + \frac{\alpha \, (\alpha - 1)}{1 \cdot 2} z^2 + \frac{\alpha \, (\alpha - 1) \, (\alpha - 2)}{1 \cdot 2 \cdot 3} z^3 + \cdots, \quad (254.7)$$

which is convergent in the disc $|z| < 1$. From this, we find that if a and b are any two complex numbers for which $|a| < |b|$, then

$$(a + b)^\alpha = b^\alpha \left(1 + \frac{\alpha}{1} \cdot \frac{a}{b} + \frac{\alpha \, (\alpha - 1)}{1 \cdot 2} \cdot \frac{a^2}{b^2} + \cdots \right).$$

255. Let z_0 be a fixed non-zero complex number and let a be any number for which

$$z_0^\alpha = a \tag{255.1}$$

holds. We can solve (255.1) for z_0, by (254.6) above, and in doing this we see that we would arrive at the same number z_0 if instead of a in (255.1) we had the product of a by any of the numbers

$$e^{\alpha \, (2 n \pi i)} \qquad (n = \pm 1, \pm 2, \ldots). \tag{255.2}$$

In general, any two of the numbers (255.2) are distinct, so that, for a given z, the power z^α has different values on any two different sheets of its logarithmically branched Riemann surface. For z^α to have the same value on two different sheets, for a given z, we must have

$$e^{\alpha \, (2 n \pi i)} = e^{\alpha \, (2 n' \pi i)} \qquad \text{or} \qquad e^{\alpha \, (n - n') 2 \pi i} = 1. \tag{255.3}$$

Thus $a (n - n')$ must be a whole number and α a (positive or negative) rational number. Conversely, if $a = p/q$, where p and q are, say, positive whole numbers, then the relation $w = z^\alpha$ is equivalent to

$$w^q - z^p = 0. \tag{255.4}$$

This function $w = z^{p/q}$ is q-valued, and its inverse $z = w^{q/p}$ is a p-valued function. For the geometric description of the function $w = z^{p/q}$, we must use, instead of the above Riemann surface with logarithmic branch points at $z = 0$ and $z = \infty$, an *algebraic Riemann surface* of q sheets with a *branch point of order q* at $z = 0$, and another at $z = \infty$. Proceeding as in § 249 above, we obtain this Riemann surface by finally joining (identifying) the upper bank of the cut of the q-th sheet to the lower bank of the cut of the first sheet.

For an algebraic Riemann surface (surface with finitely many sheets), the branch points are not considered to be frontier points (as logarithmic branch points would be), but rather as *interior* points of the surface. And in fact, the inverse of the function

$$w = z^{\frac{1}{q}},$$ (255.5)

i.e., the function

$$z = w^q,$$ (255.6)

is regular at the point $w = 0$, which is the point that corresponds to the branch point $z = 0$ of the Riemann surface of (255.5). As the point $w = 0$ is an interior point of the domain of definition of (255.6), it is apparent that $z = 0$ must be considered an interior point of the domain of definition of (255.5).

Regular Functions with a Many-Valued Inverse (§ 256)

256. We can now calculate the inverse of a power series of the form

$$w = a_k z^k + a_{k+1} z^{k+1} + a_{k+2} z^{k+2} + \cdots \quad (k \geq 2,\ a_k \neq 0). \quad (256.1)$$

To this end, we set

$$w = t^k,$$ (256.2)

$$t = a_k^{\frac{1}{k}} \cdot z \left(1 + \frac{a_{k+1}}{a_k} z + \frac{a_{k+2}}{a_k} z^2 + \cdots \right)^{\frac{1}{k}}.$$ (256.3)

Here,

$$a_k^{\frac{1}{k}} = b_0$$ (256.4)

is any (fixed) one of the k-th roots of a_k. There is a positive number r_0 such that for all $|z| < r_0$,

$$\left| \frac{a_{k+1}}{a_k} z + \frac{a_{k+2}}{a_k} z^2 + \cdots \right| < 1$$ (256.5)

holds. For all such z, we know from (254.7) above that the last of the factors on the right-hand side of (256.3) can be expanded in a convergent power series in z, and we can therefore write

$$t = b_0 z + b_1 z^2 + b_2 z^3 + \cdots \quad (b_0 \neq 0). \quad (256.6)$$

By § 228 above, this implies that

$$z = c_0 t + c_1 t^2 + c_2 t^3 + \cdots \quad \left(c_0 = \frac{1}{b_0} = a_k^{-\frac{1}{k}}\right), \quad (256.7)$$

where the power series in (256.7) is convergent for, say, $|t| < \varrho$. To any given point w of the disc $|w| < \varrho^k$ we can assign k different values of t for each of which equation (256.2) holds. If t_1 is any one of these k values, we obtain all k of them from the formula

$$t_j = t_1 e^{2\pi i \cdot \frac{j-1}{k}} \quad (j = 1, 2, \ldots, k). \quad (256.8)$$

By (256.7), each of these t_j determines one and only one corresponding z_j which when substituted for z in (256.1) produces the given value of w.

Thus equation (256.1) represents a one-to-one mapping of a certain neighborhood of $z = 0$ in the z-plane onto a region of a Riemann surface of k sheets over the w-plane.

For (256.7) we can also write

$$z = c_0 w^{\frac{1}{k}} + c_1 w^{\frac{2}{k}} + c_3 w^{\frac{3}{k}} + \cdots .$$

But there are no particular advantages to this notation as against the one above.

Bounds for $n!$ (§ 257)

257. From formula (253.5) we can derive rather close bounds for $n!$, as follows. We first re-write (253.5) in the form

$$1 < l\left(1 + \frac{1}{y}\right)^{y + \frac{1}{2}} < 1 + \frac{1}{12\,y} - \frac{1}{12\,(y+1)}, \quad (257.1)$$

from which we obtain

$$e^{-\left(\frac{1}{12\,y} - \frac{1}{12\,(y+1)}\right)} \left(1 + \frac{1}{y}\right)^{y + \frac{1}{2}} < e < \left(1 + \frac{1}{y}\right)^{y + \frac{1}{2}}. \quad (257.2)$$

In the last relation, we replace y successively by $1, 2, \ldots, (n-1)$ and multiply the resulting $(n-1)$ inequalities; from this we obtain, if we make use of the identity

$$\left.\begin{array}{l} \left(1 + \frac{1}{1}\right)^{\frac{3}{2}}\left(1 + \frac{1}{2}\right)^{\frac{5}{2}} \cdots \left(1 + \frac{1}{n-1}\right)^{n - \frac{1}{2}} \\[2mm] = 2^{\frac{3}{2}} \cdot \frac{3^{\frac{5}{2}}}{2^{\frac{5}{2}}} \cdots \frac{n^{n - \frac{1}{2}}}{(n-1)^{n - \frac{1}{2}}} = \frac{n^{n - \frac{1}{2}}}{(n-1)!}, \end{array}\right\} \quad (257.3)$$

that

$$e^{-\frac{1}{12}} \frac{n^{n-\frac{1}{2}}}{(n-1)!} < e^{n-1} < \frac{n^{n-\frac{1}{2}}}{(n-1)!}. \tag{257.4}$$

Hence if we set

$$n! = A(n) \, n^{n+\frac{1}{2}} \, e^{-n}, \tag{257.5}$$

then for all values of n,

$$e^{\frac{11}{12}} < A(n) < e, \tag{257.6}$$

that is,

$$2.50 < A(n) < 2.72. \tag{257.7}$$

Thus the above formulas serve to calculate $n!$ with an error of not more than about 10%.

Bounds for the Series $\displaystyle\sum_{n=1}^{\infty} \frac{1}{n^{1+x}}$ (§ 258)

258. Let x be a positive real number. We wish to establish the convergence of the series

$$S(1+x) = 1 + \frac{1}{2^{1+x}} + \frac{1}{3^{1+x}} + \cdots = \sum_{n=1}^{\infty} \frac{1}{n^{1+x}} \tag{258.1}$$

and to obtain at the same time an estimate for its remainder.

To this end we let u range over the ray $-1 < u < \infty$ and consider the function

$$v(u) = (1+u)^{-x} + x\,u,$$

whose derivative with respect to u is

$$\frac{dv}{du} = -x\,(1+u)^{-(1+x)} + x.$$

In the interval $-1 < u < 0$, we have $0 < 1+u < 1$ and $(1+u)^{-(x+1)} > 1$, hence $dv/du < 0$; similarly, if u is positive we find that $dv/du > 0$. Therefore the function $v(u)$ assumes its only minimum at $u = 0$, whence

$$(1+u)^{-x} > 1 - u\,x \quad (u > -1, u \neq 0). \tag{258.2}$$

Hence if n is any integer greater than unity, we see from (258.2) that

$$\left(1 - \frac{1}{n}\right)^{-x} > 1 + \frac{x}{n}, \quad \left(1 + \frac{1}{n}\right)^{-x} > 1 - \frac{x}{n},$$

that is,

$$1 - \frac{n^x}{(n+1)^x} < \frac{x}{n} < \frac{n^x}{(n-1)^x} - 1.$$

The last relation yields

$$\frac{1}{n^x} - \frac{1}{(n+1)^x} < \frac{x}{n^{1+x}} < \frac{1}{(n-1)^x} - \frac{1}{n^x}. \tag{258.3}$$

Replacing n by $(n+p)$ in (258.3) and then adding the results for $p = 1, 2, 3, \ldots$, we obtain

$$\frac{1}{x(n+1)^x} < \sum_{p=1}^{\infty} \frac{1}{(n+p)^{1+x}} < \frac{1}{x\,n^x}. \tag{258.4}$$

But by (258.3),

$$\frac{1}{x\,n^x} < \frac{1}{x\,(n+1)^x} + \frac{1}{n^{1+x}}. \tag{258.5}$$

From (258.4), (258.5) and (258.1) we finally obtain the relation

$$\left. \begin{array}{c} \displaystyle S\,(1+x) = \sum_{p=1}^{n} \frac{1}{p^{1+x}} + \frac{1}{x\,(n+1)^x} + R_n, \\[2mm] \displaystyle 0 < R_n < \frac{1}{n^{1+x}}. \end{array} \right\} \tag{258.6}$$

By taking n sufficiently large, we can make R_n as small as we please; for if we break the series off after n terms and add the expression $1/[x\,(n+1)^x]$ to the partial sum, then the remaining error is positive and less than the last term used.

The Partial-Fraction Decomposition of
π ctg πz (§§ 259-261)

259. The analytic function

$$z \,\mathrm{ctg}\, z = z\,\frac{\cos z}{\sin z} = 1 - \frac{1}{3}\,z^2 - \frac{1}{45}\,z^4 - \cdots \tag{259.1}$$

is even and regular in a neighborhood of $z = 0$, and the first few terms of its power series expansion are as shown in (259.1). Therefore we have

$$\pi \,\mathrm{ctg}\, \pi\,z = \frac{1}{z} - \frac{\pi^2}{3}\,z - \frac{\pi^4}{45}\,z^3 - \cdots. \tag{259.2}$$

Hence the function π ctg πz has a pole of order unity at the point $z = 0$, and its residue at this point is 1. Also, it is a periodic function, of period 1;

therefore it has poles of order unity and with residue $=1$ at each of the points $z = \pm n$ $(n = 0, 1, 2, \ldots)$. This last condition, however, is also satisfied by the function

$$\psi(z) = \frac{1}{z} + \sum_{n=-\infty}^{\infty}{}' \left(\frac{1}{z+n} - \frac{1}{n} \right), \tag{259.3}$$

which by § 223 above represents a meromorphic function in the whole complex plane; that it is permissible to take all of the n_j of formula (223.5) to be $=1$ in the case of the series (259.3) follows from the fact that by the preceding section, the series

$$S(2) = \sum_{n=1}^{\infty} \frac{1}{n^2}$$

is convergent. The prime on the summation symbol in (259.3) is to indicate that the index n of summation runs through all of the positive and negative integers but *omits* $n = 0$.

The function $\pi \operatorname{ctg} \pi z$ has no further poles beyond those indicated above. Hence by § 222 above, we may set

$$\pi \operatorname{ctg} \pi z = g(z) + \psi(z), \tag{259.4}$$

where $g(z)$ is an *integral function* that we shall determine presently. For the simplest method of doing this, the author is indebted to G. Herglotz who communicated this method to him orally.

260. From (259.1) and (259.3) it follows that

$$\lim_{z=0} \left(\pi \operatorname{ctg} \pi z - \frac{1}{z} \right) = 0, \quad \lim_{z=0} \left(\psi(z) - \frac{1}{z} \right) = 0,$$

which implies first of all that

$$g(0) = 0 \tag{260.1}$$

holds. Since by § 204 above, relation (259.3) can be differentiated term by term, we obtain by differentiation with respect to z of (259.4) that

$$g'(z) = -\frac{\pi^2}{\sin^2 \pi z} + \sum_{n=-\infty}^{\infty} \frac{1}{(z+n)^2}, \tag{260.2}$$

where we note that there is no prime on the summation symbol to modify its meaning. If we replace the variable z in (260.2) by $z/2$ or by $(z+1)/2$, we obtain, respectively,

$$g'\left(\frac{z}{2}\right) = -\frac{\pi^2}{\sin^2\dfrac{\pi z}{2}} + \sum_{n=-\infty}^{\infty}\frac{4}{(z+2n)^2},$$

$$g'\left(\frac{z+1}{2}\right) = -\frac{\pi^2}{\cos^2\dfrac{\pi z}{2}} + \sum_{n=-\infty}^{\infty}\frac{4}{(z+2n+1)^2}.$$

Adding the last two equations and comparing the result with (260.2), we obtain the functional equation

$$g'\left(\frac{z}{2}\right) + g'\left(\frac{z+1}{2}\right) = 4\,g'(z), \tag{260.3}$$

which the integral function $g'(z)$ must satisfy. Now let M stand for the least upper bound of $|g'(z)|$ in the disc $|z| < 2$. If the point z belongs to this disc, then so do the points $z/2$ and $(z+1)/2$. Hence (260.3) implies that

$$\left|g'(z)\right| \leq \frac{1}{4}\left|g'\left(\frac{z}{2}\right)\right| + \frac{1}{4}\left|\frac{g'(z+1)}{2}\right| \leq \frac{M}{2}.$$

Since this last relation holds for all points of the disc $|z| < 2$, we must have $M \leq M/2$, whence $M = 0$. Therefore $g'(z)$ vanishes in the disc and hence also in the whole plane, so that the integral function $g(z)$ must be a constant. By (260.1), we therefore have $g(z) \equiv 0$, and we finally have the formulas

$$\pi\frac{\cos \pi z}{\sin \pi z} = \frac{1}{z} + \sum_{n=-\infty}^{\infty}{}'\left(\frac{1}{z+n} - \frac{1}{n}\right) \tag{260.4}$$

and

$$\pi\frac{\cos \pi z}{\sin \pi z} = \frac{1}{z} + \sum_{n=1}^{\infty}\frac{2z}{z^2 - n^2}, \tag{260.5}$$

the second of which is derived from the first by combining the terms of (260.4) in twos, for n and $-n$.

261. Each of the terms of the last series can be developed in a power series in z, namely

$$\frac{2z}{z^2 - n^2} = -\frac{2z}{n^2} - \frac{2z^3}{n^4} - \frac{2z^5}{n^6} - \cdots; \tag{261.1}$$

using Weierstrass' double-series theorem (cf. § 212) and (258.1) above, we therefore obtain

$$\pi \operatorname{ctg} \pi z = \frac{1}{z} - 2\, S(2)\, z^3 - 2\, S(4)\, z^5 - \cdots, \qquad (261.2)$$

which implies that

$$\pi z \operatorname{ctg} \pi z = 1 - 2 \sum_{n=1}^{\infty} S(2\,n)\, z^{2n}, \qquad (261.3)$$

$$\frac{z}{2} \operatorname{ctg} \frac{z}{2} = 1 - \sum_{n=1}^{\infty} \frac{S\,(2\,n)}{2^{2n-1}\,\pi^{2n}} \cdot z^{2n}. \qquad (261.4)$$

Here, $S(n)$ has the same meaning as in § 258 above.

The Product Formula for $\sin \pi z$, and Wallis' Formula (§ 262)

262. If we integrate relation (260.4) above term by term from 0 to z and make use of the fact that

$$\frac{d}{dz}\, l \sin \pi z = \frac{\pi \cos \pi z}{\sin \pi z}, \qquad (262.1)$$

we find that

$$l \sin \pi z = A + l z + \sum_{n=-\infty}^{\infty}{}' l\left[\left(1+\frac{z}{n}\right)e^{-\frac{z}{n}}\right], \qquad (262.2)$$

whence

$$\sin \pi z = e^A\, z \prod_{n=-\infty}^{\infty}{}' \left(1+\frac{z}{n}\right)e^{-\frac{z}{n}}.$$

Since

$$e^A = \lim_{z=0} \frac{\sin \pi z}{z} = \pi,$$

we finally obtain the formula

$$\sin \pi z = \pi z \prod_{n=-\infty}^{\infty}{}' \left(1+\frac{z}{n}\right)e^{-\frac{z}{n}}, \qquad (262.3)$$

where the infinite product converges for all values of z. If we combine the terms for n and $-n$, we may also write the last relation in the form

$$\sin \pi z = \pi z \prod_{n=1}^{\infty} \left(1-\frac{z^2}{n^2}\right). \qquad (262.4)$$

For $z = 1/2$, this yields

$$\frac{2}{\pi} = \prod_{n=1}^{\infty} \left(1-\frac{1}{4\,n^2}\right) = \prod_{n=1}^{\infty} \frac{(2\,n-1)\,(2\,n+1)}{2\,n \cdot 2\,n}, \qquad (262.5)$$

a formula that was discovered by Wallis (1616-1703).

We can also find, and just as easily, a convergent infinite product that represents $\cos \pi z$. To this end, we write

$$\cos \pi z = \frac{\sin 2 \pi z}{2 \sin \pi z} = \frac{2 \pi z \, \Pi' \left(1 + \dfrac{2 z}{n}\right) e^{-2 \frac{z}{n}}}{2 \pi z \, \Pi' \left(1 + \dfrac{z}{n}\right) e^{-\frac{z}{n}}}, \qquad (262.6)$$

which after cancellation of the common factors in the numerator and denominator yields

$$\cos \pi z = \prod_{n=-\infty}^{\infty} \left(1 + \frac{2 z}{2 n + 1}\right) e^{-\frac{2 z}{2 n + 1}}. \qquad (262.7)$$

To each negative value n' of n, there corresponds a value $n \geq 0$ such that $(2n' + 1) = -(2n + 1)$. By always combining two such corresponding terms in (262.7), we finally obtain

$$\cos \pi z = \prod_{n=0}^{\infty} \left(1 - \frac{4 z^2}{(2 n + 1)^2}\right). \qquad (262.8)$$

CHAPTER THREE

THE BERNOULLI NUMBERS AND THE GAMMA FUNCTION

The Inverse of Differencing (§ 263)

263. Jakob Bernoulli (1654-1705) introduced polynomials $s_n(x)$ that satisfy the equation

$$s_n(x) = 0^n + 1^n + \cdots + (x-1)^n \quad (0^0 = 1, \ 0^n = 0 \ \text{if} \ n > 0) \quad (263.1)$$

for all non-negative integral values of n and x. In this connection he discovered a certain infinite sequence of rational numbers which are called the Bernoulli numbers and which are useful for many problems of Analysis and of Number Theory.

The problem treated by Bernoulli is closely related to the study of the inverse of the basic operation of the Calculus of Finite Differences.[1] Let

$$f(x) = c_0 + c_1 x + \cdots + c_n x^n \qquad (c_n \neq 0)$$

be a polynomial of degree n. We wish to find a polynomial $g(x)$ for which

$$\Delta g(x) = g(x+1) - g(x) = f(x) \qquad (263.2)$$

holds. If

$$g^*(x) = g(x) + h(x)$$

is a second polynomial for which $\Delta g^*(x) = f(x)$, then

$$h(x+1) = h(x)$$

must hold, whence

$$h(0) = h(1) = \cdots = h(n) = h(n+1) = \cdots.$$

---

[1] The pertinent investigations by Bernoulli are to be found in his *Ars Conjectandi*, published posthumously (1713). The first five of the Benoulli numbers appear on p. 97 of this treatise.

For the state of the inverse Calculus of Finite Differences in the eighteenth century, see the book by S. F. Lacroix, *Traité du Calcul Différentiel et du Calcul Intégral*, 2nd ed., Vol. 3 (1819), p. 75 ff. and the bibliography on p. ix.

Therefore the polynomial $h(x) - h(0)$ has an infinite number of zeros, so that $h(x)$ must be identically equal to the constant $h(0)$. Hence there exists at most one polynomial $g(x)$ that satisfies both equation (263.2) above and the relation $g(0) = 0$.

To prove the existence of such a polynomial $g(x)$, we first write $f(x)$ in the form

$$f(x) = a_0 + a_1 x + a_2 x (x - 1) + \cdots + a_n x (x - 1) \ldots (x - n + 1). \quad (263.3)$$

It is easy to show that it is possible in one and only one way to write $f(x)$ in the form (263.3). For if $n = 1$, then clearly $a_0 = c_0$ and $a_1 = c_1$; also, if $n > 1$ then clearly $a_n = c_n$. Thus if we assume, as an induction hypothesis, that the statement holds true for $(n - 1)$, then it follows that it is possible in one and only one way to determine the numbers $a_0, a_1, \ldots, a_{n-1}$ in such a way that the equation

$$f(x) - c_n x (x - 1) \ldots (x - n + 1) = a_0 + a_1 x + \cdots + a_{n-1} x (x - 1) \ldots (x - n + 2)$$

holds, and this equation implies (263.3).

A similar proof by mathematical induction shows that all of the coefficients $a_0, a_1, \ldots, a_n$ are integers if and only if all of the coefficients $c_0, \ldots, c_n$ are integers.

We now introduce the notation

$$b_0 = a_0, \quad b_1 = a_1, \quad b_\nu = a_\nu \, \nu! \quad (\nu = 2, \ldots, n), \quad (263.4)$$

$$\binom{x}{0} = 1, \quad \binom{x}{1} = x, \quad \binom{x}{\nu} = \frac{x (x - 1) \ldots (x - \nu + 1)}{\nu!} \quad (\nu = 2, 3, \ldots), \quad (263.5)$$

and we observe that

$$\varDelta \binom{x}{\nu + 1} = \binom{x + 1}{\nu + 1} - \binom{x}{\nu + 1} = \binom{x}{\nu} \quad (\nu = 0, 1, \ldots). \quad (263.6)$$

Hence by (263.3), (263.4) and (263.5), we can write

$$f(x) = b_0 \binom{x}{0} + b_1 \binom{x}{1} + \cdots + b_n \binom{x}{n} = \sum_{\nu = 0}^{\infty} b_\nu \binom{x}{\nu}, \quad (263.7)$$

and (263.6) shows that the polynomial

$$g(x) = \sum_{\nu = 0}^{n} b_\nu \binom{x}{\nu + 1} \quad (263.8)$$

satisfies not only condition (263.2) but also the condition $g(0) = 0$.

We note finally that if x is a positive integer, then

$$g(x) = [g(1) - g(0)] + [g(2) - g(1)] + \cdots + [g(x) - g(x-1)],$$

so that

$$g(x) = f(0) + f(1) + \cdots + f(x-1) \qquad (x = 1, 2, \ldots) \quad (263.9)$$

holds.

The function $g(x)$, which satisfies both $\Delta g(x) = f(x)$ and $g(0) = 0$, will be denoted in what follows by

$$\Delta^{-1} f(x) = g(x). \qquad (263.10)$$

The Bernoulli Numbers (§ 264)

264. Bernoulli's polynomials mentioned at the beginning of the preceding section can now be found by setting

$$s_n(x) = \Delta^{-1} x^n. \qquad (264.1)$$

By the method of the preceding section, we can calculate the $s_n(x)$, obtaining—for the first few of them—

$$\left. \begin{aligned}
s_0(x) &= x, \\
s_1(x) &= \frac{x(x-1)}{2} = \frac{x^2}{2} - \frac{1}{2}x, \\
s_2(x) &= \frac{x(x-1)(2x-1)}{6} = \frac{x^3}{3} - \frac{1}{2}x^2 + \frac{1}{6}x, \\
s_3(x) &= \frac{x^2(x-1)^2}{4} = \frac{x^4}{4} - \frac{1}{2}x^3 + \frac{1}{4}x^2 + 0 \cdot x, \\
s_4(x) &= \frac{x(x-1)(2x-1)(3x^2-3x+1)}{30} = \frac{x^5}{5} - \frac{1}{2}x^4 + \frac{1}{3}x^3 + * - \frac{1}{30}x.
\end{aligned} \right\} \quad (264.2)$$

The pattern of the coefficients of these polynomials does not seem transparent at all. In order to find a simple law of formation for the coefficients, we shall now given an alternate method for determining the polynomials $s_n(x)$. Our defining equations for the $s_n(x)$ are

$$s_n(x+1) - s_n(x) = x^n, \quad s_n(0) = 0 \qquad (264.3)$$

(*cf.* (264.1) and (263.10) above). Differentiation of the first of these yields

$$s_n'(x+1) - s_n'(x) = n\,x^{n-1}, \qquad (264.4)$$

whence

$$s_{n-1}(x) = \frac{1}{n}\,[s_n'(x) - s_n'(0)]. \qquad (264.5)$$

Now let us assume that we had already calculated the coefficients of $s_n'(x)$, i.e. let us assume that in the equation

$$s_n'(x) = h^0 x^n + h^1 \binom{n}{1} x^{n-1} + \cdots + h^n = \sum_{\nu=0}^{n} \binom{n}{\nu} h^\nu x^{n-\nu} \qquad (264.6)$$

the numbers h^ν are given. (The superscripts ν of these numbers are *not* meant to be exponents.) Then we obtain from (264.5) and (264.6) that

$$s_{n-1}(x) = \frac{1}{n} \sum_{\nu=0}^{n-1} \binom{n}{\nu} h^\nu x^{n-\nu}, \qquad (264.7)$$

and since $\binom{n}{\nu}(n-\nu)/n = \binom{n-1}{\nu}$ holds, (264.7) implies that

$$s_{n-1}'(x) = \sum_{\nu=0}^{n-1} \binom{n-1}{\nu} h^\nu x^{(n-1)-\nu} \qquad (264.8)$$

The numbers $h^0, h^1, \ldots, h^{n-1}$ appearing in (264.8) are the same as those in (264.6). Thus the only difference between equations (264.8) and (264.6) consists in the replacement of the n of (264.6) throughout by $(n-1)$ in (264.8) and in the omission of the term h^n in (264.8). But for $x = 0$ and $n \geqq 2$, relation (264.4) becomes $s_n'(1) - s_n'(0) = 0$, and this relation together with (264.6) yields the identity

$$h^0 + \binom{n}{1} h^1 + \cdots + \binom{n}{n-1} h^{n-1} = 0 \qquad (n \geqq 2). \quad (264.9)$$

Thus we can calculate h^{n-1} provided we know $h^0, h^1, \ldots, h^{n-2}$, and since $h^0 = 1$ by (264.2), relation (264.9) enables us to determine successively the numbers of the sequence $h^1, h^2, \ldots$, as far as we please.

The Symbolic Calculus of E. Lucas (§§ 265-268)

265. The relations derived above, as well as those we wish to derive from them, can be written in a very transparent form if we consider the numbers h^ν, which are called the *Bernoulli numbers*, as "symbolic powers," and operate with them just as though this deliberate misinterpretation were valid. This artifice was first suggested by E. Lucas (1842-1891). Accordingly, we write equation (264.6) in the form

$$s_n'(x) = (x + h)^n, \qquad (265.1)$$

and equation (264.9) in the form

$$(h + 1)^n - h^n = 0 \qquad (n = 2, 3, \ldots). \quad (265.2)$$

In this way, we calculate the first few of the Bernoulli numbers as follows:

$$2 h^1 + 1 = 0, \qquad\qquad h^1 = -\frac{1}{2},$$

$$3 h^2 + 3 h^1 + 1 = 0, \qquad\qquad h^2 = \frac{1}{6},$$

$$4 h^3 + 6 h^2 + 4 h^1 + 1 = 0, \qquad\qquad h^3 = 0,$$

$$5 h^4 + 10 h^3 + 10 h^2 + 5 h^1 + 1 = 0, \qquad\qquad h^4 = -\frac{1}{30},$$

$$6 h^5 + 15 h^4 + 20 h^3 + 15 h^2 + 6 h^1 + 1 = 0, \qquad\qquad h^5 = 0,$$

$$7 h^5 + 21 h^5 + 35 h^4 + 35 h^3 + 21 h^2 + 7 h^1 + 1 = 0, \qquad h^5 = \frac{1}{42},$$

$$\vdots \qquad\qquad\qquad \vdots$$

266. The symbolic calculus of Lucas represents a kind of shorthand in terms of which many other relations involving the Bernoulli numbers can be set up. Consider, for instance, the polynomial

$$\varphi(t) = c_0 + c_1 t + c_2 t^2 + \cdots + c_m t^m. \tag{266.1}$$

Using relation (265.2), we have that

$$\varphi(h + 1) - \varphi(h) = c_1 + \sum_{\nu = 2}^{m} c_\nu \left[(h + 1)^\nu - h^\nu\right] = c_1,$$

so that the Bernoulli numbers satisfy the relation

$$\varphi(h + 1) - \varphi(h) = \varphi'(0). \tag{266.2}$$

Furthermore, if z is any real or complex number and if we set

$$\varphi(t) = f(z + t), \tag{266.3}$$

then (266.2) implies that

$$f(z + h + 1) - f(z + h) = f'(z). \tag{266.4}$$

This last relation in turn yields

$$\Delta^{-1} f'(z) = f(z + h) - f(h), \tag{266.5}$$

which leads to another very simple way of solving the problem mentioned at the beginning of § 263. Specifically, we obtain

$$s_n(x) = \Delta^{-1} x^n = \frac{1}{n + 1} \left[(x + h)^{n+1} - h^{n+1}\right]. \tag{266.6}$$

From relation (266.4) we further obtain, if x denotes any natural number, the equation

$$f'(0) + f'(1) + \cdots + f'(x-1) = f(x+h) - f(h), \qquad (266.7)$$

which represents a generalization of Bernoulli's summation formula.

267. We next set

$$\varphi(t) = f(z\,t)$$

and obtain from (266.2) that

$$f\big(z(h+1)\big) - f(z\,h) = z\,\varphi'(0). \qquad (267.1)$$

This relation remains valid also if $\varphi(t)$ is a power series, since the formal rules of calculation are the same for power series as for polynomials. In particular, if we set

$$\varphi(t) = e^t,$$

then (267.1) yields

$$e^{z(h+1)} - e^{zh} = z.$$

We thus obtain also the symbolic equation

$$e^{zh} = \frac{z}{e^z - 1}. \qquad (267.2)$$

Hence the Bernoulli numbers can be obtained directly from the coefficients in the power-series development of the right-hand side of (267.2), a fact that was discovered by Euler. Now we note that

$$\frac{z}{e^z - 1} = -\frac{z}{2} + \frac{z}{2} \cdot \frac{e^z + 1}{e^z - 1} = -\frac{z}{2} + \frac{z}{2} \cdot \frac{e^{\frac{z}{2}} + e^{-\frac{z}{2}}}{e^{\frac{z}{2}} - e^{-\frac{z}{2}}}, \qquad (267.3)$$

and that the second term on the right-hand side is an even function of z. Hence the coefficients of $z^3, z^5, \ldots$ in the power-series expansion of e^{zh} all must be zero, which yields the equation

$$h^{2k+1} = 0 \qquad (k = 1, 2, \ldots). \qquad (267.4)$$

If we replace z by iz in (267.2) and (267.3), we obtain

$$e^{izh} + i\,\frac{z}{2} = \frac{z}{2}\,\operatorname{ctg}\,\frac{z}{2}. \qquad (267.5)$$

Hence by (261.4),

$$\sum_{n=1}^{\infty} (-1)^n \frac{h^{2n}}{(2n)!} z^{2n} = - \sum_{n=1}^{\infty} \frac{2 S(2n)}{(2\pi)^{2n}} z^{2n}, \qquad (267.6)$$

so that the "even" Bernoulli numbers satisfy the relation

$$h^{2n} = (-1)^{n-1} \frac{2(2n)!}{(2\pi)^{2n}} S(2n). \qquad (267.7)$$

Thus the "even" Bernoulli numbers are alternately positive and negative. For this reason, it is customary to consider instead of the numbers h^{2n} other numbers B_n that are defined by

$$B_n = (-1)^{n-1} h^{2n}, \text{ gives } B_1 = \frac{1}{6}, \ B_2 = \frac{1}{30}, \ B_3 = \frac{1}{42}, \ \dots . \qquad (267.8)$$

We note two implications of relation (267.7). First, it enables us to evaluate the series

$$S(2n) = \sum_{v=1}^{\infty} \frac{1}{v^{2n}} \qquad (267.9)$$

in terms of h^{2n} (or B_n), thus:

$$S(2) = \frac{\pi^2}{6}, \ S(4) = \frac{\pi^4}{90}, \ S(6) = \frac{\pi^6}{945}, \ \dots, \ S(2n) = \frac{(2\pi)^{2n}}{2(2n)!} B_n. \qquad (267.10)$$

Second, since the numbers $S(2n)$ decrease monotonically as n increases and converge rapidly to unity, we can use (267.7) to find bounds for the Bernoulli numbers. If for no other reason, such bounds are of importance because even for moderately large values of n, the numbers B_n become tremendously large, as can be seen from the formula

$$\frac{B_{n+1}}{B_n} = \frac{(2n+1)(2n+2)}{4\pi^2} \cdot \frac{S(2n+2)}{S(2n)} . \qquad (267.11)$$

Therefore if we make use of bounds for $S(2n)$ and $(2n)!$—for example, those obtained in §§ 258 and 257, respectively—we can find approximations for the B_n.

268. We obtain a further application of formula (266.2) by setting

$$\varphi(t) = (2t-1)^{2p+1}, \quad \varphi'(0) = 2(2p+1),$$

where p is a natural number; this gives

$$(2h+1)^{2p+1} - (2h-1)^{2p+1} = 2(2p+1)$$

or

$$(2p+1) = \frac{(1+2h)^{2p+1} + (1-2h)^{2p+1}}{2}$$

$$= 1 + \frac{(2p+1)\,2p}{2!}\,(2h)^2 + \frac{(2p+1)\,2p\,(2p-1)\,(2p-2)}{4!}\,(2h)^4 + \cdots.$$

After some simplifications, this becomes

$$\left.\begin{aligned}
\frac{1}{2p+1} &= \frac{(2h)^2}{1\cdot 2} + \frac{(2p-1)\,(2p-2)}{1\cdot 2}\cdot\frac{(2h)^4}{3\cdot 4} + \cdots \\
&= \sum_{\nu=1}^{p} \binom{2p-1}{2\nu-2}\,\frac{(2h)^{2\nu}}{(2\nu-1)\,2\nu}.
\end{aligned}\right\} \quad (268.1)$$

With the notation

$$u_0 = \frac{1}{2p+1}, \quad u_\nu = (-1)^{\nu-1}\binom{2p-1}{2\nu-2}\frac{(2h)^{2\nu}}{(2\nu-1)\,2\nu}, \qquad (268.2)$$

formula (268.1) assumes the form

$$u_0 - u_1 + u_2 - u_3 + \cdots + (-1)^p\,u_p = 0. \qquad (268.3)$$

Now it is easy to see that for $p \geq 2$,

$$0 < u_0 < u_1 < \cdots < u_{p-1} \qquad (268.4)$$

holds. For to begin with, we have

$$u_0 = \frac{1}{2p+1} \leq \frac{1}{5} < \frac{1}{3} = 2B_1 = u_1 \quad (p\geq 2), \qquad (268.5)$$

and furthermore, using (267.11),

$$\left.\begin{aligned}
\frac{u_{\nu+1}}{u_\nu} &= \frac{(2p-2\nu+1)\,(2p-2\nu)}{(2\nu+1)\,(2\nu+2)}\cdot\frac{4B_{\nu+1}}{B_\nu} \\
&= \frac{(2p-2\nu+1)\,(2p-2\nu)}{\pi^2}\cdot\frac{S(2\nu+2)}{S(2\nu)}.
\end{aligned}\right\} \qquad (268.6)$$

Now for $1 \leq \nu \leq (p-2)$, we have, first,

$$S(2\nu+2) > 1, \quad S(2\nu) \leq S(2) = \frac{\pi^2}{6}, \text{ thus } \frac{S(2\nu+2)}{S(2\nu)} > \frac{6}{\pi^2},$$

and second,

$$(2p-2\nu+1)\,(2p-2\nu) \geq 5\cdot 4 = 20.$$

This implies that

$$\frac{u_{\nu+1}}{u_\nu} > \frac{120}{\pi^4} > \frac{120}{100} > 1, \qquad (268.7)$$

and from this we see that the numbers of the sequence

$$u_0, \ u_0 - u_1, \ u_0 - u_1 + u_2, \quad \ldots, \quad u_0 - u_1 + \cdots + (-1)^{p-1} u_{p-1} \quad (268.8)$$

are alternately positive and negative. Hence if k is any natural number for which $1 \leq k \leq p - 1$, then there exists a number ϑ_{pk} for which the two conditions

$$u_0 - u_1 + \cdots + (-1)^{k-1} u_{k-1} + (-1)^k \vartheta_{pk} u_k = 0, \quad 0 < \vartheta_{pk} < 1 \quad (268.9)$$

both hold. If $k = p$, then by (268.3) we can take $\vartheta_{pp} = 1$ in formula (268.9); the same holds for $k > p$, as we can see from the fact that the relations

$$u_{p+1} = u_{p+2} = \cdots = 0$$

follow from the definition (268.2) of the u_ν. Hence for every natural number $k \geq 1$, we have the equation

$$\left. \begin{array}{c} \dfrac{1}{2p+1} = \displaystyle\sum_{\nu=1}^{k-1} \binom{2p-1}{2\nu-2} \dfrac{(2h)^{2\nu}}{(2\nu-1)\,2\nu} + \vartheta_{pk} \binom{2p-1}{2k-2} \dfrac{(2h)^{2k}}{(2k-1)\,2k} \\[2mm] 0 < \vartheta_{pk} \leq 1, \end{array} \right\} \quad (268.10)$$

which we shall find of use in the proof of Stirling's formula (cf. § 276 below).

Clausen's Theorem (§ 269)

269. We shall derive an important number-theoretic property of the Bernoulli numbers before we take leave of them. If we set

$$\varphi(t) = \binom{t}{m+1} = \frac{t\,(t-1)\,(t-2)\,\ldots\,(t-m)}{(m+1)!},$$

then

$$\varphi'(0) = \lim_{t=0} \frac{\varphi(t)}{t} = (-1)^m \frac{1}{m+1}.$$

Applying (266.2) and using (263.6), we obtain

$$\binom{h}{m} = (-1)^m \frac{1}{m+1}, \quad h\,(h-1)\,\ldots\,(h-m+1) = (-1)^m \frac{m!}{m+1}. \quad (269.1)$$

Now let $f(x)$ be any n-th degree polynomial whose coefficients are integers. If we transform $f(x)$ into the form (263.3), then by a remark in § 263 above, all of the coefficients a_ν must likewise be integers. Comparing (263.3) and (269.1), we obtain

$$f(h) = \sum_{v=0}^{n} (-1)^v \frac{a_v \, v!}{v+1}. \tag{269.2}$$

Whenever $(v+1)$ in the last sum can be written as the product of two different integers $l \geqq 2$ and $m \geqq 2$, then $v!$ is divisible by $(v+1)$. The same conclusion holds whenever $v+1 = m^2$ and $m \geqq 3$; for in this case we also have $2m \leqq v$. Therefore each of the terms on the right-hand side of (269.2) is an integer, with the possible exception of the terms for $v+1 = 2, 4$, or p, where p is an odd prime $\leqq n+1$. Hence we deduce from (269.2) that

$$\left.\begin{aligned}
f(h) = \quad & \text{integer} \quad - \frac{a_1}{2} - \frac{3\,a_3}{2} + \sum_p a_{p-1} \frac{(p-1)!}{p} \\
= \quad & \text{integer} \quad + \frac{2\,(a_1 + a_3)}{4} + \sum_p a_{p-1} \frac{(p-1)!}{p},
\end{aligned}\right\} \tag{269.3}$$

where p goes through all the prime numbers > 2 and $\leqq n+1$.

Frobenius (1849-1917) found a similar equation, in which it is not necessary to calculate the coefficients a_v. To obtain this equation, we consider any prime number $p \geqq 3$ and set

$$s_n(p) = 0^n + 1^n + \cdots + (p-1)^n. \tag{269.4}$$

If g is any number not divisible by p, then the residues modulo p of the numbers $0g, 1g, \ldots, (p-1)g$ represent a permutation of the numbers $0, 1, \ldots, (p-1)$ themselves, and we therefore have

$$s_n(p) \equiv g^n \, s_n(p) \; (\text{mod } p). \tag{269.5}$$

Now if g is a *primitive root* of p, then $g^n \equiv 1 \pmod{p}$ holds if and only if n is divisible by $(p-1)$. Hence if n is not divisible by $(p-1)$, then we have $s_n(p) \equiv 0 \pmod{p}$. But if n equals $(p-1)$ or is a multiple of $(p-1)$, then by Fermat's Theorem we have

$$s_n(p) \equiv (p-1) \pmod{p}.$$

Thus we finally have

$$\left.\begin{aligned}
s_n(p) &\equiv -1 \;(\text{mod } p), \quad \big(n = k\,(p-1),\; k = 1, 2, \ldots\big), \\
s_n(p) &\equiv \quad 0 \;(\text{mod } p), \quad \big(n = 0,\; n = k\,(p-1) + r,\; 0 < r < p-1\big).
\end{aligned}\right\} \tag{269.6}$$

Hence if

$$\varphi(x) = a_0 + a_1 x + a_2 x\,(x-1) + \cdots + a_{p-2} x\,(x-1)\ldots(x-p+3),$$

$$\psi(x) = f(x) - \varphi(x) = a_{p-1} x\,(x-1)\ldots(x-p+2) + a_p x\,(x-1)\ldots(x-p+1) + \cdots,$$

then we have

$$\varphi(0) + \varphi(1) + \cdots + \varphi(p-1) \equiv 0 \ (\mathrm{mod}\ p),$$

$$\psi(0) + \psi(1) + \cdots + \psi(p-1) = a_{p-1}(p-1)!\ .$$

Therefore

$$f(0) + f(1) + \cdots + f(p-1) \equiv a_{p-1}(p-1)!\ (\mathrm{mod}\ p). \qquad (269.7)$$

On the other hand, we can calculate that

$$f(0) + f(1) + f(2) \overset{\cdot}{+} f(3) = 4\,a_0 + 6\,a_1 + 8\,a_2 + 6\,a_3 \equiv 2\,(a_1 + a_3)\ (\mathrm{mod}\ 4). \quad (269.8)$$

Hence we can replace (269.3) by the much more convenient formula

$$f(h) = \quad \text{integer} \quad + \sum_p \frac{f(0) + f(1) + \cdots + f(p-1)}{p}\ ; \qquad (269.9)$$

here p goes through all the odd primes $\leqq n + 1$ and in addition takes on the value 4.

If we apply the last formula to the Bernoulli numbers h^{2n}, we obtain

$$h^{2n} = \quad \text{integer} \quad + \sum_p \frac{s_{2n}(p)}{p}\ .$$

Now

$$s_{2n}(4) = 1 + 2^{2n} + 3^{2n} \equiv 1 + 9^n \equiv -2\ (\mathrm{mod}\ 4)$$

holds true, and by (269.6) we have $s_{2n}(p) \equiv 0$ or -1. By crossing out in the last sum all those terms for which $s_{2n}(p)/p$ is an integer, we obtain the following final result:

$$\left.\begin{array}{l} h^{2n} = A_n - \left(\dfrac{1}{2} + \sum_p \dfrac{1}{p}\right), \\[2mm] p \text{ runs through all the odd primes } \leqq 2n + 1 \text{ for which } 2n \\ \text{is divisible by } p-1;\ A_n \text{ is a positive or a negative integer.} \end{array}\right\} \quad (269.10)$$

This theorem was proved independently and published almost simultaneously, by T. Clausen (1801-1885) and C. von Staudt (1798-1867). It is very useful for the calculation of the higher Bernoulli numbers, since the value of A_n follows even from a preliminary estimate of h^{2n} that one might obtain in one way or another. For the Bernoulli numbers h^2 through h^{20}, which we can calculate directly, we obtain the following values, which of course are seen to be in agreement with Clausen's theorem (269.10) above:

$$h^2 = \quad 1 - \left(\frac{1}{2} + \frac{1}{3}\right) = \frac{1}{6},$$

$$h^4 = \quad 1 - \left(\frac{1}{2} + \frac{1}{3} + \frac{1}{5}\right) = -\frac{1}{30},$$

$$h^6 = \quad 1 - \left(\frac{1}{2} + \frac{1}{3} + \frac{1}{7}\right) = \frac{1}{42},$$

$$h^8 = \quad 1 - \left(\frac{1}{2} + \frac{1}{3} + \frac{1}{5}\right) = -\frac{1}{30},$$

$$h^{10} = \quad 1 - \left(\frac{1}{2} + \frac{1}{3} + \frac{1}{11}\right) = \frac{5}{66},$$

$$h^{12} = \quad 1 - \left(\frac{1}{2} + \frac{1}{3} + \frac{1}{5} + \frac{1}{7} + \frac{1}{13}\right) = -\frac{691}{2730},$$

$$h^{14} = \quad 2 - \left(\frac{1}{2} + \frac{1}{3}\right) = 1 + \frac{1}{6},$$

$$h^{16} = \quad -6 - \left(\frac{1}{2} + \frac{1}{3} + \frac{1}{5} + \frac{1}{17}\right) = -7 \quad -\frac{47}{510},$$

$$h^{18} = \quad 56 - \left(\frac{1}{2} + \frac{1}{3} + \frac{1}{7} + \frac{1}{19}\right) = 54 \quad -\frac{775}{798},$$

$$h^{20} = -528 - \left(\frac{1}{2} + \frac{1}{3} + \frac{1}{5} + \frac{1}{11}\right) = -529 - \frac{41}{330}.$$

Euler's Constant (§ 270)

270. We introduce the following notation:

$$C'_n = 1 + \frac{1}{2} + \cdots + \frac{1}{n} - l\,n, \quad C''_n = 1 + \frac{1}{2} + \cdots + \frac{1}{n} - l\,(n+1). \quad (270.1)$$

Then we have, first,

$$C'_n - C''_n = l\left(1 + \frac{1}{n}\right) > 0, \quad \lim_{n=\infty} (C'_n - C''_n) = 0, \qquad (270.2)$$

and second, by (253.4) above,

$$C'_n - C'_{n+1} = l\left(1 + \frac{1}{n}\right) - \frac{1}{n+1} > 0,$$

$$- C''_n + C''_{n-1} = l\left(1 + \frac{1}{n}\right) - \frac{1}{n} < 0.$$

(270.3)

Therefore $C'_1 > C'_2 > C'_3 > \cdots$ and $C''_1 < C''_2 < C''_3 < \cdots$, and hence by (270.2) above,

$$\lim_{n=\infty} C'_n = \lim_{n=\infty} C''_n = C.$$

The number

$$C = \lim_{n=\infty}\left(1 + \frac{1}{2} + \cdots + \frac{1}{n} - l\,n\right)$$

is called *Euler's constant*. The numbers C_n' or C_n'' are not very well suited for the numerical calculation of C. However, we note that the numbers

$$C_n = 1 + \frac{1}{2} + \cdots + \frac{1}{n} - l\left(n + \frac{1}{2}\right)$$

lie between C_n' and C_n'', for every n, so that the C_n must themselves converge to C. By using the sequence of C_n, we can easily determine quite a few of the decimals in C; to this end, we note that by (251.3) above,

$$C_{n-1} - C_n = l\left(\frac{1 + \dfrac{1}{2n}}{1 - \dfrac{1}{2n}}\right) - 2 \cdot \frac{1}{2n}$$

$$= 2\left(\frac{1}{3} \cdot \frac{1}{(2n)^3} + \frac{1}{5} \cdot \frac{1}{(2n)^5} + \cdots\right),$$

so that we have

$$C = C_n - (C_n - C_{n+1}) - (C_{n+1} - C_{n+2}) - \cdots$$

$$= \left[1 + \frac{1}{2} + \cdots + \frac{1}{n} - l\left(n + \frac{1}{2}\right)\right] - 2\sum_{p=n+1}^{\infty}\left(\frac{1}{3} \cdot \frac{1}{(2p)^3} + \frac{1}{5} \cdot \frac{1}{(2p)^5} + \cdots\right).$$

By taking, say, $n = 12$ in this formula, we can find the first three of the decimals of C even if we ignore the entire series development under the summation symbol; by taking into account just the first two terms of this series, we obtain the first ten decimals of C. Thus we have

$$1 + \frac{1}{2} + \frac{1}{3} + \cdots + \frac{1}{12} = 3.10321\ 06782\ 10 \ldots$$

$$l\,\frac{25}{2} = 2.52572\ 86443\ 28 \ldots$$

$$\frac{1}{12} \cdot \sum_{13}^{\infty} \frac{1}{p^3} = 0.00026\ 62415\ 82 \ldots$$

$$\frac{1}{80} \cdot \sum_{13}^{\infty} \frac{1}{p^5} = 0.00000\ 01273\ 22 \ldots$$

whence we obtain

$$C = 0.57721\ 56649 \ldots .$$

The Function $\Gamma(z)$ (§§ 271-273)

271. For any two natural numbers s and n, the following identity holds true:

$$(s-1)! = \frac{1}{s} \cdot \frac{1\ \cdot\ 2\ \cdot\ \ldots\ \cdot\ n}{(s+1)\,(s+2)\ldots(s+n)}\ n^s \cdot \left[\frac{n+1}{n} \cdot \frac{n+2}{n} \cdot \ldots \cdot \frac{n+s}{n}\right]. \quad (271.1)$$

If we hold s fixed and let n go to ∞ in (271.1), the factor in brackets converges to unity, and we therefore have the relation

$$(s-1)! = \lim_{n=\infty} \frac{n^s \cdot n!}{s\,(s+1)\ldots(s+n)}. \quad (271.2)$$

We shall now prove that the right-hand side of (271.2) represents a function that is meromorphic in the entire complex plane if s is replaced by a complex variable z. This meromorphic function is denoted by $\Gamma(z)$.

To prove our statement, we set

$$\left.\begin{aligned}
\Gamma_n(z) &= n^z \cdot \frac{1}{z} \cdot \frac{1\ \cdot\ 2\ \cdot\ \ldots\ \cdot\ n}{(z+1)\,(z+2)\ldots(z+n)} \\
&= e^{z\left(ln-1-\frac{1}{2}-\cdots-\frac{1}{n}\right)} \cdot \frac{1}{z} \cdot \frac{e^{\frac{z}{1}}}{1+\frac{z}{1}} \cdot \frac{e^{\frac{z}{2}}}{1+\frac{z}{2}} \cdots \frac{e^{\frac{z}{n}}}{1+\frac{z}{n}} \cdot
\end{aligned}\right\} \quad (271.3)$$

It suffices to show that the $\Gamma_n(z)$ converge continuously to $\Gamma(z)$. By the preceding section, the first factor converges continuously to e^{-Cz}, so that we need only prove that in

$$\Gamma(z) = e^{-Cz} \frac{1}{z} \prod_{n=1}^{\infty} \frac{e^{\frac{z}{n}}}{1+\frac{z}{n}}, \quad (271.4)$$

the infinite product converges continuously, or which is the same, that in

$$l\,\Gamma(z) = -\,C\,z - l\,z - \sum_{n=1}^{\infty}\left[l\left(1+\frac{z}{n}\right)-\frac{z}{n}\right] \qquad (271.5)$$

the infinite series converges continuously. But this is very easy to see, as follows. If R is any positive number and N a natural number $> 2R$, then for all $n > N$ and for all $|z| < R$ we have $|z/n| < 1/2$, so that by (253.1),

$$\left|l\left(1+\frac{z}{n}\right)-\frac{z}{n}\right| \le \frac{R^2}{n^2} \qquad (n > N). \quad (271.6)$$

From the convergence of the majorizing series

$$\sum_{n=N}^{\infty}\frac{R^2}{n^2} < \frac{\pi^2\,R^2}{6} \qquad (271.7)$$

we now deduce, by § 204 above, the continuous convergence of the series (271.5) and hence of the product (271.4), which proves the above statement.

From (271.4), we obtain the formula

$$\frac{1}{\Gamma(z)} = e^{C z}\,z\prod_{n=1}^{\infty}\left(1+\frac{z}{n}\right)e^{-\frac{z}{n}}, \qquad (271.8)$$

which shows that $1/\Gamma(z)$ is an integral function the only zeros of which are at $z = 0,\,-1,\,-2,\,-3,\cdots$.

272. The first of the expressions for $\Gamma_n(z)$ in (271.3) yields $\Gamma_n(1) = n/(n+1)$, whence

$$\Gamma(1) = 1. \qquad (272.1)$$

We also have

$$\Gamma_n(z+1) = \frac{n^{z+1}\,n!}{(z+1)\,(z+2)\ldots(z+n+1)} = z\,\Gamma_n(z)\cdot\frac{n}{n+z+1},$$

whence

$$\Gamma(z+1) = z\,\Gamma(z). \qquad (272.2)$$

Relations (271.1) and (272.2) further imply that

$$\Gamma(n) = (n-1)! \qquad (n = 2, 3, \ldots). \quad (272.3)$$

By (272.2) and (271.8), we can write

$$\frac{1}{\Gamma(1-z)} = -\frac{1}{z}\cdot\frac{1}{\Gamma(-z)} = e^{-C z}\prod_{n=1}^{\infty}\left(1-\frac{z}{n}\right)e^{\frac{z}{n}}. \qquad (272.4)$$

Multiplying relations (271.8) and (272.4) and using (262.4), we obtain

$$\frac{1}{\Gamma(z)} \cdot \frac{1}{\Gamma(1-z)} = z \prod_{n=1}^{\infty}\left(1 - \frac{z^2}{n^2}\right) = \frac{\sin \pi z}{\pi}. \tag{272.5}$$

By setting $z = 1/2$ in (272.5), we find that

$$\Gamma\left(\frac{1}{2}\right) = \sqrt{\pi}, \tag{272.6}$$

and from this together with the functional equation (272.2) of the gamma function, we obtain

$$\Gamma\left(-\frac{1}{2}\right) = -2\sqrt{\pi}, \quad \Gamma\left(\frac{3}{2}\right) = \frac{\sqrt{\pi}}{2}. \tag{272.7}$$

273. By relation (271.5) above, logarithmic differentiation of (272.2) yields

$$\frac{\Gamma'(z+1)}{\Gamma(z+1)} = \frac{\Gamma'(z)}{\Gamma(z)} + \frac{1}{z} = -C - \sum_{n=1}^{\infty}\left(\frac{1}{z+n} - \frac{1}{n}\right). \tag{273.1}$$

From this we obtain the power-series development

$$\frac{\Gamma'(z+1)}{\Gamma(z+1)} = -C + S(2)\, z - S(3)\, z^2 + S(4)\, z^3 - \cdots \tag{273.2}$$

valid in the disc $|z| < 1$. Term-by-term integration and use of (272.1) lead to

$$l.\Gamma(z+1) = l\,\Gamma(z) + l\, z = -C\, z + \frac{S(2)}{2}\, z^2 - \frac{S(3)}{3}\, z^3 + \cdots . \tag{273.3}$$

Hence for positive real values x of z, the function $l\Gamma(z)$ assumes real values and $\Gamma(z)$ itself assumes positive real values, as can also be seen immediately from the product representation (271.4) of the gamma function.

Finally, differentiation of (273.1) yields

$$\frac{d^2\, l\, \Gamma(z)}{dz^2} = \frac{\Gamma(z)\,\Gamma''(z) - \Gamma'(z)^2}{\Gamma(z)^2} = \sum_{n=0}^{\infty} \frac{1}{(n+z)^2}. \tag{273.4}$$

The Bohr-Mollerup Theorem (§§ 274-275)

274. The function $\Gamma(z)$ was discovered by Euler, who defined it in terms of definite integrals. For a long time afterwards, mathematicians searched for a simple definition that would determine this function uniquely. The difficulty here was that unlike in the case of most of the more common analytic functions, it was not possible to find an algebraic differential equation that has $\Gamma(z)$ as a solution. In fact, it was proved by O. Hölder (1859-1919) that $\Gamma(z)$

cannot satisfy any algebraic differential equation.[1]   On the other hand, the functional equation (272.2) is not in itself sufficient to define $\Gamma(z)$; for if $p(z)$ is any periodic function of period 1 and if we set $g(z) = p(z)\Gamma(z)$, then we clearly have $g(z + 1) = zg(z)$.

It was not until 1922 that H. Bohr and J. Mollerup[2] discovered a marvelously simple characterization of $\Gamma(z)$.

A real-valued function $f(x)$ that is defined, say, for all $x > 0$ is said to be *convex* if for all $x > 0$ the function

$$\varphi(y) = \frac{f(x + y) - f(x)}{y} \tag{274.1}$$

is monotonically increasing in its entire domain of definition (i.e. for $y > -x$ and $y \neq 0$). It is easy to prove that every convex function must be continuous.

If the first two derivatives of $f(x)$ exist and are continuous, then $f(x)$ is convex if and only if $f''(x) \geqq 0$.   For we obtain from (274.1) that

$$\varphi'(y) = \frac{y f'(x + y) - f(x + y) + f(x)}{y^2} . \tag{274.2}$$

If we set $x + y = u$, then by Taylor's theorem,

$$f(x) = f(u - y) = f(u) - y f'(u) + \frac{y^2}{2} f''(u - (1 - \vartheta) y),$$

where ϑ is a number between 0 and 1.   If we substitute this expression for $f(x)$ in (274.2), we obtain

$$\varphi'(y) = \frac{1}{2} f''(x + \vartheta y).$$

Hence if $\varphi'(0) \geqq 0$, then $f''(x) \geqq 0$; and conversely, if the latter condition holds for all $x > 0$, then it follows that $\varphi'(y) \geqq 0$.

We note that for all positive real values of z, the right-hand side of (273.4) is itself positive.   Hence by what has just been proved, the logarithm of $\Gamma(x)$ is a convex function of x for $x > 0$.

275.   The theorem of Bohr and Mollerup states the following:

The function $\Gamma(x)$ is the only function defined and positive on the ray $x > 0$ that

    1.   *satisfies the functional equation $\Gamma(x + 1) = x\Gamma(x)$,*
    2.   *is logarithmically convex,*
    3.   *satisfies the condition $\Gamma(1) = 1$.*

---

[1] O. Hölder, Math. Ann. *28*, 1-13 (1887).—For other proofs, see E. H. Moore, Math. Ann. *48*, 49-74 (1897), and A. Ostrowski, Math. Ann. *93*, 248-251 (1925).

[2] H. Bohr and J. Mollerup, *Laerebog i matematisk Analyse* (Copenhagen, 1922), Vol. III, pp. 149-164. *Cf.* also E. Artin, *Einführung in die Theorie der Gammafunktion*, Hamb. math. Einzelschr. *11* (Leipzig, 1931), which we have followed in many details.

To prove this theorem, let $f(x)$ be any function satisfying the conditions of the theorem, let n be a natural number > 2, and let x lie in the interval $0 < x \leq 1$.

Then by the logarithmic convexity of $f(x)$, the four points

$$n - 1 < n < n + x \leq n + 1$$

satisfy the relations

$$\frac{l\,f(n-1) - l\,f(n)}{(n-1) - n} < \frac{l\,f(n+x) - l\,f(n)}{(n+x) - n} \leq \frac{l\,f(n+1) - l\,f(n)}{(n+1) - n}. \quad (275.1)$$

Now by properties 1. and 3. of $f(x)$, we have

$$f(n-1) = (n-2)!, \quad f(n) = (n-1)!, \quad f(n+1) = n!, \quad (275.2)$$

$$f(n+x) = x\,(x+1) \ldots (x+n-1)\,f(x). \quad (275.3)$$

By (275.1), it follows from (275.2) that

$$l\,(n-1)^x < l\,\frac{f(n+x)}{(n-1)!} \leq l\,n^x,$$

so that—the logarithm being a monotonically increasing function—

$$(n-1)^x < \frac{f(n+x)}{(n-1)!} \leq n^x. \quad (275.4)$$

This together with (275.3) implies that

$$\frac{(n-1)!\,(n-1)^x}{x\,(x+1) \ldots (x+n-1)} < f(x) \leq \frac{(n-1)!\,n^x}{x\,(x+1) \ldots (x+n-1)}.$$

These inequalities hold for all values of n. Replacing $(n-1)$ by n in the left-hand side, we obtain

$$\frac{n!\,n^x}{x\,(x+1) \ldots (x+n)} < f(x) \leq \frac{n!\,n^x}{x\,(x+1) \ldots (x+n)} \cdot \frac{x+n}{n},$$

or, using the notation of (271.3) above,

$$\Gamma_n(x) < f(x) \leq \Gamma_n(x)\,\frac{x+n}{n} \quad (n = 2, 3, \ldots). \quad (275.5)$$

From this it follows that

$$f(x) = \lim_{n=\infty} \Gamma_n(x) = \Gamma(x), \quad (275.6)$$

and since we saw earlier that the function $\Gamma(z)$ actually does satisfy all of the conditions of the theorem, our proof of this theorem is complete. To be sure, we have verified (275.6) only for the interval $0 \leq x < 1$; but for all remaining positive values of x, (275.6) follows from the functional equation (272.2).

Stirling's Series (§§ 276-277)

276. We shall now use the Bohr-Mollerup theorem to derive a formula that will enable us to calculate $\Gamma(x)$ for large positive values of x. From the developments in § 257 above, it is to be guessed that if we set

$$\Gamma(x) = a \, x^{x - \frac{1}{2}} e^{-x} e^{\mu(x)} \tag{276.1}$$

then the function $\mu(x)$ will remain bounded. We first obtain from (276.1) that

$$x = \frac{\Gamma(x+1)}{\Gamma(x)} = \frac{(1+x)^{x+\frac{1}{2}}}{x^{x+\frac{1}{2}}} \, x \, e^{-1} \, e^{\mu(x+1)-\mu(x)},$$

so that the function $\mu(x)$ is seen to satisfy the difference equation

$$\mu(x) - \mu(x+1) = \left(x+\frac{1}{2}\right) l\left(1+\frac{1}{x}\right) - 1. \tag{276.2}$$

We write, for short,

$$g(x) = \left(x+\frac{1}{2}\right) l\left(1+\frac{1}{x}\right) - 1, \tag{276.3}$$

and as a solution of equation (276.2), let us try

$$\mu(x) = g(x) + g(x+1) + g(x+2) + \cdots \tag{276.4}$$

By (251.5), $g(z)$ can be represented by the series

$$g(z) = \frac{1}{3} \cdot \frac{1}{(2z+1)^2} + \frac{1}{5} \cdot \frac{1}{(2z+1)^4} + \cdots \tag{276.5}$$

at every point z of the complex plane that lies outside the circle $|z + 1/2| = 1/2$. For any such z, we then have

$$|g(z)| < \frac{1}{3} \cdot \frac{1}{|2z+1|^2 - 1}, \tag{276.6}$$

whence it is easy to deduce that the series

$$\mu(z) = g(z) + g(z+1) + \cdots \tag{276.7}$$

converges continuously in a region of the z-plane that is contained in the half-plane $\Re z > 0$, and represents an analytic function in this region. This function is usually named after J. Binet (1786-1856), who was the first to study it in detail. It is obvious from (276.7) and (276.3) that the function $\mu(x)$ does satisfy the difference equation (276.2).

For positive real values x of z, we can use (253.5) to find bounds for the function $g(x)$ of (276.3), obtaining

$$0 < g(x) < \frac{1}{12\,x} - \frac{1}{12\,(x+1)}\,,$$

$$0 < g(x+n) < \frac{1}{12\,(x+n)} - \frac{1}{12\,(x+n+1)}\,;$$

(276.8)

from this we infer that

$$0 < \mu(x) < \frac{1}{12\,x}\,. \tag{276.9}$$

If we differentiate (276.5) twice term by term, we find that $g''(x) > 0$ for $x > 0$; the same result follows, with a little more calculation however, directly from (276.3). We obtain

$$g''(x) = \frac{1}{2\,x^2\,(1+x)^2} > 0\,.$$

Hence we also have

$$\mu''(x) = g''(x) + g''(x+1) + \cdots > 0\,,$$

which shows that $e^{\mu(x)}$ *is logarithmically convex.*

The factor $x^{x-\frac{1}{2}} e^{-x}$, by the way, is likewise logarithmically convex for $x > 0$, since the second derivative of its logarithm is

$$\frac{1}{x} + \frac{1}{2\,x^2}$$

and is therefore positive. Thus by the Bohr-Mollerup theorem, the right-hand side of (276.1) does indeed represent the gamma function $\Gamma(x)$, provided only that the constant a is defined to be

$$a = e^{1-\mu(1)}, \tag{276.10}$$

to satisfy condition 3. of the theorem, and that $\mu(x)$ is Binet's function. Under these conditions, we also have for complex values of z that

$$\Gamma(z) = a\,z^{z-\frac{1}{2}}\,e^{-z}\,e^{\mu(z)},$$

$$\mu(z) = \sum_{p=1}^{\infty} \frac{1}{2\,p+1} \sum_{n=0}^{\infty} \frac{1}{(2\,z+2\,n+1)^{2p}}\,.$$

(276.11)

Moreover, for $x > 0$ we have that

$$\Gamma(x) = a\, x^{x-\frac{1}{2}} e^{-x} e^{\frac{\vartheta(x)}{12\,x}}, \tag{276.12}$$

where, by (276.9),

$$0 < \vartheta(x) < 1 \tag{276.13}$$

holds. In particular,

$$n! = a\, n^{n+\frac{1}{2}} e^{-n} e^{\frac{\vartheta(n)}{12\,n}} \quad (0 < \vartheta(n) < 1). \tag{276.14}$$

This approximation to $n!$ is much better than the one in § 257 above. Formula (276.14) also enables us to calculate the numerical value of a by means of Wallis' formula (cf. § 262 above); but we shall not go into this, because we shall obtain the constant a in § 278 below by a different method and without any extra work. At any rate, it follows from (276.10) and (276.9) that a lies between $e^{11/12} \approx 2.5009$ and $e \approx 2.7183$.

277. We now wish to replace the approximation

$$\mu(x) = \frac{\vartheta(x)}{12\,x} \quad (0 < \vartheta(x) < 1) \tag{277.1}$$

by something more precise. To this end, we consider the second of the two equations in (276.11) above for $z = x > 0$ and replace the factors $1/(2p+1)$ by their expansions (268.10), which we transform at the same time, as follows:

$$\left. \begin{aligned} \frac{1}{2p+1} &= \sum_{k=1}^{m-1} (-1)^{k+1} \frac{(2p-1)\,(2p-2)\,\ldots\,(2p-2k+2)}{1\;\cdot\;2\;\cdot\;\ldots\;\cdot\;(2k-2)} \cdot \frac{4^k B_k}{2k\,(2k-1)} \\ &\quad + (-1)^{m+1} \frac{(2p-1)\,\ldots\,(2p-2m+2)}{1\;\cdot\;\ldots\;\cdot\;(2m-2)} \cdot \frac{4^m B_m}{2m\,(2m-1)}\, \vartheta_{mp}. \end{aligned} \right\} \tag{277.2}$$

A rearrangement of terms yields

$$\left. \begin{aligned} \mu(x) &= a_1 \frac{B_1}{1\cdot 2} - a_2 \frac{B_2}{3\cdot 4} + \cdots + (-1)^m a_{m-1} \frac{B_{m-1}}{(2m-3)\,(2m-2)} \\ &\quad + (-1)^{m+1} \vartheta\, a_m \frac{B_m}{(2m-1)\,2m}. \end{aligned} \right\} \tag{277.3}$$

This estimate, in which $0 < \vartheta < 1$, is a consequence of the formula

$$\sum_p \vartheta_p a_p = \vartheta \sum_p a_p \quad (0 < \vartheta < 1),$$

which is valid for positive numbers a_p whose sum is finite, and for numbers ϑ_p between 0 and 1.

To calculate the a_k in (277.3) above, we note first that

$$a_k = \sum_{n=0}^{\infty} \frac{4^k}{(2\,x + 2\,n + 1)^{2\,k-1}} \sum_{p=k}^{\infty} \frac{(2\,p-1)\,(2\,p-2)\,\ldots\,(2\,p-2\,k+2)}{1 \quad \cdot \quad 2 \,\cdot\, \ldots \,\cdot\, (2\,k-2)} \left. \begin{array}{l} \\ \\ \end{array} \right\}$$
$$\times \frac{1}{(2\,x+2\,n+1)^{2\,p-2\,k+1}}. \qquad (277.4)$$

In the second sum, we have omitted the terms for $p = 1, 2, \ldots, (k-1)$, because they equal zero. For $p \geqq k$, we have

$$\frac{(2\,p-1)\,(2\,p-2)\,\ldots\,(2\,p-2\,k+2)}{1 \quad \cdot \quad 2 \,\cdot\, \ldots \,\cdot\, (2\,k-2)} = \frac{(2\,k-1)\,2\,k\,\ldots\quad(2\,p-1)}{1\,\cdot\,2\,\cdot\,\ldots\,\cdot\,(2\,p-2\,k+1)}, \qquad (277.5)$$

as we can verify by cross-multiplying.

We now note that

$$2\sum_{p=k}^{\infty} \frac{(2\,k-1)\,2\,k\,\ldots\quad(2\,p-1)}{1\,\cdot\,2\,\cdot\,\ldots\,\cdot\,(2\,p-2\,k+1)}\, u^{2\,p-2\,k+1} \left. \begin{array}{l} \\ \\ \end{array} \right\}$$
$$= (1-u)^{-(2k-1)} - (1+u)^{-(2k-1)}, \qquad (277.6)$$

which is obtained from the power-series expansions of the two terms on the right-hand side. By (277.6), (277.5), (277.4), we now have

$$a_k = \sum_{n=0}^{\infty} \frac{2^{2\,k-1}}{(2\,x+2\,n+1)^{2\,k-1}} \left. \begin{array}{l} \\ \\ \\ \\ \\ \\ \end{array} \right\}$$
$$\times \left[\left(1 - \frac{1}{2\,x+2\,n+1}\right)^{1-2\,k} - \left(1 + \frac{1}{2\,x+2\,n+1}\right)^{1-2\,k}\right] \qquad (277.7)$$
$$= \sum_{n=0}^{\infty} 2^{2k-1}\,[(2\,x+2\,n)^{1-2k} - (2\,x+2\,n+2)^{1-2k}]$$
$$= \sum_{n=0}^{\infty} [(x+n)^{1-2k} - (x+n+1)^{1-2k}]$$

which finally yields $a_k = 1/x^{2k-1}$

If we substitute the numerical values of the first few of the Bernoulli numbers (cf. § 269 and formula (267.8) above), we now obtain from (277.3) and (277.7) the final formula

$$\mu(x) = \frac{1}{12\,x} - \frac{1}{360\,x^3} + \frac{1}{1260\,x^5} - \frac{1}{1680\,x^7} + \cdots \left. \begin{array}{l} \\ \\ \\ \end{array} \right\}$$
$$\cdots + (-1)^m\,\vartheta_m \,\frac{B_m}{(2\,m-1)\,2\,m\,x^{2\,m-1}} \qquad (0 < \vartheta_m(x) < 1). \qquad (277.8)$$

This holds for all values of m. Since for fixed x the terms of the series (277.8) converge not to zero but to infinity, the formula is useful only if the series is cut off after not too many terms.

Gauss's Product Formula (§ 278)

278. Let p be a natural number. The function

$$f(x) = p^x \, \Gamma\left(\frac{x}{p}\right) \Gamma\left(\frac{x+1}{p}\right) \dots \Gamma\left(\frac{x+p-1}{p}\right) \tag{278.1}$$

is logarithmically convex, since the logarithm $x l p$ of p^x is a linear function, while each of the remaining factors is logarithmically convex. We also have $f(x+1) = x f(x)$; for, to add 1 to x has the effect of multiplying p^x by p, of transforming each save the last of the $\Gamma((x+\nu)/p)$ into the next factor, and of transforming $\Gamma((x+p-1)/p)$ into $\Gamma((x+p)/p) = \Gamma(x/p) \, x/p$. By the Bohr-Mollerup theorem (cf. § 275 above), $f(x)$ must be a multiple of the function $\Gamma(x)$, so that

$$p^x \, \Gamma\left(\frac{x}{p}\right) \Gamma\left(\frac{x+1}{p}\right) \dots \Gamma\left(\frac{x+p-1}{p}\right) = a_p \, \Gamma(x). \tag{278.2}$$

For $x = 1$, this becomes

$$a_p = p \, \Gamma\left(\frac{1}{p}\right) \Gamma\left(\frac{2}{p}\right) \dots \Gamma\left(\frac{p}{p}\right). \tag{278.3}$$

Now if k is any one of the numbers $1, 2, \dots, p$, we have from (271.3) above that

$$\Gamma_n\left(\frac{k}{p}\right) = \frac{n^{\frac{k}{p}} \, n! \, p^{n+1}}{k \, (k+p) \, (k+2p) \dots (k+np)} . \tag{278.4}$$

Let us multiply the p equations obtained from (278.4) by setting successively $k = 1, 2, \dots, p$. In the denominator of the resulting right-hand side, each of the factors is of the form $(k + hp)$, where h assumes all values from 0 to n, and k all values from 1 to p. Thus for $h = 0$ the factors $1, 2, \dots, p$ occur; for $h = 1$, the factors $(p+1), \dots, 2p$; finally for $h = n$, the factors $(np+1), \dots, (np+p)$. Hence we have

$$a_p = p \lim_{n=\infty} \frac{n^{\frac{p+1}{2}} \, (n!)^p \, p^{np+p}}{(np+p)!} \tag{278.5}$$

Now we have the identity

$$(np+p)! = (np)! \, (np)^p \left[\left(1+\frac{1}{np}\right)\left(1+\frac{2}{np}\right) \dots \left(1+\frac{p}{np}\right)\right], \tag{278.6}$$

where for fixed p the expression in brackets converges to unity as n goes to ∞. Thus (278.6) becomes

$$a_p = p \lim_{n=\infty} -\frac{(n!)^p \, p^{np}}{(np)! \, n^{\frac{p-1}{2}}}.$$ (278.7)

In this formula we replace $n!$ and $(np)!$ in accordance with (276.14) above, which yields

$$(n!)^p = a^p \, n^{np+\frac{p}{2}} \, e^{-np} \, e^{\frac{p}{12n}\vartheta(n)},$$

$$(np)! = a \, n^{np+\frac{1}{2}} \, p^{np+\frac{1}{2}} \, e^{-np} \, e^{\frac{\vartheta(np)}{12np}},$$

$$a_p = a^{p-1} \sqrt{p} \lim_{n=\infty} e^{\frac{p}{12n}\vartheta(n) - \frac{\vartheta(np)}{12np}}.$$

This finally gives a_p as

$$a_p = \sqrt{p} \; a^{p-1}.$$ (278.8)

Comparison of (278.8) with (278.3) for $p=2$ now yields

$$a = \frac{1}{\sqrt{2}} a_2 = \frac{1}{\sqrt{2}} \cdot 2 \, \Gamma\left(\frac{1}{2}\right) \Gamma(1) = \sqrt{2\pi},$$ (278.9)

$$a_p = \sqrt{p} \; (2\pi)^{p-\frac{1}{2}}.$$ (278.10)

We note that

$$a = \sqrt{2\pi} = 2{,}50662\;82746 \ldots$$

lies between the bounds given in § 276 above.

Compilation of Formulas; Applications (§§ 279-280)

279. Below is a summary of the various formulas obtained in connection with our study of the gamma function. The last formula of (279.1), by the way, is known as *Stirling's formula*.

$$\left.\begin{aligned}
\Gamma(x) &= \sqrt{2\pi} \, x^{x-\frac{1}{2}} \, e^{-x+\mu(x)}, \\[6pt]
\mu(x) &= \frac{\vartheta_1(x)}{12x} = \frac{1}{12x} - \frac{1}{360 x^3} + \\[6pt]
&\quad \cdots + (-1)^m \, \vartheta_m(x) \, \frac{B_m}{(2m-1)\,2m\,x^{2m-1}}, \\[6pt]
n! &= \sqrt{2\pi} \, n^{n+\frac{1}{2}} \, e^{-n+\frac{\vartheta_1(n)}{12n}},
\end{aligned}\right\}$$ (279.1)

$$\Gamma(x) = (x - 1)\, \Gamma(x - 1), \tag{279.2}$$

$$\Gamma(x)\, \Gamma(1 - x) = \frac{\pi}{\sin \pi x}, \tag{279.3}$$

$$\Gamma\left(\frac{x}{p}\right) \Gamma\left(\frac{x + 1}{p}\right) \dots \Gamma\left(\frac{x + p - 1}{p}\right) = \frac{(2\pi)^{\frac{p-1}{2}}}{p^{x - \frac{1}{2}}}\, \Gamma(x). \tag{279.4}$$

In particular, for $p = 2$ (*Legendre's identity*) and for $p = 3$,

$$\Gamma\left(\frac{x}{2}\right) \Gamma\left(\frac{x + 1}{2}\right) = \frac{\sqrt{\pi}}{2^{x-1}}\, \Gamma(x), \tag{279.5}$$

$$\Gamma\left(\frac{x}{3}\right) \Gamma\left(\frac{x + 1}{3}\right) \Gamma\left(\frac{x + 2}{3}\right) = \frac{2\pi}{3^{x - \frac{1}{2}}}\, \Gamma(x). \tag{279.6}$$

As to tabulating the Γ-function, it suffices to construct tables for the interval $1 < x < 2$, since for x outside this interval the values of $\Gamma(x)$ can then be found by using the functional equation. For actual calculation it turns out to be advantageous to construct the tables first for the interval $5 < x < 6$ by means of the formulas (279.1) and to calculate on the basis of these the values in the interval $1 < x < 2$.

280. As an application of formulas (279.2) through (279.6), we shall show how to calculate the numbers $\Gamma(k/12)$ for $k = 1, 2, \dots, 11$; these numbers are of interest in various problems of Function Theory. We set, for short,

$$x_k = \Gamma\left(\frac{k}{12}\right), \quad y_k = \sin\frac{\pi k}{12} \quad (k = 1, \dots, 11). \tag{280.1}$$

It will turn out that all of the x_k can be calculated in terms of

$$x_3 = \Gamma\left(\frac{1}{4}\right) = \eta, \quad x_4 = \Gamma\left(\frac{1}{3}\right) = \xi. \tag{280.2}$$

To begin with, if we set

$$\tau = \sqrt{3} + 1, \tag{280.3}$$

we can easily verify that

$$y_1 = \frac{1}{2^{1/2}\tau}, \quad y_2 = \frac{1}{2}, \quad y_3 = \frac{1}{2^{1/2}}, \quad y_4 = \frac{\sqrt{3}}{2}, \quad y_5 = \frac{\tau}{2^{3/2}}. \tag{280.4}$$

Now we obtain from (279.3) and (280.4) that

$$x_1 x_{11} = 2^{\frac{1}{2}} \tau \pi, \quad x_2 x_{10} = 2\pi, \quad x_3 x_9 = 2^{\frac{1}{2}} \pi,$$

$$x_4 x_8 = 2 \cdot 3^{-\frac{1}{2}} \pi, \quad x_5 x_7 = 2^{\frac{3}{2}} \tau^{-1} \pi. \tag{280.5}$$

Thus it only remains to determine the three numbers x_1, x_2, and x_5. By setting successively $x = 1/3$ and $x = 1/6$ in (279.5), and $x = 1/4$ in (279.6), we obtain

$$x_2 x_8 = 2^{\frac{2}{3}} \pi^{\frac{1}{2}} x_4, \tag{280.6}$$

$$x_1 x_7 = 2^{\frac{5}{6}} \pi^{\frac{1}{2}} x_2, \tag{280.7}$$

$$x_1 x_5 x_9 = 2 \cdot 3^{\frac{1}{4}} \pi x_3. \tag{280.8}$$

If we multiply these three equations by each other and then multiply through by $x_3 x_4$, we find by (280.5) that

$$\Gamma\left(\frac{1}{12}\right) = 2^{-\frac{1}{4}} \cdot 3^{\frac{3}{8}} \cdot \sqrt{\frac{\tau}{\pi}} \, \Gamma\left(\frac{1}{3}\right) \Gamma\left(\frac{1}{4}\right), \tag{280.9}$$

and in a similar way we obtain

$$\Gamma\left(\frac{1}{6}\right) = 2^{-\frac{1}{3}} \sqrt{\frac{3}{\pi}} \, \Gamma\left(\frac{1}{3}\right)^2, \tag{280.10}$$

$$\Gamma\left(\frac{5}{12}\right) = 2^{\frac{3}{4}} \cdot 3^{-\frac{1}{8}} \sqrt{\frac{\pi}{\tau}} \, \frac{\Gamma(1/4)}{\Gamma(1/3)}. \tag{280.11}$$

INDEX

INDEX